D1480046

HUNTER: THE VIGIL
SPIRIT SLAYERS

Martin Henley| Howard Wood Ingham| Mike Lee|
Matthew McFarland| John Newman| Stew Wilson

Concept and Design:
Justin Achilli, Richard Thomas,
Chuck Wendig

Authors:
Martin Henley, Howard Wood
Ingham, Mike Lee, Matthew
McFarland, John Newman, Stew
Wilson

Developer:
Chuck Wendig

Editor:
Scribendi.com

Art Direction and Design:
Mike Chaney

Creative Director:
Richard Thomas

Production Manager:
matt milberger

Artists: Erik Rose, Aaron
Acevedo, Jim DiBartolo, Jim
Pavelec, Dugnation, Avery
Butterworth, Juan Antonio
Serrano Garcia, Brian Leblanc,
Matt Kolbek, & James Stowe

Cover Artist:
Chad Michael Ward

Special Thanks for Translation:
Amado Guzman

WHITE WOLF PUBLISHING
2075 WEST PARK PLACE BOULEVARD
SUITE G
STONE MOUNTAIN, GA 30087

© 2008 CCP hf. All rights reserved. Reproduction
without the written permission of the publisher
is expressly forbidden, except for the purposes
of reviews, and one printed copy which may be
reproduced for personal use only. White Wolf,
Vampire and World of Darkness are registered
trademarks of CCP hf. All rights reserved.
Vampire The Requiem, Werewolf The Forsaken, Mage
The Awakening, Promethean The Created, Changeling
the Lost, Hunter The Vigil, Spirit Slayers and
Storytelling System are trademarks of CCP hf. All
rights reserved. All characters, names, places
and text herein are copyrighted by CCP hf. CCP
North America Inc. is a wholly owned subsidiary of CCP hf. The mention of or reference
to any company or product in these pages is not a challenge to the trademark or copyright
concerned. This book uses the supernatural for settings, characters and themes. All
mystical and supernatural elements are fiction and intended for entertainment purposes
only. This book contains mature content. Reader discretion is advised.
Check out White Wolf online at http://www.white-wolf.com

PRINTED IN CHINA

HUNTER: THE VIGIL

SPIRIT SLAYERS

TABLE OF CONTENTS

GUT FEELINGS

A CULINARY GUIDE TO FAST FOOD IN PHILADELPHIA

BY MATT MCFARLAND

From the TV, Morgan Freeman informs me that "Ernest Hemingway once wrote, 'The world is a fine place, and worth fighting for.'" Ernest Hemingway also blew his head off with a shotgun, of course.

I switch off the TV as the credits roll. The coffee table has a stack of DVDs, but I don't much feel like watching anything else. Thing is, I don't know what else to do. I've been puking my guts out for the last two days, no matter what I eat, so I've been knocking around my apartment, but I'm utterly bored now.

I stand up and walk to the bathroom. I don't think I'm going to be sick again. Actually, I'm starting to feel hungry, which is a good sign. I draw a glass of water and swish it around in my mouth before spitting it out. I still have the taste of vomit in my mouth, and it's not unpleasant, which is goddamn weird.

But my reflection in the mirror is even weirder. I look fine. My face is clean, my skin looks clear, and my stubble's coming in even. None of that makes any sense. When I throw up, all of the blood vessels around my eyes burst and I get these little blood-red dots on my face. I go all pale and look like a zombie for at least a day. My stubble never comes in even, always patchy and ugly. But I look… good.

And I'm definitely feeling hungry. I walk into my room, throw off my robe, and pull on a pair of jeans. I haven't been dressed in a couple of days, and it's already helping me feel more normal. I wonder if the sandwich shop up the road is still open. They keep odd hours, but they make some of the best veggie burgers I've ever had.

I yank on a sweatshirt, and take a second to inhale. My room smells good. It smells safe. I lie down on my bed and roll over a couple of times, enjoying the comfort, enjoying the contours that my body has made over the years. My pillow has my scent, my girlfriend's scent, and deep down in my memory I associate this pillow with my dad — I pulled it off his bed before I moved out on my own. It's good. It's home.

But I'm still hungry, and so I leave my room and my apartment and walk out into the ice. It's been pouring down rain since yesterday morning, but today the temperature dropped and now everything's coated. Walking on the sidewalk is tricky — it's not like anyone ever salts around here. It's probably about five or ten below freezing with the wind, and Manny Martinez is still out on his goddamn porch.

Manny beat up the old guy who lives in the building across from me last week. I don't know if he took anything or how bad the old guy was hurt. I don't even know his name. I just know Manny's a cock. I stare at him a minute, before I realize what a bad idea that is.

He's alone, at least. He usually rolls around with five of his buddies. "Thick as thieves," my mom used to say, and I had no idea what that meant. But that's Manny and his guys. They weren't all together when Manny jumped that old guy. The others were watching, and then when the cops questioned them, they were all together down at the pool hall, the whole time, you know, officer? And the guy who runs the place backed them up.

The papers called it a hate crime because the old guy was Jewish. I don't think he was, though. I used to hang with a guy who lived in his building, and I smelled bacon from his place all the time. Used to make me feel ill, but it was always there, and I thought Jews didn't eat bacon. And how would the papers know, anyway? He doesn't wear a little cap or a star — wait, actually, maybe he did. But that bacon smell—

I smell the sandwich shop and start moving faster. I try to slow down, because I don't want to fall, but damn, I'm hungry. A couple of minutes later, I'm walking in the door. I'm not winded, I'm not even that cold. I'm just pumped, which is strange, because I should feel like complete ass after not eating for three days.

"Well, hi." The girl behind the counter knows my face, if not my name. She doesn't wear a nametag, so I don't know hers, either. "You want a burger?"

"Yeah," I pant. I'm not out of breath, but my mouth is watering so much it's harder to talk. "Two. The works."

"Okay." She taps on the register keys for a minute and takes my money. "Is it really cold out still?"

I turn around and look outside, as if that's going to tell me if it's cold. "Yeah, but it's going to warm up a little before morning. Rain's not stopping, though."

"Huh." She glances at the TV in the corner. "Thought they said we were getting more snow."

I don't know, actually. I haven't looked at a weather report in a while. How'd I know that, then? Gut feeling. I can smell the rain coming, over the snow, through the wind. Rain is coming and taking the ice off. I'm glad I live on the third floor — the basements of the apartment complex are going to flood again, I'm sure.

The TV's talking about the old dude who lives in my complex. Wendell McCall. Not exactly a

EDITOR'S QUICK PICK!

A VEGGIE BURGER THAT IS SIMPLY A DELIGHT!

I've lived in the city for what sometimes seems an eternity and sometimes (and I do mean sometimes) I like to break up the monotony of it all with venturing forth into the various smaller fast food joints.

For those of you who weren't around in the late 1950's, there were many "Mom and Pop" styled fast food places. Each one had its own flavor and style, as well as a menues so varied it defied the imagining.

However, in the 80's and 90's, many of those great pieces of Americana were devoured by the giant franchises. However, our city's own Burger Keep managed to survive. Not only that, they are thriving on today's health crazes by offering the most delicious veggie burger this writer has ever eaten.

So, if you only take one piece of advice from me, hit up the Burger Keep and you won't be disappointed.

Jewish name. The counter girl looks over at me. "Did you know that guy? You live down the block, there, right?"

"Yeah. I mean, I live down there. I didn't really know him."

"Didn't?"

"Don't know him." He's not dead, after all. I nod toward the TV. "What's up?"

"Oh, he's going home tomorrow."

"Really?" I lean in to listen, but the TV is crackly with static and it makes my ears itch. "I thought he was beat up worse than that."

"Me, too." She shrugs. "They haven't caught who did it."

I shake my head. "Yeah, well, he's right down the block. Dude who lives in my complex."

"Why don't you say something?"

I look out the window, down the street. I can't see Manny, of course, but he's probably still out there. "Maybe I will." The TV switches to a weather report, and the reporter says we've got a cold front and more snow on the way. The counter girl looks at me with a smirk. She thinks I'm full of shit with my weather forecast.

I walk to the door and stick my head out again. Yep, I'm sure. Rain tonight. Warmer tomorrow. My mom used to say she could smell rain coming, and she was usually right about her predictions, but I don't remember her ever doing it in a damn snowstorm before. I pull my head back inside the shop. My burgers are ready.

"Hey, your food's ready."

"Didn't you just say that?"

She shakes her head. "Don't think so." How'd I know, then?

I sit down with my burgers. I eat the first one in three bites, and I savor the second one a little more. After I'm done, though, I still feel hungry. Not empty, exactly, but craving something. I thank the girl at the counter and walk outside.

It's still cold, and the slush on the sidewalk sneaks into my shoes. Everything's covered in ice like a worldwide sugar-coating. I think about rock candy and wonder if anywhere around here sells it. But actually that doesn't appeal to me much. Instead of walking toward my house, I start walking down the block. I'm keyed up. I'm cold, but it's not unpleasant. I feel like I'm part of the world around me, like I can hear and see and smell everything. My skin itches against my clothes. My face feels flushed. And I'm still hungry, damn it.

Family Sized Chicken Dinner. An Old Fashioned Favorite that is perfect for any Family Gathering around the holidays.

I walk by the fried chicken place, and my mouth is watering. And that stops me dead.

I haven't eaten meat in… what, 10 years now? Closest I've come is eating fish once every few months. But I haven't had beef or chicken in a decade. I hate the smell of cooked meat, and I have since I was little, but now…

I walk toward the chicken place. It's dirty and grimy and greasy in there. I can smell it before I touch the door, and I turn away, the food I've just eaten threatening to come back up. A big fat guy walks out of the place past me, and lets out a huge belch as he digs his car keys out of his pants. I smell that foul mix of digesting food, chicken grease, and cigarette smoke, and my dinner makes good on its threat.

The manager comes out of the store and yells at me, but his accent is too strong and I don't get anything except "fucker." I stagger away, back toward my place. I'm hungry again, but I don't want to go back to the sandwich shop. That'd look too weird. Maybe I'll call my girlfriend and see if she wants to come over and bring me dinner. She offered to yesterday, but I wasn't fit company.

Man, whatever this is, I hope it isn't catching.

I'm walking down the block, shoes still full of slush, mouth still tasting of puke, face flushed and nose running. I'm hunched over like   I'm in pain, but I actually feel Okay. Just hungry.

"What's up, man?" Manny Martinez. I'm on his side of the street this time.

I turn to him. I'm expecting him to tell me how crappy I look. I don't say anything, I just sniff a bit.

That apparently looks exactly like I think it does, because he furrows his brow. "Smell something bad, man?"

"Yeah," I say without thinking. But it's not bad like he's meaning. It's bad in a way I can't quite describe. I sniff, and I see things. I see blood on his knuckles. I see him yelling something I don't understand. I see purpose, like it wasn't just about the money or the watch or even the thrill. He hit that old guy for a reason. Maybe it was a hate crime, that's about the only thing that makes any sense.

I see strength in Manny, and that pisses me off, because in my gut, I know I'm stronger.

He takes a step toward me. "What you wanna do about it?"

I don't get into fights. I'm no good at it, and I'm sick anyway. But I stand up taller and take a step forward. I have this crazy idea about pushing him down and pissing on him. I bare my teeth.

He
swings. I
don't move. His fist
connects with my face and I lose
my balance, falling over into the slush. My
face stings a bit, but it doesn't really hurt. That comes
later, anyway.

Manny, true to form, doesn't quit. He kicks me in the gut once, which should completely wreck me. But I don't really feel it. He's talking at me in Mexican, which of course I don't understand, but I get the gist. His turf. His block. His home. There's none of that fire I smelled on him, though. He's not getting into this the way he did with the old guy. This is just about him strutting his stuff, being king of his block.

But I live here, too. I push myself to my feet and slam my shoulder into him. He slips backwards and lands on his ass. I follow him down, flip him over and pin him. My hips are moving, and I don't like that at all, but he needs to learn, goddammit. And he will, if I have to rip the pants off him and fucking show him that—

What the fuck am I doing?

I push back, spin around, and start running. My shoes slip on the ice, but I still make tracks. I'm going home. I'm going to my safe, warm bed, where everything smells like me. I hit the door to my build-ing
full-
speed and
the frame
splinters. I can
barely breathe. My shirt feels tight. The stairs move under me, but that's only because I'm taking them so quickly. I stop long enough to use my key, and then I'm in my bed, muddy shoes marking the floor and the sheets, shaking, whining, trying to be calm.

I was really ready to… I don't even know. It wasn't about sex. It was just that he did wrong, and I'm stronger than he is, and he needs to know that. He still needs to know that.

I stand up and pull off my shirt. It felt tight before, but it feels okay now. I stand by the window and look across the street. I see Manny coming out of his building. He's got something in his hand. It glints in the moonlight.

Moonlight? I shut my eyes, and I realize that the moon is shining tonight. It's half-full, and suddenly I

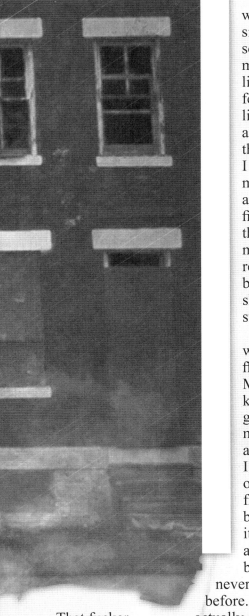

want to be outside again, just so I can see the moon. The moonlight makes me feel less empty, like it's hitting a craving. And then the craving I had before, for meat, comes back, and I'm trying to figure out how those two things, moonlight and red meat, connect, before I hear the shot and feel a sting in my chest.

I fall backwards onto the floor of my room. My window's broken, and there's glass around me. My stomach aches terribly, and I can see a stream of blood coming from my belly button. No, wait, it's from a hole above my belly button. That's never been there before.

That fucker actually shot me. I turn over and spit out a mouthful of blood, and try to struggle to my feet. I reach down to try and push myself up, but I wind up undoing my belt instead. I don't know why, but I have a gut feeling I want to be naked right now.

I start crawling out of the room. I can smell burnt flesh and shit coming from the hole in my stomach, but it's getting fainter. There's a new scent, too, something that reminds me of moonlight for some reason. Something I recognize, but I have no memory to go with it.

I'm up and running, but the perspective is weird. I still feel like I'm crawling, from the look of things. Everything's too tall. I run down the stairs and burst out the door, and see Manny across the street. He looks at me, but it doesn't look like recognizes me. That's weird.

I smell gunpowder and feel heat from the pistol. And that just pisses me off. And suddenly, my perspective changes again, except now I'm taller. I look up at the moon, and I see it, a semicircle shining down on the ice and slush and the two of us. And I lift my head and sing to it, lost for a moment in the beauty of it all. I've never sung to the moon before, but in my gut—

—I'm shot again. My eyes snap open and Manny's standing there with the gun pointed at me. He's shaking, and I smell urine laced with beer, weed and too much sugar. I launch myself across the street and hit him full-force. He is going to know I'm stronger. He is going to respect how things work around here. He is not going to beat up old men anymore.

I grind my teeth, trying to find a way to hurt him more than I already am. And then I open my mouth and snap it down over the side of his face, and pull up, ripping his cheek away. I bite down again, and my teeth somehow shatter his. I taste gold from his fillings and spit it out. I adjust my angle and my jaws close over his neck. I taste blood, thick and copper and coating my tongue like licorice and stout beer. I taste the fluid leaking out his spine, and it's bitter and sticks to the roof of my mouth, like eating a cobweb. I taste the cartilage in his throat, and he stops making sounds because I've bitten through his larynx.

I taste meat. Soft, tender, red, warm, meat. And that place inside me, that empty place in my gut, fills up again. There's a bullet hole in my shoulder, but its closing. And I keep biting, even though I know he can't feel pain anymore.

Lights start to come on around me. I hear the clicks from people's houses. I hear screams. I smell fear. I'd better go.

But before I do, I piss on his body. I guess he's not really in a position to learn anything now, but there are other people like him around here. They can learn this lesson: If you're going to act like top dog, you'd better fucking be top dog.

I turn and jog back toward my building. My perspective looks normal again. The rain's already coming down heavier, washing away my footprints… also some footprints that can't possibly be mine. I can't see the moon anymore, and that gives me a heavy, sad feeling in my gut.

But I know it's there, somewhere, and that thought comforts me. I feel sated, but it's just that the edge is off my hunger.

I could really go for some chicken.

The street gang with scarred-up faces. The eerie-eyed park ranger giving off the gamy stink of an animal's musk. The alley preachers proselytizing messages of rage. The pack of lone hikers carrying blood-caked camping gear.

Werewolves are men who become wolves, are humans with feral hearts and unnatural souls. Hunters who know of the shapechangers, whether it's from a story about stumbling into Lupine territory or getting run down by a pack of bloody-muzzled truckers, know to be afraid.

The fear has many reasons: for one, anger dominates these beasts. Two, their wild side bleeds off them like an intangible miasma, a heady musk. And three, they rarely work alone; the werewolf pack is a bestial analog to the hunter cell, for both represent a struggling minority against a cruel majority. The werewolves are themselves creatures besieged, and yet they hunt what surrounds them. Hunters, too, are outnumbered on all sides—red eyes from the forest, the gleam of white teeth from the dark of a doorway.

Yes, that means there's a common ground to be had — when either side is willing to see it. Both hunt. And quite often, they hunt each other.

Wild at Heart

Whether it's mystical, biological, or some fucked-up amalgam of the two, werewolves are men whose souls are shared with a wolf — they reek of this wildness. A Lupine's body longs to roam the edges of his territory. He shares a kill with his friends, his *pack*. His teeth need to bite, his muzzle needs to pick up every lingering scent, his claws must rend. Man's refined civilization — a costume of quiet flesh and polite manners — cannot easily contain the wolf-half of the soul, and these urges must be made manifest. They become apex predators, hunting as an expression of those untamed needs.

So, they are wild, but do not be misled: this wildness is not natural. It is not the *wilderness* that lives within the creatures, but a wild, frenzied, feral core. This is not the hand of Mother Nature at work, no. Werewolves are part of a spirit world, and the wolf that lurks within thinks in ways alien to a real wolf. Many of the Lupines worship the moon in the sky above, howling desperately and madly to her eerie face. (And any hunter who asks the werewolves about the moon comes to a swift conclusion: she's probably batshit, and the werewolves are just as batshit for worshipping her. Luna, lunatic, lunacy, it all starts to make a kind of deranged sense.)

Dark and Secret Territory

Werewolves are lords of their territories, and that plays very well with **Hunter: The Vigil**. Think of how one street gang dominates this block, and another gang dominates the next. Or how a group of young Muslims or Guardian Angels might try to "clean up" one of those blocks, or how the police control a certain part of a certain city but have *lost* control of other parts. Or, in a hunter-context, how this Union cell watches over the Dragoon Court project or this other Aegis Kai

Little girls, this seems to say
Never stop upon the way
Never trust a stranger, friend
No one knows where it may end
As you're pretty, so be wise
Wolves may lurk in every guise
Now as then, 'tis simple truth
Sweetest tongue has sharpest
tooth.

—Rosaleen,
"The Company of Wolves"

Doru cell stands Vigil over the three downtown universities. Werewolves, too, keep their territory. One pack roves Chinatown, claiming its tangled streets as hunting ground. A lone skin-changer is King of the Shantytown, where all the homeless gather beneath the overpass in tents and tin-sheet shelters.

Oh, humans don't know about these territories, not really. They go about their business, only aware of the subtle vibrations of wildness lingering: a bloody claw streak on an otherwise white sidewalk, lots of flyers advertising *missing children*, or weird reflections poorly-seen in passing storefront windows. The wilderness, too, is home to great swaths of territory — places where the wolves rule more easily, and where hunters are truly at the mercy of the beasts that wonder the aimless tracts.

Hell, territory doesn't even need to be physical, does it? One pack claims to "watch over" a women's shelter, going so far as to use the women within as "breeders." And maybe a hunter cell chooses to stand guard over that same shelter — and, inevitably, the

two clash. Territory is a great hook, and something to keep in mind of when reading this book.

Common and Dangerous Threads

That leads us to one strange and often denied fact: hunter cells and werewolf packs are, as noted, similar. Both attempt to "police" their respective domains because… well, for many, because that's what they do. They can do nothing else. (Think of them like Charles Bronson in *Death Wish*, "Well, what if the cops *can't* handle this, Jack?" They do what they do because circumstance and conscience offer them little choice.) That commonality, though, should not be comfortable to either group. They don't band together and make nice-nice. Yes, alliances are possible. Even long-term ones. But "friendly" isn't the word one might use to describe such relationships. Moreover, such discomfort living next to one another (remember, werewolves aren't necessarily opposed to outright slaying those humans who stray) is so uneasy

VIGIL AND FORSAKEN

This book is not a replacement of **Werewolf: The Forsaken**, nor do you need that book to follow this book.

That being said, if you're in possession of **Forsaken**, you have a couple of choices. First, you can use this book as a great antagonist book for **Werewolf** — the hunters here have a lot of abilities and tactics that can make the life of a werewolf pack very difficult, indeed. (Alternately, they might make good temporary allies in the fight against the Pure.) Second, you can use this book and **Forsaken** hand-in-hand. Both books can easily be mixed together, with you as Storyteller pulling bits from each to keep players (be they controlling hunter *or* werewolf characters) on their toes.

that it can lead to violent flare-ups. Where does the common ground end? Uratha are born to this, forced into it. It is instinct. Hunters must force themselves; they may be forced by compulsion, twisted to the mission, but most are not "born" this way. (That being said, the Lucifuge certainly think they're born to it, and may find more in common with werewolves than they accept as comfortable.)

An Inscrutable Spirit

This book, though, is about more than just werewolves. Werewolves aren't really part wolf: they're part *wolf-spirit*. Whether they're born to it through the genetics of a moon-tribe or they steal the shapeshifting ability from Satan himself, the soul changes. A beast emerges, a skin spirit that latches onto one's psyche and essence and won't let go.

This book is therefore as much about spirits as it is about the werewolves who deal with and are part of that world. Hunters cannot see into the spirit world; they are only barely aware at all that such an immaterial plane exists. But they *can* see the effects of spirits and ghosts, they *can* see those strange entities that manifest or steal bodies.

Some are certainly misled by the term "spirit." It sounds almost pleasant, doesn't it? *The spirits have guided me.* Except, no hunter should expect pleasantness from spirit encounters. Spirits are bizarre. They adhere to Byzantine rules (one leaves a trail of bloodied teeth in its wake, another scrawls poetic revelations on subway tunnel walls not because it wants to but because it *has to*). They are in no way human, have never been human, and do not even understand humans — yes, some are the embodiments of human emotion, but there hunters suffer the *chicken-and-egg* dilemma. Which came first, the spirits born of emotion, or the emotions born of the spirits?

Once more, just as with werewolves, hunters soon learn that there exists nothing "natural" or "pleasant" about spirits — they are selfish figments and lunatic

entities. One can deal with them in a way that doesn't involve burning down their nests or chopping apart their hot-spot "loci," but it's never, ever easy.

How to Use This Book

First things first, throughout the book you'll find short stories by Matt McFarland. These stories (preceding each of the chapters) are meant to frame the hunter-werewolf struggle in a meaningful context.

Chapter One: Untamed Territory is a heady mix of the history of the struggle betwixt hunter and werewolf. And it's not just about those werewolves who have come to their gifts and curses by birth — no, it's also about those hunters who have encountered beasts who have stolen their power from the skins of wolves or from the Devil his own self.

Chapter Two: Sheep's Clothing gives a look at how the hunters respond to the werewolf and spirit menace. How do individual cells deal with werewolves? How do the compacts and conspiracies mount their attacks on — or make alliances with — the shapeshifters in this world? In addition, you'll find three new compacts and one new conspiracy: the appropriately named Les Mystères, a loose confederation of cults whose hunters allow spirits to possess their bodies for a time, so as to gain access to new powers in the Vigil.

Chapter Three: Silver Bullets is about the tools and weapons available to both hunter and werewolf. New Tactics? Endowments? Merits? Check, check, and check. But the werewolves and spirits have their own powerful tricks, and hunters should be wary.

Chapter Four: Moonstruck provides advice to Storytellers hoping to tell a story or chronicle based around the hunter-werewolf struggle. In addition, we are once more granted a look at Philadelphia. This time, the City of Brotherly Love is painted in strokes of blood spilled from cruel tooth and claw, showing how the tumult of the city's existence has shaped — and is shaped by — the war between hunter and Lupine.

35

The history of human endeavor and progress has, in some respect, always been about the separation of humanity and nature. We build walls and roofs. We dress ourselves in ever more elaborate clothing. We create machines. We deny the fact that in each and every one of us lives an animal, a mortal being of blood and secretions and bone.

And over time, we've feared people who seem to be closer to the animal nature. Because they shouldn't be. Because we've made it impossible to understand the animal without some paradoxically unnatural agency to make it happen. We accuse people who love their dogs or their cats of being witches. We equate closeness to the animals with sexual deviancy, with cannibalism, with murder.

And... aren't we right to do this? Alone and naked, humans are vulnerable to the dangers presented by a hostile world. The hunter doesn't perform the Vigil for long before he has hard evidence that behind the world we see another world that informs the visible world around us with malice. Spirits swarm in the shadowy depths that wait at the corner of your eye. The Earth itself throbs with an intelligence, a power that would reach inside you, twist you, take away everything that makes you human, leaving you as nothing more than a beast, howling at the stars, tearing at the flesh of those you love with gore-stained teeth. If we allow these powers to triumph, humanity becomes no more than the illusion we maintain to protect us from becoming the animals we left behind. In some respects, it always has been.

Skins for Wearing

At what point in our evolution did the human race become more than apes? When did we gain self-consciousness, the ability to reason? When did we leave behind our innocence?

The story of Adam and Eve is to some the story of a fall, the story of curiosity leading to the mistake that robbed humanity of our enlightened innocence. But in some interpretations, the exile from Eden is a metaphor of the dawn of consciousness. The Fruit from the Tree of Knowledge of Good and Evil is the signifier of the dawning awakening of human language and thought. Eden is the animal state. In eating of the Fruit — in gaining knowledge — humanity must leave behind Eden and can never return.

The example of the werewolf gives the lie to that particular part of the story.

Either way, the exile from Eden ends in enmity. Adam and Eve are barred from ever coming back by an angel bearing a flaming blade, and from then on, they suffer and die without ever really being in communion with the world.

Right from the beginning of history, that hostility between the human and the animal expressed itself in a fear of the animal world. The accusation of shape-shifter, so often

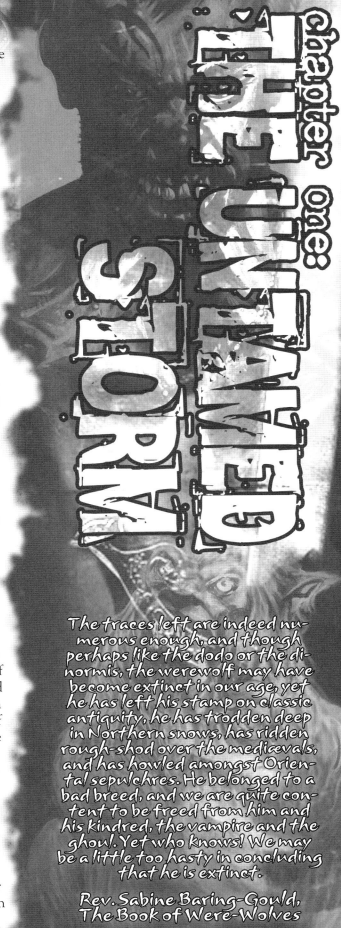

chapter one: THE UNTAMED STORY

The traces left are indeed numerous enough, and though perhaps like the dodo or the dinormis, the werewolf may have become extinct in our age, yet he has left his stamp on classic antiquity, he has trodden deep in Northern snows, has ridden rough-shod over the mediævals, and has howled amongst Oriental sepulchres. He belonged to a bad breed, and we are quite content to be freed from him and his kindred, the vampire and the ghoul. Yet who knows! We may be a little too hasty in concluding that he is extinct.

Rev. Sabine Baring-Gould, The Book of Were-Wolves

cognate with "vampire" and "witch" was leveled at those we most feared. Our enemies were, more than anything, shapechangers, both in the transitive and intransitive senses of the term: they changed their own shapes, and they changed the shapes of others. And yet, to take the form of the animal was a divine characteristic, too. The gods represented the forces of nature

Horus became the falcon, Anubis the jackal, Hathor the cow, Seth the incomprehensible Typhon Beast. The gods of Greece and Rome, particularly Zeus and Apollo, adopted a menagerie of shapes, the better to interact with mortals, and sometimes to love them. And in return they forced changes upon the mortals whom they judged worthy to be changed, or unworthy to be human.

The shapechanger must understand his form, and must understand the rules that govern changing, the use of the tools one uses to change. Witness the tale of Lucius the Greek, who spies on his hostess Pamphile one night, as she strips her clothes and coats herself with an unguent taken from a cellar shelf; she shrinks, sprouts feathers and beak, and is a bird. She flies. Lucius watches her go and something changes inside him. It's another danger of seeing another change shape: along with the strangeness and the slight revulsion, it creates curiosity; it creates a burning desire to experience the new body, inside and perhaps out. He becomes eager to fly himself. He snatches a jar from the shelf and strips off his clothes. Coated with ointment, he spreads out his arms to fly away, but his back cramps and his arms fall to the ground; his face elongates, his ears grow high and bushy. His genitals swell. He is a donkey, and for nearly a year, Lucius is forced to remain a donkey. Thieves steal him. He experiences abuse. But at the same time, people treat him strangely; the animal form creates that same revulsion/curiosity/desire in others that the sight of Pamphile created in him. He faces more cruelty than the other animals, and one day a woman sees him without truly knowing what he is, and desires him, and takes him to her bed. A god of Egypt returns him to his shape, but only after the allotted time has passed.

The shapechanger can be cursed to change; and it can be hotly desired. Sometimes, only a fine line divides the two.

Pasiphaë

From a fragmentary poem engraved on a clay tablet in Linear B, now held in the Library of the Aegis Kai Doru in Athens:

I WANT YOU FOR MY OWN; THAT SILKEN HIDE,
THAT MUSCLE RIPPLING LIKE THE SEA,
THE BODY THAT STEAMS AND
GRUNTS IN THE DAWN, THAT TAIL.
BLACK AS NIGHT YOU ARE,
DUMB AND WET-NOSED AND ROUGH-TONGUED.
YOUR EYES ARE DEAD,
AND NO SIGN OF MY DESIRE REFLECTS.
I CANNOT LOVE YOU ANY MORE
THAN YOU LOVE ME.
I WANT YOU.
I IMAGINE YOU WITHIN ME, ATOP ME, LOWING.
I CONFIDE; THE ARTIFICER OBLIGES;
THE MANTLE HE MAKES.
MY SHAPE IS CHANGED.
I AM WHITE COW; YOU ARE BLACK BULL.
UNMINDED, MINDLESS, I CHEW GRASS, I WAIT.
THE SMELLS CHANGE; BODIES DO THEIR WORK.
I AM YOURS.
I LOW, I SCREAM, I AM WOMAN AND COW
AND AFRAID AND EXULTED
AND YOU HAVE GONE AND I AM NAKED
AND BREATHING AND WEEPING

FACE-DOWN IN THE GRASS.
AND I HAVE DONE A TERRIBLE THING, AND I
CANNOT BEAR TO SEE YOU,
AND MY HUSBAND HAS YOU BUTCHERED,
AND MAKES ME TO EAT OF THE MEAT.
AND MY BELLY SWELLS, AND I FEEL YOUR CHILD
MOVE INSIDE ME,
BUTTING AGAINST THE WALL OF MY FLESH.
AND HE HUNGERS.
AND HE WILL NEED MEAT WHEN HE IS BORN, THE
MEAT OF HIS MOTHER'S KIN,
AS HER KIN FED UPON HIS FATHER.
AND I WILL LOVE HIM.
AND I WILL THINK HIM BEAUTIFUL.
FOR HE IS HIS FATHER'S SON.

Story Hooks: Hybridization

• Unnatural Unions

The tale of Pasiphaë is one of the strangest and perhaps most perverse in a body of mythology that has no shortage of bestiality and weird sex. The wife of the queen of Crete develops an unnatural desire for a fine black bull that will only be relieved by the act of consummation. Transformed into the shape of a bull with a deviously clever costume, she gets her wish. She conceives the Minotaur: a beast with a bull's head and a hunger for human flesh. This much is a matter of myth.

Anyone with a basic knowledge of biology — even assuming the knowledge of an inhabitant of Archaic Greece — knows that you can't conceive a man-bull hybrid, flesh-eating or not, by just having sex with a bull. But in the World of Darkness, it's not impossible... it just depends on the bull.

Spirits can take many forms, and have the ability to possess animals. It's not outside the realms of possibility that a spirit personifying lust or fertility could possess ("claim") an animal and create an animal-human hybrid, or shape-shifter.

In fact, it's a possible origin for the first werewolf — a woman impregnated by an event, or a she-wolf impregnated by an event.

Here's the thing: if such a thing could happen (and why not?) back in the age of heroes, why can't it happen now? The answer is of course that it does happen, and that it is happening right now. It happens to people in remote places. It happens to people trapped in the middle of cities, locked inside the labyrinthine slums that make up so much of the modern urban experience. It happens to the great and the good.

A woman in a tenement block gives birth to a mewling cat-thing. The cat-child runs away one night; and although his mother never sees him again, people walking the stairwells of the vast decaying block of flats sometimes see round eyes, shining in the dark. A man on a farm far from anywhere, possessed for a season by a goat-spirit fathers a goat-girl on his wife (like the one in Joyce Carol Oates' short story "Secret Observations on the Goat-Girl"). His wife goes mad, and he puts the goat-girl out into the paddock and forbids his other children from having anything to do with her. He means to kill her when she is too old to hide, when he can gather up the nerve.

More famously, perhaps, one might think of the beast of Glamis Castle: in this royal residence, something resided in a hidden room for a hundred years or more, a supposed scion of the house of Hanover that could never be revealed, whose nightly howled echoed across the glens of the Scottish estate.

Spirits may also create things that are hybrids of humans and creatures that don't exist outside of our nightmares. The scenario of Lovecraft's classic story "The Dunwich Horror" becomes all too possible — a degenerate occultist subjects his daughter to a terrible union. A precocious child develops into a form of terrible evil...

Whether the creature is a flesh-eating minotaur, a man-dog, a furred, clawed cat-child or some other creature, hunters may find themselves facing something terrible, bestial, flesh-eating, and intimately familiar with the lie of the land. Who are the hunters, and who the hunted?

It's sometimes far too easy to just assume that people out in the sticks are evil, though. It's one of

the tropes of horror fiction, and really, poor people and uneducated people are just as likely to be good or bad as rich, educated people (it's just that wealth and education allow people to manifest evil in different ways. But we're digressing here). Let's go back to the farmer whose family tragedy is to have to deal with the aftermath of a spirit having fun in his body for a single night: a goat-girl. It is an innocent creature that can do no harm... and whose conception and birth drove his wife mad and has, in his opinion blighted his crops, a permanent reminder of his shame, and his weakness.

A hunter may be drawn to tales of domestic violence and madness, of a family that has turned inward, that hides a secret in its old barn... And the father will kill to hide it.

What will the hunters do when they discover the goat-girl is harmless? Does the simple fact that she is a spirit-born, barely intelligent mixture of girl and beast remove from her the right to live? But then, what hope does she have of survival in the greater world? The superiors of Task Force: VALKYRIE and the Cheiron FPD wouldn't hesitate to take her away

and dissect her. But will the field agents allow that? Can they, and get out with their consciences intact?

• Sex and the Human Animal

A real-world Roman carving exists, which is seen in very few textbooks, of a Herm and a Panisca. A Herm is a fertility-statue, a pedestal on which rests the head and shoulders of a God, and which has on its front an erect phallus. This one has the face of a horned Pan. A Panisca is a female satyr. The Panisca is, not to put too fine a point on it, using the Herm to pleasure herself. What makes this carving so very important is that it's not from a brothel, or a bedroom, or some dirty old man's home. It's from a coffin-lid. It's a sacred object.

The divinely or supernaturally created man-animal of the ancients had a sexual power and frankness it's difficult to imagine the people of the ancient world ascribing to anything. The minotaur was born of lust, and in Greek myth lust characterized human-animal hybrids. The Centaurs were a race of rapists. And the half-goat Satyrs were a byword for phallic obsession. But whatever these creatures were like, they were divine in nature. The lust they both experi-

THE UNWANTED SISTER

Her nose, like her ears, is goatish: snubbed and flat with wide, dark nostrils. But her eyes are human eyes. Thickly lashed and beautiful. Except they are so very pale. The tiny blood vessels are exposed which is why they look pink; I wonder, does the sunshine hurt her? ...do tears form in her eyes? (of my eight brothers and sisters, it is the older, for some reason, who argue that the goat-girl is blind and should be put out of her misery. One of my sisters has nightmares about her—about her strange staring eyes—though she has seen the goat-girl only once, and then from a distance of at least fifteen feet. Oh the nasty thing, she says, half-sobbing, the filthy thing!—Father should have it butchered).

Joyce Carol Oates, "Secret Observations on the Goat-Girl"

enced and inspired in others was combined with awe. It was mixed in with the awe of the human animal when faced with a vision of the living world's totality and potency, distilled in a single vital body.

In modern-day story terms, what this means is that people who can shapeshift into certain animals — predators like wolves or big cats, athletic animals like horses or bulls, fertile animals like goats — have a strange kind of magnetism. Imagine a vampire, a werewolf and a warlock all going out to some singles bar to seduce someone, for whatever reason. The vampire stares into his victim's eyes and twists his mind: she makes her victim want her. The mage shrouds himself with mystery and misdirection: all paths lead to him, and he knows exactly what his mark wants and needs. But the werewolf simply stands there and lets her victim come to her. All it takes is a look, a flash of the eye, the sight of a jawline, a shoulder, the light glint-ing from a droplet of sweat on a finely-shaped neck, a flick of the tongue over perfect white teeth that could *eat you right up…*

The werewolf's sensual physicality draws the ordinary humans to her without her doing anything. Because she is divine.

Think of this another way: a vampire's hapless slaves are probably controlled by supernatural powers that grip their minds or their emotions. The warlock's slaves probably have no idea what they're doing. But the followers of the werewolf *want* her. The werewolf has a group of hangers-on, men and women who really want her and who will do anything to get the attention and approval of the object of their desire. It'll take a lot to turn people who worship a werewolf like that.

But crushes can turn into loathing really easily, and while the werewolf's powers of sexual attraction are potent enough that a single touch or a kiss or the tracing of a finger on a shoulder blade can wipe out all doubts, limits exist, and people who once thought themselves madly in love with the werewolf can turn on her if she doesn't throw them the scraps of affection they need.

The Neurian Slave (490 BCE)

From a paper given by Dr. Curt Ransmayr, of the Loyalists of Thule, West Berlin, in 1987:

Among the more unusual, underrated and dare I say useful historians of Late Antiquity, Julius Piso Minor the Kinsman stands alone in the intimate quality of his information. As far as we know, he exists only in a fragmentary form, but the tales he tells, although as arcane and peculiar as his cognomen (to whom is he "Kindred," wonders the scholar?) are lurid and yet have a ring of truth that only the seasoned inquirer into the supernatural is really able to appreciate.

This story concerns a nameless, lone traveler, which is by no means unusual in ancient tales of the supernatural. The man is a merchant, an Athenian heading through the Tauri, which is now firmly in the Soviet Union. We think of the region now as Cossack country, and the Cossacks, right up to the time of Stalin, lived much as the Scythians must have lived millennia before. I have been to the place once, and I could not imagine it looking any different in the time of Herodotus and Piso Minor. The sky stretches forever; the flatlands seem conducive to the strangest form of agoraphobia. You imagine that the sun is an eye, staring at you, that the sky will crush you if only you offend it.

I digress somewhat. The traveler in the story employs a band of Scythians for protection; they speak to him of the blue-eyed Budini, of the Melanchaeri, who wear only black. They advise that he not approach the Androphagi, who of course subsist on human flesh. The traveler asks of the Neuri.

Here the writer remarks on the Scythians' blinded slaves, previously noticed by the traveler. One of these wretches bears silver chains, as if he were some noble, but nonetheless receives worse treatment than any of the others, having only the lowest scraps to eat, and being the brunt of the Scythians' worst excesses of violence. No slave is whipped more. No slave is a more popular subject for a recreational beating at the hands of drunken Scythians.

And when the Athenian asks about the Neuri, the Scythians only nod, and indicate this man. What has he done? asks the Athenian. The Scythians refuse to tell him, again indicating the slave.

Eventually, the curious traveler finds a slave who can speak both Greek and the language of the Neuri, and this individual facilitates communication between traveler and slave. The abused slave is a Neurian, a prisoner of inter-tribal war. As such, he is only there to suffer. He pillaged the settlements of the Scythians; they in turn captured him. The slave is philosophical: this is the way of war in this country.

The Athenian shrugs, his curiosity satisfied. He is content now, and continues his journey without any more questions to ask of his companions. But over the days to come he saw fit to show kindness to the Neurian, giving the man morsels of food, and occasionally offering him water.

When the caravan reaches its destination, it delays for some reason or other; a few nights later, the weather turns. The inclement conditions force the caravan to change course, into the country of the Neuri. The Scythians tremble to go into the region, but have no choice. They will not tell the Athenian why they fear this place so.

They make camp in a relatively sheltered spot. A commotion wakes the Athenian on the first night. The Neurian slave is making a commotion. He is howling, like some animal. No matter how hard his slave-masters try to silence him, he will not be silent. Eventually, the Scythians beat him into unconsciousness. The wind rises and it begins to rain, but over the squall of the wind and rain, the travelers can now hear another howling: the cry of wolves. The horses panic; a rope snaps, and they bolt, leaving the Scythians without their mounts.

The Scythians take up what defensive positions they can, but the beasts are upon them before they are ready to face the foe, and the Athenian, clutching his sword, watches as the largest, most terrifying wolves he has ever seen leap upon his guides, one by one, ignoring blows from spears and arrows. The slaves, too, chained together, are helpless. A particularly vicious-looking wolf bounds into full view of the traveler. He raises his sword, and prepares to sell his life, dearly. A second appears, and a third. They surround him. They snarl. A grizzled beast appears among the animals, a blind, emaciated creature with matted fur. It is blind, although this seems to cause it little hindrance, and although it bears countless scars, criss-crossing its ragged fur, it is larger than any of the other animals.

It makes a low growl and tosses its head. The beasts, their snarls changing tone, turn and leave, leaving the Athenian alone with the wreckage of the caravan and the corpses of his guides.

In the morning, the rain stops, and the traveler must take stock of what little in the way of supplies he has. The plain is dark with the blood of men. His comrades are no more than a jumble of gnawed bones and half-devoured corpses. It would be tempting to claim that he looked for the Neurian slave and found no trace of him, but in the account the man is unsure: the bodies are so mangled, he cannot even tell how many bodies are there. He must find a safe haven, he thinks, and determines that he must salvage what supplies he can carry on foot.

The Athenian finds that the caravan's supplies of food have entirely gone. Only one source of possible sustenance is here: the half-eaten corpses of his comrades...

Story Hooks: The Remote Places

• The Other

Throughout history, majority cultures have always held foreigners in suspicion, and particularly suspicious are nomads. Whether tribespeople or gypsies, nomads, with their closed family circles and equally closed cultures excite our fear.

Their otherness invites superstition and dread, and in earlier days that excited the suspicion of witchcraft, vampirism and shapeshifting. So it was with the Neuri, whom Herodotus heard described as a race of werewolves. In the middle ages, the people of Sweden ascribed to the Russians and the Finns the power to force others to become wolves.

The Buda lived in Ethiopia up to the colonial era. Less a people than a caste, they were metalworkers and blacksmiths by trade, and could be known by the ear-rings they habitually wore. No matter how useful their trade, the people avoided them, for the Buda could become hyenas at will.

Now imagine an isolated village in a valley or up a mountain somewhere, one of those places where everyone is somehow related to everyone else by about two or three degrees and where no one ever seems to leave. People down the river or in the big town up the highway avoid the place, and say, *they're not right over there. They're strange.* Stories of inbreeding and abuse follow. Hunters turning up there looking for explanations for recent spates of cattle mutilation and one or two disappearances may find themselves in deep trouble when night falls and the moon rises. They run—but where to? What hope do they have when their pursuers know the ground intimately? Whom can they trust when the whole town seems to be half-beast?

It doesn't have to be on such a large scale. Here's a family of werewolves. They're out hunting. Our hunters, out looking for the culprit of the recent cannibal killings, get more than they bargained for and find themselves running in the forest from huge, vicious beasts. They see a house, and of course, they take shelter, only later realizing who the real owners are (at about the time they raid the kitchen and dining room and discover that the family doesn't have any silverware, anywhere). Which is more or less the scenario from the movie *Dog Soldiers.*

The advantage for the Storyteller in having a pack of werewolves who are all related, or who all grew up together lies in the simple fact that they all know each other. They have a realistic reason to care about each other and to side with each other beyond the affirmation that they're all, you know, werewolves. It's a case of *us* and *them,* and the hunters aren't "us." The werewolves don't even have to like each other — the hunters are outsiders, and the other members of the society, the pack, are on the inside.

Hunters who kill a ravening beast in a far-off region may not find the locals necessarily grateful. That beast may be someone's father, or sister, or cousin, or son.

• Societies Changed at a Stroke

The flipside of having an entire caste, or tribe, or village or family being werewolves is that, like the Neuri in Herodotus' original story, they may not have control over when they change.

Going back to the trope of the remote close-knit village that everyone shuns, it might well be that they don't have any say in the matter as to when they change. For example: our remote village has a history of unsolved murders of the most horrible kind, bodies torn limb from limb, half-eaten corpses left lying on rocks, that sort of thing.

The horrors go back a century. It happens every few years, maybe even less frequently than that, although the horrors have increased in frequency in recent decades (say, three deaths in the last ten years). Every one of these murders happens at roughly the same time. An enterprising and intelligent hunter works out that the happenings coincide with the nearest full moon to May 1st. The hunters load up with everything they can and dutifully set off to the village, which they hope to make their base of operations (as well as being the most likely place they'll find their suspect). Imagine their terror when they realize that when the May-day full moon arrives, every single man, woman and child becomes a wolf.

Will the hunters get out alive? The chances are that whatever happens, the community wake up none the wiser a day or two later. No one remembers, and if someone wakes up with something like a hangover, and vomits up the ear of a large dog, or the foot of a sheep, or three fingers from an adult human woman... he keeps quiet. Because even if some people in the village suspect what happens when everyone blacks out once a year, no one talks about it. If someone dies, it's their fault for getting in the way.

What can the hunters do when they find out that everyone in a whole community is, unwittingly, a werewolf? Violence may be out of the question (some of these werewolves are children, some are elderly — and none of them really knows what he's doing when the change comes), although the masters of some of the more extreme organizations may not agree with that. Some extreme members of the Long Night discover the secret of place and see it as the first skirmish

THE NEURI

The Neuri share the customs of Scythia. A generation before the campaign of Darius, they were forced to quit their country by snakes, which appeared all over the place in great numbers... It appears that these people are magicians. A story doing the rounds among the Scythians and the Greeks who live in Scythia tells how every Neurian turns into a wolf for a few days, once a year, and then turns back into a man. I do not believe the tale. But they tell it, and they swear that it is true.

Herodotus, IV. 105

in the Final Battle. Higher powers in the Malleus Maleficarum, no strangers to ruthlessness, might see mass-murder as preferable to allowing such creatures to exist — not knowing is no excuse, and absolution is available for the perpetrators of such sanctioned horrors. The top echelon of the Cheiron Group makes an order to sweep in by night and "harvest" every inhabitant of the town, leaving the place a ghost-town by morning. Project TWILIGHT sends in the black helicopters under cover of a CDC disease-control operation; they say it's Ebola or something like that, quarantine the town and intern the inhabitants. No one sees anyone there ever again.

People in the local community might not miss the strange inhabitants of the local town, but that's beside the point. They may be werewolves, and some might even know for certain what happens to them once a year and even be prepared to keep that secret, but the fact is that the vast majority of the people here are innocent. Can our hunters live with themselves if they allow their masters to wipe this place from the face of the earth? Or do they take part in the destruction?

• Metamorphoses

Ancient Greek and Roman mythology is full of people with shapes changed and changing. The definitive collection, perhaps, is in the *Metamorphoses* of the Augustinian poet Ovid. His stories are bleak and Tereus marries Procne the daughter of Pandion; by her he has a son, Itys. But he becomes consumed with lust for Procne's sister Philomela. Tereus rapes her, and to silence her wailings he tears out Philomela's tongue.

Procne discovers what has happened to her sister, and takes her revenge on the only thing that Tereus loves; Itys, whose throat she cuts, and who she serves up in a stew to her husband. In a rage, Tereus pursues his wife and his sister-in-law, but they become a blood-red swallow and a nightingale; Tereus himself becomes a hoopoe, a bird which Ovid describes as "looking like war."

Ascalaphus betrays his mistress Proserpina: he tells Pluto that she has eaten a pomegranate while exiled in Hell. The god of the dead condemns her never to return to the higher world, and Proserpina transforms Ascalaphus into a screech-owl, the bringer of foul omen. Alcyone finds her beloved husband washed up ashore after having waited for him to return home for years. By her love, she becomes a heron; she pecks at the face of her husband's corpse and he too lives once more, transformed into a bird.

Actaeon sees the virgin goddess Diana bathing naked in a stream. He betrays his position, and is forced to become a stag, the quarry of Diana's hounds, who run him down and tear him to pieces.

Arachne angers Minerva by proving that she can weave more beautifully than the goddess of arts and crafts; the goddess destroys Arachne's work. When the weaver tries to hang herself, Minerva transforms her into a spider, who weaves forever.

Cyparissus, the beloved of Apollo, kills by accident the tame stag that he adores. He mourns, and becomes a tree, a guardian of mourners.

Battus breaks an oath given to Mercury, and becomes stone. Lichas, who poisons Hercules and is thrown off a cliff by the dying demigod, becomes stone before he hits the ground. On the other hand, Deucalion creates a whole race of people from pebbles after a flood destroys the human race, and the Myrmidons were people made from ants.

The point of all this is that transformations are a powerful tool in the Storyteller's arsenal. They have symbolic force. Ants symbolize industry and unstoppable energy; owls are creatures of ill omen, black cats are lucky or unlucky depending on which side of the Atlantic you live on, hounds are vicious but obey orders, rabbits are fecund, spiders are skilled, and so on. Every aspect of man has the animal that represents it.

Some shapechangers — the ones who adopt a tribal culture at any rate — are skilled shamans, and as such, they are in league with the spirits of the animals, who of course represent the notional symbolic force of each animal as much as they do the animal itself. By channeling the powers of these animals, the werewolves can adopt their powers. The animal itself may make an appearance, which, although it may not have much to do with the creature's shamanic magic, does have the effect of tipping off the sensitive and intuitive individual that something is going wrong.

LYCAON

Cecrops was the first to name Zeus the Supreme god, and refused to sacrifice anything that had life in it, but burnt instead on the altar the national cakes which the Athenians still call pelanoi. But Lycaon brought a human baby to the altar of Lycaean Zeus, and sacrificed it, pouring out its blood upon the altar, and according to the legend immediately after the sacrifice he was changed from a man to a wolf.

I for my part believe this story; it has been a legend among the Arcadians from of old, and it has the additional merit of probability.

Pausanias, Description of Greece, 8.2.

Going back to that whole idea of spirits having a connection with the notional symbolic abilities of the creatures they connect to, sometimes this can be terribly dangerous for humans who are perhaps too closely representative of the animal's symbol. They can become targets for possession: a spirit finds one of these people an attractive home. A homeless man who scavenges and festers with diseases becomes the target for a rat-spirit that gnaws its way inside his body; he grows animalistic and rodent-like, capable of horrible violence and disgusting acts. He subsisted on garbage before, but now he revels in it. He touches people and they grow ill. He grows to look more and more like a rat-headed man. He haunts the sewers. He begins to prey upon people who walk too close to the alleys of his home town.

An office-bound workaholic becomes the host for a bee while working late one night. The office becomes everything to her; and worse, she begins to organize the people around her, creating a strange hive of activity that may not have anything to do with the business at all. The fellow employees find themselves drawn into a mindless drone-state. They begin to suck more people into the hive. The original never leaves the hive; her drones bring her food and care for her. She grows monstrously fat, and begins to lay spirit eggs, and the larvae that hatch eat her very soul, until at last, her body crumbles into a swarm of bees that crawl away, and her maggot-spawn grow into shapechanging insect-people with an urge to organize, a desire for efficiency at all costs, even at the cost of life itself.

A shaman (maybe a shapechanger, maybe a human witch) grows sick with the actions of a mining town or a steelworking town and calls a horde of spirits. Ovid's *Metamorphoses* re-live themselves once more as smelters become hoopoes and whippoorwills, their women become cats and nightingales, church ministers become seagulls and albatrosses. Hunters come to the city and witness the entire place gone mad, as trees that were once people grow in the middle of streets, as butchers turn to marble statues and women burst into spontaneous tears in the street and dissolve into short-live babbling streams. The town becomes one with nature, and the hunters find the effect spreading. It's up to them to find out what is going on, and who is behind this… before they themselves become snakes, falcons and standing stones.

The Centurion (58CE)

From the Catalogue of the Malleus Maleficarum's Black Museum:

ITEM 291/307/IT: STATUARY, ITALY, 1ST CENTURY AD.

WHAT APPEARS TO BE A LIFESIZE STATUE OF A PILE OF, AS FAR AS THE VIEWER CAN TELL, ROMAN MEN'S CLOTHES, ARMS AND ARMOR, DATING TO THE FIRST CENTURY AD, ALL PART OF A SINGLE PIECE OF STONE. THE HELMET, BREASTPLATE AND SWORD ALL SUGGEST A CENTURION OF ONE OF THE GALLIC LEGIONS. THE TUNIC, MOSTLY HIDDEN UNDERNEATH THE BREASTPLATE, BEARS SIGNS OF HAVING BEEN TORN AND REPAIRED AT SOME TIME IN THE PAST.

THE AESTHETIC SENSITIVITY OF ROMAN ART HAD NOT YET FALLEN WHOLLY INTO DECADENCE BY THIS POINT, AND IT IS CONCEIVABLE THAT THIS PIECE COULD BE A PARTICULARLY WELL-DONE PIECE OF FIGURATIVE SCULPTURE, IN WHICH CASE IT WOULD BE PART OF SOME LARGER TABLEAU, PERHAPS LOST, INCLUDING OF COURSE A NAKED FIGURE.

HOWEVER, ONE MUST NOT DISCOUNT THE POSSIBILITY, HOWEVER BIZARRE IT MAY SEEM, THAT THESE ARE IN FACT REAL CLOTHES, PETRIFIED BY A PROCESS UNKNOWN TO US.

FROM THE ANONYMOUS RES GESTAE AVIUM MINERVAE, EXTANT IN THE VATICAN LIBRARY CACHE OF THE MALLEUS MALEFICARUM:

ACCOUNTED BY S. SALVIUS CLEMENS, IN THE THIRD CONSULSHIP OF NERO CLAUDIUS CAESAR GERMANICUS AUGUSTUS. AN ADJUNCT TO THE ACCOUNT OF THE VAMPIRE OF MONA. OUR MAN, HAVING BEEN ASSIGNED WITH THE INVESTIGATION OF CERTAIN TROUBLESOME AND UNUSUAL EVENTS IN THE WEST OF BRITAIN, AS DESCRIBED PREVIOUSLY, HAD TRAVELED OUTSIDE OF THE LANDS WE CONTROL AND INTO THE REGION OF THE SILURES, BEARING THE INSIGNIA OF A MERCHANT. HE HAD FALLEN INTO THE COMPANY OF A MAN WITH A FEARSOME REPUTATION NAMED PANDIRA, A BY-MERIT CENTURION OF XX VALERIA VICTRIX. THIS PANDIRA HAD BEEN GIVEN DISPENSATION TO SCOUT THE LANDS OF THE SILURES.

CLEMENS ASSERTS THAT HE DID NOT LIKE THE MAN, FINDING HIM TO BE UNCULTURED AND CRUEL OF TEMPER, BUT THAT HE PROVED TO BE A VALUABLE ASSET IN DANGEROUS LANDS. AN ASSAULT BY A DOZEN SILURIAN TRIBESMAN ENDED WITH CLEMENS ACCOUNTING FOR THREE. PANDIRA MEANWHILE HAD SLAIN THE REST BEFORE CLEMENS HAD RUN THROUGH HIS THIRD.

BY NIGHT, PANDIRA AND CLEMENS EACH TOOK WATCH. ON THREE NIGHTS, CLEMENS WOKE TO FIND PANDIRA GONE. ALTHOUGH NO ANIMAL OR BARBARIAN EVER CAME NEAR TO THE CAMP, CLEMENS BEGAN TO WONDER WHY PANDIRA WAS SO PRONE TO LEAVE HIS POST. HE ASKED PANDIRA ON THE FIRST NIGHT AND THE CENTURION EXPLAINED THAT HE HAD HEARD A SOUND AND HAD BRIEFLY MOVED AWAY TO INVESTIGATE; ON THE SECOND NIGHT, PANDIRA HAD NEEDED TO RELIEVE HIMSELF; ON THE THIRD, PANDIRA FLEW INTO A RAGE AND DENIED THAT HE HAD EVER LEFT HIS POST AT ALL.

THAT LAST NIGHT, CLEMENS PURPOSED NOT TO SLEEP; HE FEIGNED SLEEP WHEN IT WAS HIS TURN TO PASS OVER WATCH, AND WATCHED AS THE CENTURION REMOVED HIS CLOTHES, ARMS AND ARMOR, COLLECTED THEM INTO A PILE. THE CENTURION PISSED IN A CIRCLE AROUND THE PILE OF CLOTHING, AND THEN VANISHED INTO THE SHADOWS. CLEMENS, DRAWING HIS SWORD, LEAPT UP AND RAN OVER TO THE CLOTHING AND ARMS, WHICH HE FOUND HAD TURNED INTO STONE.

HEARING A NOISE IN THE BUSHES, CLEMENS PURPOSED TO INVESTIGATE, ONLY TO FIND HIMSELF CONFRONTED WITH A BAND OF BRITONS IN WAR ATTIRE, WHO IMMEDIATELY SET UPON HIM.

AFTER A DESPERATE FIGHT, OUR SALVIUS, ALTHOUGH HE ACQUITTED HIMSELF WELL, WAS WOUNDED IN THE LEG AND BEATEN TO THE GROUND. BEFORE THE SNEERING BRITONS COULD DELIVER THE DEATH-BLOW, A WOLF OF VAST SIZE RUSHED FROM THE BUSHES AND SET UPON THE BARBARIANS, WHO WERE NO MATCH FOR IT, ALTHOUGH ONE, BEFORE HE FELL, WAS LUCKY ENOUGH TO PUT ONE OF THE WOLF'S EYES OUT WITH HIS SPEAR.

EXPECTING THE BEAST TO ATTACK HIM NEXT, CLEMENS PREPARED TO FIGHT HIS LAST, BUT THE WOLF TURNED INTO THE FOREST AND LEFT HIM.

CLEMENS LIMPED BACK TO THE CAMP. THERE HE FOUND PANDIRA, PRESSING A BANDAGE TO A TERRIBLE WOUND IN HIS EYE.

HAVING BEEN CONVINCED THAT PANDIRA WAS A WEREWOLF, CLEMENS WALKED BEHIND HIM, SPEAKING CONVERSATIONALLY AS IF UNAWARE THAT ANYTHING WAS WRONG, RAISED HIS STILL-DRAWN SWORD AND BEHEADED THE CENTURION.

HE RETURNED TO HIS MISSION ALONE.

Story Hooks: In Plain Sight

• Soldiers and Policemen

Ironically, werewolves can make fabulous soldiers and policemen. The pack-dog mentality that werewolves develop drives them to protect their chosen group and fight for it. A werewolf soldier treats his sergeant as his alpha; his fellow privates as his family. And, of course, he fights and kills.

Clemens was lucky. He got Pandira on his own, far from anywhere.

You might think that it would be difficult to hide a werewolf's presence from his military masters. This is perhaps true. But then, would they care? Going back to the film *Dog Soldiers*: the hapless squaddies in that film discover about halfway through that the British military has sent them out on maneuvers as bait to capture the werewolves and somehow learn how to get werewolves involved with Special Forces. Or something to that effect. Obviously, it doesn't work out, but that's just a movie — in the World of Darkness, what's to say that some high-level conspiracy hasn't succeeded in not only finding the werewolves... but recruiting them? Given the way that secret organizations work, it's not outside the realms of possibility that Task Force: VALKYRIE ends up investigating the

mayhem these creatures called, not realizing until it's too late that they're working for the government. Which, as any fool can tell you, is not by any means the same as saying "on *our* side." TFV's hunters find their investigation blocked at every turn; frustrated, they push it. Suddenly their nation has abandoned them. They're at the wrong end of the government's most secret military project.

Here's another story: some soldiers, known to our hunters as family, friends or even colleagues, come back from active service in Iraq or Afghanistan. They're in trouble. Some pictures surfaced of imprisoned "illegal combatants" being abused in a military prison, and the hunters' buddy is in the photos, happily playing along. He's not that sort of guy to get mixed up in something stupid like that.

A message gets to the hunters: their friend has changed his story: he's starting to protest his innocence. Somehow, someone lets them know that he wants to see them. He needs their help. The next day, he's found hanged in his cell.

Information begins to filter through to the characters. The photos were faked. The military set up the scandal — to draw attention away from what they were really doing, and who was really doing it. And the closer they get, the more the

Jim Di Bartolo

likelihood that the real military monsters are on their tails...

A werewolf who works in the police is another spectacularly difficult quarry. With a literal aptitude for sniffing out evidence, a police officer, particularly a detective, with a secret wolf-skin is incredibly successful. But suspects disappear, and sometimes evidence vanishes, too. A cell of hunters tracks down a serial cannibal. The police are never much help in situations like this, but here the local constabulary proves to be downright obstructive, almost as if they don't want anyone to find out the truth. By the time the hunters figure out that the killer is the investigating detective, they're on the run themselves: the detective has managed to pin it on them. But clearing themselves is least of their worries. They have to avoid being the next victims.

• Injuries

The classic trope of the werewolf story is the part of the story where the wolf gets injured... and the people who met the beast later meet a human with the same injury. Fact is, most werewolves heal remarkably quickly and this doesn't really happen a whole lot. Even so, a particularly badly injured werewolf may not have the time or the supernatural resources to heal his wounds before he has to change back. Storytellers using this trope should feel free to subvert it, though. Lots of people break their legs, for example, and while the werewolf may have managed to heal the injury he got from the impact of a two-by-four and his ankle, the hunters don't necessarily know that. Shapechangers excite suspicion, just by being able to change shape. You don't know who the werewolf is. Playing with that (but not too much) can add a level of uncertainty and paranoia to a game.

The People of the Wolf

Throughout the Middle Ages and into the Renaissance, the people of mainland Europe feared werewolves above all other monsters. While on the British Isles witches excited the public imagination and across the Rhine they feared vampires, in France, Germany, Italy and Spain, hardly any creature amassed quite so much terror and folklore as the werewolf, so much so that for centuries being a werewolf was a crime you could be tried for, and burnt for. Even at the time, the nature of the werewolf excited hot debate among divines and folklorists alike. Was he a worshiper of Satan? A throwback to the time of the heathen barbarians of the north? A dead man, forced to rise and adopt a lupine form? Or a simple cannibal or a murderer?

The stories are inconclusive, and the great books on the subject are contradictory. Sabine Baring-Gould's 1865 *Book of Were-Wolves*, for instance, which is a seminal work on the subject, dedicates three chapters to the case of serial child-murderer Gilles de Rais, and references the tale of Erzsébet Báthory, which is more often included in tomes of vampire lore.

The point of all this is that the werewolf is really a nebulous figure, a horror without a real definition. We fear the werewolf, but we don't really know what he is.

The compacts and conspiracies that have risen and fallen over the course of the centuries have their own ideas about werewolves, but who knows if they really have the faintest idea what these creatures are, how long they have been among us and how much power they really have?

The Beast at the Door (898)

From the anonymous Life of Saint Honoria, the Prostitute:

And when the third day had come, the woman put aside her fine clothes and called to her the maidservants and pages whom she was wont to employ; and she said to them, You are free to go now, and see, all my riches and wealth are yours, for I have renounced them. I only ask you this, that you look to the state of your souls, and consider the Word of God while you are young.

And the servants left her. Honoria returned to the convent and met Sister Elizabeth, and the Sister gave her a cloak, and Honoria cut her hair, for she said, My pride is not in earthly appearances but in God.

And Honoria tied a cloth around her head, and then returned to a cell, where she took to praying. And as she prayed, Satan came to her, and said, You are foolish to abandon me, for I can give you wealth that shall make your former estate seem poor. And he showed her a vision of gold and gems and fine cloths and linen, of houses with pillars and indentured servants.

But Honoria turned away from him, and did not speak to him, but continued to raise prayers to Heaven.

And Satan said to her, But see the pleasures you have rejected, and the pleasures I have in store for you, should you only decide to follow me once more.

But Honoria turned away from Satan, and said, Begone, for I have served you enough, and have no need of such things. For what do these phantoms matter when I have had a vision of the true bliss that awaits me in Heaven?

And Satan was sore vexed, and said to her, Look then to your self, for I shall send my servants to assault you.

And Honoria said, I am not afraid to die.

And Satan left her.

Presently, a frightful sound was heard through the convent, of a great wild beast outside, snarling, and grinding its teeth, and scraping its claws against the outside of the door. And Sister Elizabeth and the other nuns were terribly afraid. Honoria said to them, Take heart, for the Lord is with us and the sign of the cross will protect us.

And the nuns said to Honoria, What shall we do? For our door is weak and we are not able to fight such a thing, and while we do not fear ourselves, we must protect the children and the elderly for whom we care in this place.

And Honoria told them to hide in the convent garden and to garland themselves with the monkshood that grew there, for she said, The Lord has shown to me that the followers of Satan fear the holy flower. And she said, I shall face this creature, and God shall decide my fate.

And when the sisters had hidden themselves, and the children and elderly folk for whom they cared, Honoria went to the chapel and took in her hands the silver cross that stood upon the altar, and held it before herself, and waited by the door.

And the beast sent by Satan hit the door hard, and it burst into splinters. And it stood at the threshold, a beast with the head and claws of a wolf that walked like a man. And Honoria did not step back, but held aloft the cross, and bade the beast retreat.

But Honoria's faith failed her, and the beast leapt forward, so to devour her.

And it leaped through the air. And Honoria raised the silver cross from the altar and thrust it under the beast's ribs, and pierced it, and crushed its heart, and it breathed out its life.

And when the beast had died, and had left its blood upon the silver cross from the altar, which bubbled and boiled against the sacred metal, it lay back, Honoria saw that its hair and fangs and claws and muzzle vanished, and it became a man, a man whom she recognized, who had been reputed a witch, and who had bought her when she was given to sin.

Story Hooks: By the Word of God

• Saints and Sinners

It was commonly believed that the werewolf was in some way in league with Satan. Some werewolves were the children of witches who had fornicated with devils; some had made a pact with the Evil one. Either way, werewolves were the work of Old Nick, and being infernal in origin, heavenly signs and miracles could stop them. Take the story of Saint Honoria. The Malleus Maleficarum honors Saint Honoria as the patron of monster-hunters and werewolf-slayers, and her feast day is September 25th.

The old-school Catholic line is that Honoria destroyed the werewolf that the Devil sent against her through her faith, and the use of a sacred object as a weapon.

More knowledgeable readers will no doubt be aware that the efficacy of the altar cross probably had more to do with the simple fact that its pointy end was solid silver (as a lot of ecclesiastical tat was, particularly in places where having the stuff in solid gold was prohibitively expensive).

Which goes to show that actually, hunters and fighters of monsters can get the wrong end of the stick, whoever they are, and whatever they're fighting. Honoria seemed to have a good idea of what worked against the werewolves, or at least a grasp of the folklore. Monkshood, for example, is another name for aconite, which is also sometimes called "wolfsbane." Some werewolves are repelled by it (but not all of them). But some of Honoria's contemporaries believed that werewolves could be cured if you took away the tools that made them werewolves (more on that later), or if you kept them from eating flesh for a month and prayed for their souls, or if you performed rites of exorcism on them. The thing is, on some werewolves, some of these things might actually work. But they're in the minority here. That doesn't stop hunters even today passing around these things as foolproof remedies. They're in for a shock.

The Malleus Maleficarum's members take it as a point of faith that the Benediction rituals they use against werewolves work better on Saint Honoria's Day. Do they? Kindly Storytellers may be prepared to give a one-die bonus to a single Benediction dice pool on that day, but it's not mandatory, and it doesn't settle the question of whether or not Benedictions are really signs of divine favor or not (it might represent the agent's increased confidence, for example).

The feast of Saint Honoria is, unsurprisingly for those who don't discount her story as mere myth, a favored time to hunt werewolves for Catholic and Orthodox hunters the world over, whether members of the Malleus Maleficarum or not. Around the time of the harvest moon, werewolves start getting hassle from old-school religious warriors. The Harvest Crusade doesn't carry with it any guarantee of success; in fact, given the nature

of the opponent and the martial prowess of your average priest, it's a good time, as they say, to die.

The flip side of this is of course that the werewolves aren't stupid. More than that, a lot of them have their own unique religious views which have no space for a Christian worldview, and have suffered for centuries at the hands of its most patriarchal and conservative practitioners. Some werewolves are organized into tribes and families. Now imagine that a group of zealous Catholic hunters have been dutifully calling werewolf season every year for decades, for generations.

Are the werewolves going to take lightly the fact that around the harvest moon, they start getting persecuted by the Catholics again? Are they going to lie down like good doggies and take it?

Cue some persecution coming right back at the Catholics. Innocent churchgoers get preyed upon. The Catholic church gets firebombed. So does the Catholic hospital. Beasts break into a convent and massacre the nuns. And then they lay siege to the Catholic boarding school...

It's war. Now our Catholic hunters must retaliate; escalation is inevitable. The Christians have the numbers. But the werewolves have terrible strength, and some of them have even more terrible allies. Maybe those allies aren't strictly the demonic slaves of Satan, but in the field, who's going to be able to tell the difference?

The Boy Lame of Leg (1194... or thereabouts)

WENDIGO GROUP PUBLISHING

TALES

EERIE TALES MAGAZINE

WOLFSHEAD

A TALE OF GORY HORROR TO CHILL YOUR BONES BY VINCENT MOON

III

Partha Mac Othna wiped the last of the brigand's blood from his sword, and surveyed his handiwork with an appreciative eye. He grunted, half with approval, half with exhaustion. Nearby, his faithful companion Franz sat upon a rock and bound a cut on his arm with a strip of rag.

"They weren't the monsters, of course," said the big Briton, looking across the forest clearing, across the five men who lay dead at his feet, their gore steaming in the cold air and dying the snowy ground a rich, bright red. He regarded the corpses with the cool detachment of a man who has killed many in his time and will kill many more.

"Still, it seems too convenient that they came for us here, now," said Franz, gritting his teeth as he pulled the knot tight. "They must have been sent. Here, look," he said, suddenly, as he leaped to his feet and strode across to one of the bloodied brigands.

He crouched, and with a single tug, took a necklace from the man's neck. "I saw this as we fought," he said, holding up a leathern thong on which hung an iron pendent, crudely fashioned into the shape of a wolf. "They all have them."

"The sign of Alaric Wolfshead," said Mac Othna, setting his chin. "His power reaches far into these woods."

"They were doubtless sent here to keep us from the village," said Franz, sheathing his sword. We have no time to lose. The demon's agent will arrive at Stregoicavar in mere hours."

The two men had pursued the man called Wolfshead across the warring states of the East, until at last they came here to Livonia, his ancient hold. Tonight would be Christmas Eve, the night before the traditional dawn of hope, on which the forces of evil and darkness made their last assault on the world.

As the two men rode purposefully towards the village of Stregoicavar, night hung over the blasted landscape like a sullen threat, pregnant with doom. The village itself appeared deserted; the villagers would stay inside until the bells rang for midnight and Christmas day. And so, the snow lay thinly over the settlement like a shroud, and life was absent.

The two men dismounted at the edge of the village square. "Now what?" said Franz, rubbing his hands together and pulling his cloak more tightly around him.

"Now we wait," said Mac Othna.

Each man was no stranger to the cold, but even so, the waiting chilled in other ways. The darkness was deep and complete, but as they waited, the full moon arose and lit the town in ghoulish white. And then it came: they heard the rhythmic tap of a stick or crutch on the icy cobbles of the square.

32

EERIE TALES MAGAZINE

WOLFSHEAD

A TA...

Partha M...
veyed his han...
exhaustion. N...
his arm with ...
"They we...
clearing, acr...
and dying th...
detachment ...
"Still, it...
his teeth as ...
suddenly, as ...
He cro...
this as we f...
crudely fas...
"The ...
reaches fa...
"They ...
his sword ...
mere hou...
The ...
East, unt...
mas Eve...
darkness ...
As ...
over the...
appeare...
Christ...
was abs...
Th...
rubbin...
"N...
Ea...
ways. ...
lit the...
or cru...

32

EERIE TALES MAGAZINE

A figure of a young boy, wearing only rags and shivering in the cold, lame of one leg and leaning on a crutch, hobbled to the center of the village square and called out: "Come!"

"This cannot be Wolfshead's agent," whispered Franz, but Mac Othna hissed silence.

The boy cried out a second time: "Come!" and this time his voice was like the howl of some maddened wolf, a howl that tore through the hearts of the doughty warriors, that made their blood run colder than the ice and snow that covered this cursed land.

Although neither man would ever admit it, even to himself, both Franz and his dour companion felt an urge to run. But is not the nature of courage to conquer one's fear? Both had driven back the specter of fear too many times to turn and fly, and so both witnessed as one by one, doors in certain houses of the village began to open and a number men and women, as if in a dream, walked into the square. Each man and woman was naked, and each bore on his or her shoulder a mark like a strangely-shaped mole or blemish, a figure with open jaws.

"This is no boy; this is a demon in the form of a child," whispered Mac Othna through his teeth.

Franz nodded. "These are they who bear the Devil's mark. It must be time for Wolfshead's sabbat."

The lame child turned and began to walk away towards the forest, leaning on the crutch and rocking from side to side as one who really was lame, but bearing an expression on his face that no human child ever bore, an expression of infinite age and infinite malice.

The men followed at a distance on foot, as the boy led the blank-faced thralls of Satan into the woods, and witnessed a bizarre transformation. As each of the Satanists crossed the perimeter of the woods, his face elongated, he stooped, and fur sprouted from his skin, leaving a dark patch where Wolfshead's mark remained: with each step, Satanist became wolf, and as they entered the depths of the forest, the change was complete and the lame devil-child led a pack of wolves.

EERIE TALES MAGAZINE

They followed him meekly to a clearing in the center of the forest, in the middle of which a huge bonfire blazed. Human skulls, some still bearing shreds of flesh, hung on branches that hung across the open space, while the decaying hands and feet of men, women and children were nailed to the trunks of trees that had grown fat and evil-looking through being watered with blood. Beside the fire stood something like a stone table, or an altar, to which a naked young woman was tied. She was unconscious, and her hair obscured her face.

And from behind the fire strode a man fully the size of Mac Othna, but where the Briton had a certain nobility to his glowering countenance, this man looked like nothing more than an animal, a scar-faced, red-eyed villain who bared yellow teeth filed to vicious points as his pack gathered around him. He wore a shirt and breeches made of tanned human skin, and bore a wickedly-curved blade like a Turk's at his hip.

"Wolfshead," hissed Franz. He tightened his grip on the hilt of his sword.

The boy with the crutch began to cackle, and Wolfshead motioned with one hand. The lame child dropped the crutch, and rushed forward into the blazing fire, and was gone.

Partha Mac Othna unslung his crossbow from his back, loaded the silver-tipped bolt that the Wallachian priest had given him, and began to wind back the string. But Franz put his hand on the Briton's arm.

"Who knows whether your bolt will strike true, my friend?" whispered the German. "Besides, the moment they know we are here—"

"Partha Mac Othna! Franz von Beckenbauer!" Wolfshead's voice rang out across the clearing. The Briton and the German looked up. "He knows," whispered Franz.

"I have led you this far, cowards. Now see what I have as my prize!" Wolfshead lifted the head of the unconscious girl and pulled her hair back from her face.

Franz gasped again. "Drusilla! The fiend has my Drusilla!"

Mac Othna grasped Franz' shoulder with a single big hand. "An illusion. It must be—"

"It is no illusion," said Franz, regaining calm with a superhuman effort. "It is our doom."

Wolfshead, meanwhile, leered over the unconscious form of Franz' beloved. He called out again: "Come face me, cowards. Let me see the faces of those I would kill this day."

"If we die today," said Mac Othna, taking a deep breath and preparing for the worst, "We die as men."

"Aye," said Franz, raising his sword high. Franz let out a cry rich with righteous fury and leaped into the clearing. Partha Mac Othna stepped forward beside, and raised his crossbow, knowing that if this was his last shot, it must fly true...

TO BE CONTINUED...

Story Hooks: The Howls of the Damned

• The Harbinger

The tale of the lame child who wanders across Livonia on Christmas Eve gathering together the followers of Satan comes from medieval folklorist Olaus Magnus. It comes packed with a weird kind of symbolic irony: the werewolf of folklore primarily preyed on innocents, and the weak and crippled always got eaten first. The picture of a lame child, the prey of the werewolf, gathering the wolves together for their sabbat, carries a particular kind of ironic symbolism, a perversion of the Christian image of the innocent leading the wild beast. In one version of the story, the lame boy is Satan in disguise; in another he's a demon; other versions fail to explain his provenance at all.

Maybe he's a spirit, or a demon, or a hallucinatory projection. Maybe he was conjured by a werewolf (like Wolfshead in Vincent Moon's pulp story) as a means of creating a temporary pack—which is an interesting point in its own right: there are good reasons why different kinds of werewolves might be found together.

It doesn't really matter — the Storyteller can deal with that detail. What matters is that this figure is a harbinger of disaster.

He comes at night, and the werewolves have no choice but to come out of their homes and follow him to their conclave or sabbat, or moot, or whatever they want to call it.

It could be that the lame child has the power to force werewolves to change. Or he might awaken dormant werewolf blood in people who are hitherto unaware that they have werewolf heritage. Or perhaps he can temporarily force people to become werewolves — in the case of Olaus Wormius' story, it was all those who had dealt with the devil, but the lame boy might be able to do this to anyone who's been bitten by a werewolf, or anyone who saw a certain supernatural event happening (being "infected" by the appearance of a ghost, or a spooky video, for example, *Ring*-style). Or he might be the harbinger of the event that makes an entire community make the change (as we talked about above).

People known to the hunters start having dreams of the demonic child. Nightmares come to everyone in an apartment block, or a village, or a tenement. When the night comes, everyone who has the dream leaves their homes naked, and becomes a wolf. Is the change permanent? Is it just for the night? Do the subjects of the demonic "child's" weird power remember what they did on the night they spent as a wolf? All of these questions may have terrible answers.

• Keeping it in the Family

Not everyone with werewolves in their family is a werewolf. Their kids might be, and one of their parents might be, but the blood of the wolf isn't at all consistent. Still having werewolf blood in you does have one real advantage: the fear and post-facto rationalization that werewolves engender in the minds of those who see them isn't nearly as intense for a person with wolf's blood.

The relatives of werewolves are sometimes completely unaware that their relatives are werewolves. But sometimes they realize without ever being told. And sometimes they know all along.

And often, they end up working for their more frightening relatives. Maybe they do it out of fear. Maybe they do it out of love. Maybe they just do it because the wolves are family.

Our two sword-swinging pulp heroes face several of these folks, the werewolf Wolfshead's hapless kin.

Hunters looking for the more dangerous, more organized, tribal sort of werewolf may find that long before they get anywhere near the werewolves, they're facing opposition from people who aren't werewolves at all. In a small town, where everyone knows everyone, a werewolf's dad might be the county sheriff (or local Inspector of Police). His sister may be an important part of the local club scene, or the local magistrate, or the nearest general practitioner. His uncle's the medical examiner or the coroner. His brother's tied up with organized crime. His cousin's just a local landowner with a gun collection. They've all got the means to obstruct hunters, violently or not, but more importantly, they add another moral element to the hunt: many of these people are not bad people, and not everything they do to protect their kin is even all that wrong. And they will grieve for their relative if he dies. The hunters may think of a werewolf as a menace that must be stopped, but these are people to whom she is a sister, or a daughter, or a cousin... and to three small children, she's "mommy."

Eaters of Children

The Middle Ages came to an end, but the fear of werewolves continued. Enlightened thinkers came to the conclusion that werewolves were a delusion, either of the masses who still feared monsters, or of the benighted souls who fooled themselves into thinking they were werewolves.

The general public took a long time to really come to any understanding of how the human psyche could really make someone a changer of shapes.

In 1521, two men named Pierre and Michel were tried by an inquisitor in Besançon for being werewolves: they had devoured several women and children. They had, so the account went, been duped into becoming servants of the Devil, who had promised security for their livestock. They turned into wolves by smearing a particular salve on themselves, and both men entered a state of exhaustion after having run as wolves. In 1598, a girl named Pernette Gandillon began to run on all fours and behave like a beast. She attacked some children, and killed and ate a boy of four. When the local people caught her, they tore her to pieces with their bare hands. Her brother Pierre, her nephew Georges and her sister Antoinnette all confessed deals with Satan. They claimed that they had ointments that would transform them into wolves. The local inquisitors hung and burned them all. In the same year, a man in the town of Châlons was burned for being a werewolf. He had killed and eaten countless children. His confession was so awful that the court commanded it be burned. And a homeless man named Roulet was accused of being the wolf that was seen devouring a teenage boy. Circumstantial evidence was damning: when men stumbled across the boy's corpse being eaten by a wolf, the wolf ran from the scene; giving chase, the men ran into the vagrant, who was covered in blood and gore. He, too, had a salve given to him by Satan that changed his shape.

The infamous French witch hunter Pierre de Lancre tells of an incident in 1603. It began in Bordeaux: three young girls, who were tending their parents' flocks, found their dogs in a state of some distress. Following the animal, they came upon a strange-looking red-haired boy of about thirteen. His teeth were filed to points, his hands were large and knotted and his fingernails were more or less talons. He told the girls that his name was Jean Grenier and he was the son of a priest. He adopted an attitude of cocky arrogance, which isn't really all that surprising, given his age. He described Hell to the girls, and said it was the home of his master, the man who had given him the skin of a wolf. He said that on Mondays, Fridays and Sundays, he and nine others would wrap wolf-skins around themselves and would hunt for blood and flesh. Grenier maintained that his favorite food was the flesh of little girls: their meat was sweet and tender, and their blood ran warm. The girls, frightened by the glee with which he told them these things, and by the unnatural sound of his laughter, ran in fear. They told their parents.

About the same time, a girl named Marguerite Poirier, from the nearby village of St. Antoine de

Pizon, who had been sent to look after livestock with Jean Grenier, told how he had developed a preoccupation with blood and death, and how one day he had derived evident pleasure he derived from frightening her with revolting stories. He'd told her that day much the same thing as he told the other girls, but had also described in some detail how he had killed and eaten a number of children.

Marguerite escaped from Grenier and went home in what the documents describe as a "fit of terror." On her way, a wolf, or something like a wolf, attacked her: she fought it off with her staff and it withdrew a short distance. Marguerite got a good look at it. It sat on its hind legs like a dog does when it's begging, and had what can only be described as an unsettling *human* expression of hate and rage on its oddly-shaped face. It was smaller and stouter than a real wolf. Its tail was stunted, and its head was strangely flat. Its fur was reddish rather than gray.

The people of the local area began to panic: a number of small children had vanished. The local magistrates stepped in and after something of a chase, ran Grenier to ground. He was the son, not of a priest, but of a common laborer. He confessed everything.

He'd sold his soul to the Devil — who appeared to him as a black man, as was often the case in tales of witches and werewolves at this time. The Devil had given him, he said, a jar of a magical ointment and a wolf-skin. It was his habit to hide his clothes, smear himself with the ointment and put on the wolf-skin which adhered to his flesh and made him a wolf, of sorts. He claimed he had never seen Duthillaire kill anyone, but that his father was a werewolf too, and had eaten many children himself. He had been warned by the Devil never to bite or break the long, thick thumbnail of his left hand, presumably because this would cost him his powers.

Grenier told of how he stolen a baby from a cradle and had eaten most of her, and had given the rest to a wolf. He had murdered a child who had been keeping sheep with his nails and teeth and had eaten her. He had found a child crossing a bridge, and devoured her. Other children had been saved by their parents and their own efforts. Marguerite Poirier testified as

WAIT: "EATERS OF CHILDREN?"

The fact is that werewolves in folklore eat children; the real individuals who were tried for werewolfism all murdered boys and girls.

The abuse and murder of children is a touchy subject, and not necessarily one for a game. The author, as a parent, finds it particularly hard to deal with, and probably wouldn't be comfortable playing in a game where this was dealt with in any detail. Games don't have to reflect every aspect of the folklore, and frankly, the werewolves in the World of Darkness bear only a passing resemblance to the stories anyway.

A horror game can deal with difficult and nasty issues, but at the same time, it's a game, and we're here to enjoy ourselves. Everyone has buttons that shouldn't be pushed. This author's is cruelty to children, and yours may be something else. If issues like child-killing are too close to home, please ignore them and deal with frights and horrors that chill without removing any sense of enjoyment you might have.

to the monster that had attacked her, but the judge discounted this, saying that the red-headed boy was simply deluded: by the thinking of the day, the boy was an "imbecile" (in modern terms, we'd probably describe him as developmentally disabled).

The judge ignored the stories and ordered that Jean Grenier spend the rest of his life in a monastery, which he must never leave on pain of death.

De Lancre, who was, unlike the judge who sentenced Jean Grenier to the monastery, a firm believer in witchcraft and werewolves, visited Jean in 1610. Now aged 20, Grenier was short and skinny. His teeth were still long and his nails were still like talons. He was barely able to talk at all. He said that he still craved young girls' flesh and that the Devil would come to take him away. He was dead not long after de Lancre met him.

All of these cases now fall under the umbrella of psychoanalysis: lycanthropy is an order of delusion. But, especially in the World of Darkness, certain things don't make sense, certain coincidences are too common to comfortably accept. Wolves appear and disappear. What was the deformed creature that attacked Marguerite Poirier, and why did the judge ignore it so very quickly?

The werewolf panic consumed the European mainland, and in some cases stretched across to the new colonies in America, where Europeans came into contact with tribal peoples who had long held to beliefs in the continuity of man and animal, and the spirit world. Vast religious conflicts consumed the West, and these reflected themselves in the preoccupations of witch finders and werewolf hunters... and perhaps then they reflected in the monsters themselves.

The Beast of Amanges (1573)

Translated and modernized from an anonymous French document, supposedly from the early 17th century, held in the Paris library of the Loyalists of Thule:

The common belief is that the werewolf derives his powers from a skin; or from a salve which he applies to his form. I do not know if this is true. I know this: in the autumn of 1573 I was among employed by the Court of Parliament at Dôle in Franche Comté to lead the peasants of that region in a hunt for the werewolf that plagued the region.

It had savaged the livestock. It had carried away and killed several children. And it had even grown bold enough to attack a pair of mounted armed men.

On the thirteenth day of the month, a group of peasants from the region assembled; and I inspected them. They were neither hardened troops nor even particularly effective. Their discipline was poor, and their arms were not of any good standard: several pikes and halberds, not in good order; some swords and knives, some quarterstaves, farming implements, two arquebuses, only one of which was in working condition. The best of them had finely-maintained longbows. One or two of them had pieces of plate from old campaigns. I wondered if we might be able to find the creature without any of these men dying, without any of them depriving a child of his father or a wife of her husband. Their sergeant, a large, ferociously bearded man named Villet, was capable enough, but he seemed indolent, unwilling to master the troops with the discipline they required.

For my part, I had my breastplate, my rapier and my trusty caliver. And one more thing, a ball for my gun made of pure silver, given to me by a priest who belonged to the "Witches' Hammer," for whom I had worked and fought, many times. I had no intention of using it. But the priest had blessed it in the name of St. Martin and Ste. Honoria, and it was the nearest I had to a rosary or a crucifix, for I am not by nature a religious man.

We scoured the fields. We guarded the flocks. We patrolled the forests. We interviewed every peasant we could about any sighting of the wolves we had seen, but we found no werewolf.

We searched across the last dyings of summer and into October, towards the time of rain and cold. Several of the men had to return home for the harvest, and returned again, and while we had found and destroyed a number of wolves, and had even brought to justice a small band of bandits, we had still not found our werewolf. It seemed to know we were looking for it, for in the whole time, not one report of a werewolf's attack arose. I began to wonder if the werewolf had left our vicinity altogether, the better to trouble a new region.

It was not until November 8 that any news of the creature arose. It happened that four peasants of Chastenoy, not of our militia, had been returning home that evening through the forest. They heard the howls and snarls of a wolf and the screams of a child. Running to help, they drove off a creature that was attacking a little girl, and which, although she was defending herself as best she could, had already wounded her gravely.

They drove the creature off, and it snarled and made its escape on all fours. In the darkness, the four men could not agree that they had seen a wolf. One of them did not gain much of an impression of the beast at all. Two thought it was a wolf. But one of them swore that he had seen, as the creature turned on him, the face of Gilles Garnier, a recluse who lived with his wife near Amanges in a ruin of a cottage and whom, without any religious association, the peasants had begun to call the Hermit of St. Bonnot.

M. Garnier's home at Amanges was not often visited; it lay in the midst of a forested region, and lay in a unique and extreme degree of dilapidation. Its garden was overgrown, and the doors and shutters of the cottage were barely attached to their hinges.

The hermit himself was of somewhat repellent aspect: he stooped; his hands were gnarled and bore long, thick nails. The third finger of his left hand was longer than his middle finger. His teeth were uneven, sharp and protruding through a filthy gray beard. Heavy brows joined in the middle over a flat nose. He habitually breathed out a stench to make the eyes of a steady man water.

And he grew nothing, and traded nothing, and we could not see how he and his wife survived. And yet they did, year after year.

When we heard the news, several of the peasants purposed to travel directly to the hermit's home to arrest him, but I counseled caution: a single man's brief impression of the face of someone he already distrusted? Is that enough to kill a man?

The peasants, and in particular Villet, protested, telling me that this was not my home and that I could not understand of what the hermit might be capable, but I told them that I had taken part in too many hunts, and had seen too many innocent men impaled or burned to allow this to happen again without being sure of whom I was accusing. The peasants grumbled, but allowed me to make the point.

The child recovered, and we returned to the hunt, paying especial attention to the region. But the trail had grown cold. On the 14th it happened that a 10-year-old boy was missing. His parents had last seen him near the gates of Dôle. The peasant militia who accompanied me grew impatient. They ignored my orders, and worse, Villet over-ruled me and supported them. He had, he said, decided that the only way to end the werewolf's reign of terror would be to seize Garnier and his wife. I pursued them to Garnier's house, only for Villet to raise a hand and for the peasants to drag me from my horse and hold me back with punches and kicks as they raided the house and seized the two old people.

They led the pair to the inquisitor, and Garnier and his wife were put to torture, and of course they confessed everything they had been asked and more besides, to the kidnap and capture of five missing children while Gilles had taken the form of a wolf. And how they had both eaten them raw.

But no wolf-skin was found in Gilles Garnier's hovel, and no salve. No sign of a witch-mark was on his body. And his confession... he was old, and he was addled, and they had tortured him, and they had done the same to his wife while he had watched. He would have confessed to having been Satan himself if they had asked him.

But I could do nothing. At the trial at which Garnier had been found guilty, some of the peasants jeered at me. One woman, the mother of the boy who had vanished outside of Dôle, spat at my feet.

I attended the burning, although I was not welcome there, and was forced to remain at the edge of the square. I forced myself to hear Garnier's screams, and those of his wife, and, even more terrible, the cheers and laughter of the peasants. Across the crowd I saw

Villet, who was not cheering, and he nodded at me, sardonically and left the square. I pushed through the crowd, suddenly imagining that I should speak to him. I lost him.

And so it was that I rode alone through the forest of Amanges, seeking the home of the old man and woman they had accused of being a werewolf. I didn't know what I would find there. A strange compulsion had taken me, and I did not know from whence it came.

I sat in the ruins of the house for an hour or more, staring at the moon through the broken shutter, and waiting for God to show me a sign. I prayed, and I am not a praying man.

Eventually, although I had heard no sound of an approach, the ruined door of the hovel opened, and Villet entered. He asked me why I was there, and I told him that I hoped God would send me a sign and show me the truth. He told me that the truth had been found by the Inquisitor, and I said that it had not, and that I knew that Gilles Grenier had been an innocent.

He began, calmly and in good humor, to tell me how the God I worshiped was a sham, and that only the spirits were there, and they were on his side. I asked him if they were the spirits of Hell, and he said that he did not think so. He was of noble blood, he said, and it was his divine right to hunt, and if he should deprive himself of a less than palatable item of prey, so be it.

I did not understand him. But he spoke to me for much of the evening. It was as if I were the priest, and this were his confession, but the sins he spoke of were alien to me, and he did not see them as sins, rather as marks of pride. He told me that the wolf must hunt, and that the low must honor the high. He defied our Lord, and denied Him, and abused His name as the creator of the religion of failure. And he said the herd must not know, and I realized that by the herd, he meant the lower order of men, the men who were not werewolves. For he was a werewolf, the werewolf who had eaten those children, and who would eat me, for I realized also that he was not telling me these things by way of confession, but by way of answering my questions, that I might know who was about to devour me, and how I had failed. He gloated.

And he began, as he told me with relish how he had eaten children, and how strong and gamy my meat would be, to remove his breastplate and his shirt, and I turned and ran, and as I tried to light the match on my caliver, I fell in the gnarled and overgrown garden of innocent Gilles Grenier and turned onto my back and saw, close upon me, the beast that Villet had become, something the size of a bear with a head like some vast slavering wolf, and claws like pike-blades. And he was smiling at me, and with a long purple tongue, he licked his chops, and smiled with jagged brown and black teeth, like the nails that pinned Our Lord to His Cross.

And as Villet tensed his muscles to fly, I raised the caliver with one hand as if it were a pistol and saw that the match was still lit, and I sent the silver bullet through the monster's mouth as it sprang, and the bullet went through the roof of Villet's mouth and out through the back of his head, and the creature fell upon me and nearly crushed me with its weight.

But as Villet died, he shrank, and the hair folded back beneath his skin, and his muzzle faded away. And soon I had the corpse of a dead man lying upon me and his blood and brains across my face, and I pushed him off, and found his shirt and wiped his gore off me. And then I made a pyre from the ancient furniture of Gilles Grenier's hovel, and though it was hard to light and took a long time to burn, burn it did, and by the time the villagers came to see what had happened, he was ash, and the last of Gilles Grenier was ash with him.

Story Hooks: Witch-Hunts

• The Wrong Man

A whole load of ways for spotting a werewolf exist — eyebrows meeting in the middle, bad teeth, a long, thick thumbnail on the left hand, a Devil's mark — but while werewolves certainly exist who have one or more of these features, a lot of people who aren't werewolves have them too, and a lot of werewolves don't have them. Likewise, while we live in a more enlightened age, hunters live in a world where there's a chance that this stuff just might be true. And that the people who are the most likely to believe in it... act on it.

A member of Null Mysteriis probably isn't likely to pay the blindest bit of notice to such superstitions, and if he is, he'll only see them as physical symptoms of some genetic or cellular disease. The Aegis Kai Doru are far too clued on werewolves to fall for such things, and the Ascending Ones likewise have more experience than to accept medieval superstitions based on human experience. Likewise, few members of the Malleus Maleficarum have much time for these things, having gotten past that particular phase of knowledge and found new ways of finding these beasts a long time ago. Les Mystères, much like the Aegis Kai Doru, have too much knowledge (and hell, some of them probably have the very physical characteristics that are supposed to be for werewolves). On the other hand, Task Force: VALKYRIE might have the black helicopters and the medical facilities and the sci-fi gadgets, but all too often their agents rely on tactics a researcher from Null Mysteriis would just call "voodoo science."

The Cheiron Group's not-really-reliable Field Projects Division Handbook actually includes some of these characteristics as pointers to tracking down shapeshifters (in fact, at least one of TCG's major European and American facilities includes in its vault, among the monsters, at least one perfectly innocent human who agents have mistaken for a werewolf and have left to rot in the vault, because she's seen too much). The Long Night, surprisingly, doesn't have a lot of time for these superstitions, perhaps correctly identifying their provenance with Catholicism.

The Union, not being the most informed hunters in the world (its members have better things to do), do sometimes rely on pointers like these, and certainly they crop up from time to time on the forums, but whether or not a hunter takes them seriously varies from hunter to hunter.

Still, getting the wrong suspect is really an occupational hazard for werewolf hunters, what with the shapechanging and that. What happens when a cell of hunters finds one of their friends, one of their loved ones, or one of their colleagues in the sights of a rival compact or conspiracy whose werewolf lore is dodgy?

Suddenly, our hunter isn't just facing up against the werewolves, they're facing agents of TFV or TCG (or even both) who haven't just arrested his girlfriend/wife/brother/best friend, but have tipped off the enemy that the hunters in town are in on the process? How are they going to get their loved ones back? A lot of TCG and TFV agents (at least the ones who aren't player characters) are cold and inefficient bureaucrats—spies and security are kind of like that—who rely on their organizations and their kit rather than their common sense. It's no coincidence that the two best-supported organizations are among the most clueless. Hunters stave off werewolf attacks; meanwhile, the men with the big guns are so busy with their own agenda that they're more of a hindrance than a help.

On the flip side, player character agents of TCG or TFV may be far more enlightened about what werewolves are and how you can stop them, but that doesn't stop these two paradoxically unimaginative conspiracies having superiors or same-rank colleagues who will go out the way to get the result *their* way, the book's way, regardless of how incontrovertible the proof is that the book is a load of bunk.

The Recipe (1588)

The last entry in a notebook belonging to Dr. Bryan Wray Davis, researcher for Null Mysteriis:

One of the most persistent strands of folklore relating to werewolves (and shapechanging creatures in general) concerns the use of salves and ointments. From the witches of Apuleius through to the French trials of the sixteenth and seventeenth centuries, the idea that a werewolf can change shape through the simple action of rubbing a magical unguent into his skin seems to be universal.

Let's assume that in the vast majority of observed cases, the act of literally changing one's shape is a fiction, that the "werewolf" is really a person who for whatever reason is deluded into thinking he or she has become a wolf. Certainly, it's the upshot of most of the more famous werewolf trials, most of which include at some point a mention of a jar of salve or ointment, either brewed by witches, or bestowed upon the "werewolf" by Satan or some analogous figure (a "Lord of the Forest," for example). The deluded person covers himself with ointment and may or may not wrap himself with a wolf-skin. Then he's a wolf, and he goes out and eats livestock and children.

While I haven't been able to analyze a pot of "werewolf" ointment myself, several examples of recipes have survived. Here's one, which is found in an English "werewolf's" grimoire from 1598:

Monkshood.

Henbane.

Devil's Cherries.

Poppy flowers.

Sweet Flag.

Water-Parsnip.

Moon's Allure.

Boil them down in the fat of a virgin child, no more than five years old until all is made fluid. Add the blood of a bat.

Rub upon the skin, and do not eat; for to eat is death.

Note that this is it in its entirety. No amounts, no order, no directions. Little about which part of the plant to use (with the exception of the "Devil's Cherries," of course, and the flowers of the poppy). One assumes that the trained witch just knows these things from experience and personal instruction.

The addition of human fat — particularly that of a child — is chilling, of course, but it does add to our understanding of the makers' pathology. One commits a terrible act of murder to create a tool which, he hopes, will make him a more efficient killer, and more than that, a killer without conscience or self-control. In some ways, it's a self-fulfilling prophecy: you kill in order to kill. You can just as easily use other animal fats or vegetable fat to make the medium for the unguent. A "werewolf" wanting to make a new batch could just as easily make it by mixing the other ingredients with a tub of Vaseline.

As for the rest of the ingredients, well. The bat's blood is probably there for color. I don't think it does anything. All but one of the rest of the ingredients are fairly easy to identify and locate, and although I'm no herbalist, it doesn't take a degree in Botany to figure out why they're there.

Henbane, or stinking nightshade, is hyoscyamus niger, of the family solanaceae. Henbane creates visual hallucinations and the sensation of flying. It was a favorite with witches. In excessive doses, it's poisonous.

Monkshood is aconitum, or aconite. Beloved of homeopaths in miniscule doses, aconite slows the human heartbeat. It relaxes you. Interestingly, it's sometimes referred to as Wolfsbane, and is thought to repel werewolves.

"Devil's Cherries" is a colloquial English name for the berries of Atropa Belladonna, or deadly Nightshade, which is highly toxic in every part, leaves, berries and root. It's another favorite of witches, and once again, it's a hallucinogen. Water-Parsnip is Sium Suave, part of the parsnip family. It's well-known as a danger to livestock, since the leaves look a lot like the leaves of parsnips and carrots and can kill a cow stone dead. It's another hallucinogen.

Sweet Flag is a common name for Calamus (acorus calamus) of the family acoraceae. It's another hallucinogen, which is currently illegal in the US as an ingredient of medicines and food products. Entheogen groups use it as a psychotropic, and apparently, it's one of the classic ingredients of absinthe. Poppies, when prepared properly, are of course an opiate.

The only one of the herbs I haven't been able to place is "Moon's Allure." I have no idea what it is. None of the botanical or herbological works I have consulted have it under any name.

Obviously, you'd only need small quantities of any of these. I imagine that the effects of use would be dramatic to say the least, a cocktail of hallucinogens and poisons which, although most certainly lethal if ingested, probably has extremely interesting psychoactive effects when applied to the skin.

I suspect that the tingling and itchiness that a direct application of belladonna to the skin would, I think, create, would translate with the help of the other psychoactives into the illusion that hair is sprouting from the skin. Expectation and the wishes of the user would, I suppose, do the rest.

I can't help thinking that the only way to be sure would be to try it myself. Obviously, I'll use some more humanely acquired fat and leave out the bat blood. The "Moon's Allure" is probably just another hallucinogen anyway. No one has ever published on what it is like to try one of these salves.

Which is something of an oversight. Yes, there are risks, but a real scientist has to be prepared to put himself on the line. It's the least you can do.

Story Hooks: Skins and Salves

• In the Wrong Paws

The most numerous, organized and dangerous werewolves are born that way (although mostly they don't really know that until adolescence). But hunters know quite a bit about the other kinds of werewolves, who you can divide up into two main groups: the ones who became werewolves by accident, through a curse or through being bitten by a werewolf (in whom lycanthropy is a transmissible disease); and the sort who achieve their werewolf status through some order of witchcraft.

This second group includes those werewolves about whom the largest body of writing exists. They became werewolves out of their own free will (or they were duped into agreeing to become werewolves). They may have made a deal with the Devil, or with demons and spirits. And these are the ones who most often use tools to effect the transformation from human being into wolf.

Theoretically, anyone can use one of these objects, but what's the effect? And if you don't know what you're dealing with, how do you know if you have actually got it right? A lot of the psychoactive chemicals in the 16th century grimoire that Dr. Davis read are deadly poisons: use the wrong quantities and you could be in for an agonizing death.

Whether you really turn into a wolf or not, do you manage to keep control over your new "form?" Do you even remember what you did when you ran wild? Chances are, you don't.

A hunter gets hold of a pelt or a jar of ointment belonging to a werewolf. Does he know what it is? Does he know what it does? And is he tempted to try it out? And what happens if he does? Does he change into a werewolf? Or does he just believe himself to be a werewolf?

There's the question of ingredients. The missing ingredient, "Moon's Allure" is actually much more than just a psychotropic herb. It's made from magically treated flower petals, and only a certain number of people with actual magical powers know how to use one. It could be the difference between a really bad trip and an actual transformation into a werewolf. Likewise, a wolfskin impregnated with LSD and one actually enchanted are very different things.

There's the question of addiction, too. The recipe as stands has what amounts to a tiny amount of heroin in it. Psychoactive chemicals aren't usually enough to addict someone, but other things about the experience of being a wolf can be addictive: the feeling of health and power, the new physical strength, the sense of being set loose from all moral and social restrictions can all be powerfully intoxicating. Even if the character doesn't really become a werewolf, the illusion is enough, and is likely the only thing that the character remembers after he "changes back." If it's real, the effect is multiplied tenfold, meaning that before she knows it, even though she's aware of the newspaper headlines about the missing kids, even though she's sworn never to look at that jar of ointment again, she's using. And the following morning, she wakes up covered in blood and there's a human ear in her crap when she next goes to the bathroom.

It doesn't have to be a hunter. A bunch of teenagers break into the creepy old man's house and come out with the jar of... moisturizer? Vaseline? Some sort of ointment. One of them tries it on for a laugh. When he comes to, he's naked and miles away. His friends don't answer his texts or calls. Later on, he finds out they're all dead. He's scared. He runs. But at the same time, he realizes that the ointment gives an amazing high.

Maybe he starts dealing it on the streets for a few extra bucks, not realizing the literal connection between the ointment and the death of his friends. Maybe he starts using it again himself. Either way, the terrors happen and the killings escalate, made worse by the creepy old man and his own, rather unpleasant friends, who are tearing the town apart trying to find who's got the jar of ointment.

These friends might have their own jars of ointment, or may be those organized werewolves we were talking about, who have found a way to give relatives who don't naturally have the power to change the ability to do so.

• **The Dividing Line**

The kind of werewolf who uses a salve or skin to change straddles the line between werewolf and witch, and may actually *be* a witch. Several witches and warlocks, particularly those with a more shamanic outlook, know how to change shape.

A witch begins to become addicted to the rush gained from changing shape, and begins to make some terrible, bloody mistakes. Her former friends decide to stop her before she's going completely feral. So do the hunters, who of course don't count her as anything other than a dangerous menace. Do the hunters bury the hatchet and join forces with the witches or do they try to fight both groups? Is it even possible for the two outfits to get close enough to talk without killing each other? And do they have any chance of agreeing on what to do when they finally catch the errant shape changer? And when it's all over, can the magicians really let the characters go, knowing what they now know? Expect double-crosses on both sides.

In the literature, the werewolf often has some of the characteristics of the vampire. This sort of werewolf might also be a thrall or minion of a vampire. Who knows what powers the undead can bestow upon their followers? A werewolf scare might be the result of a vampire's slaves trying to hide the true crimes of their blood-sucking master.

And of course, the Devil comes in as a master of werewolves too. A whole pack of skin-wearing, ointment-using werewolves is the doing of a man with the blood of Devils in him, a Child of the Seventh Generation who never joined the Lucifuge. His half-brothers and half-sisters may be able to detect him a mile off (with the right Castigation) but there's no guarantee that they will immediately identify his works.

Any of these rationales is a great way to use the classic bait-

and-switch technique in a story: the hunters think they're facing one thing, and the enemy turns out to be quite another.

Croatoan (1590)

From Divination, *vol. 21, no.7, July 1982:*

DIVINATION

THE CROATOAN MYSTERY
by *Scott Nestel*

Among the people of the US, the legend of Roanoke Island holds pride of place in a small but growing corpus of legendry and folklore. The story goes like this: in 1587, the English, led by John White and financed by none other than Sir Walter Raleigh, made a second attempt at setting up a colony on Roanoke Island, which now lies just off the coast of North Carolina.

It looked so hopeful: the settlers landed on July 22, 1587, and soon established themselves. John White's daughter was pregnant, and on August 18, she gave birth to a daughter, Virginia Dare, the first English child born in the colonies. The settlers made contact with the Croatan Indians, who were friendly, but then things went wrong. The other local tribes, who had fought with the settlers of the first Roanoke Colony, would not meet with them or speak with John White.

The natives even killed one of the colonists while he was hunting for crabs. Eventually, the colonists sent John White back home to England to ask for help. The war with Spain and a lack of funds meant that it wasn't until 1590 that White arrived back at Roanoke Island... to find the colony gone. The cabins had been taken down, the livestock had vanished, and of the people the only traces were two graves... and a message, carved on a tree: "CROATOAN." On a lone post, someone had carved only three letters: "CRO."

White took it to mean that the colonists had gone to live on nearby Croatoan Island with the friendly Croatan Indians. But circumstances prevented him from ever visiting that island again, and more, an Indian chief convinced him that the colonists had all died.

No one ever found out what happened to the colonists. Stories emerged over the next century or more of white people intermarrying with the Indians. Explorers in the region would report grey-eyed

DIVINATION

Indians, or of natives who explained how their white forebears could "talk out of books." And let us not forget the splendid tale of the Welsh missionary who, captured by Indians and sure his time was up, was treated kindly by an old Indian medicine man who spoke to him in Welsh!

But none of this really explains the significance of that carved "CROATOAN" on the tree trunk.

Was it really a sign that the settlers had moved on to Croatoan Island, and had gone to live with the Croatans? Or was it instead a warning? Had the Croatan Indians instead decided to wipe the settlers out? Stranger reverses have happened. You may ask, if the Croatans had really turned on the settlers, why were no bodies there? Why had the cabins been so neatly taken down? Surely it was the way of the natives to leave the dead where they lay?

Perhaps it was, but perhaps none of this is true, either. Perhaps the truth lies on Croatoan Island still, even though the Croatan Indians are long gone. Stories persist of magic being buried in the land. The Indians have always believed that spirits live in the territories where they live. What if the spiritual powers of the land had begun to reach out and change the colonists? What if the people searching for them were looking in the wrong place?

A document by an English explorer early in the seventeenth century has him conversing with a Croatan Indian about his beliefs. The Indian tells a fine story about an entire tribe of strangers who angered the spirits of the island. The Spirit of the Island had tested them, and had told them that they could stay, but that they would have to spend a season as animals and plants, until they had understood what it meant to be in harmony with the world around them.

The strangers did not believe the Spirit, and the Spirit became angry again, and made them change, one by one, until they were all birds, and beavers, and skunks and bears and squirrels and trees and wolves.

No one really paid much credence to the story, considering it at best as a charming parable of the settlers' acclimation to the lifestyle of the Indians. Perhaps this is so, but this does not explain the constant reappearance of the word "CROATOAN" that has accompanied inexplicable disappearances in North America in the last few centuries, often in places far away from the Roanoke Island? When Edgar Allen Poe vanished in the few days before he was found, and brought to his death bed, what really happened to him? What shock had he seen? What led him to whisper the word "Croatoan" in his delirium? Why is the word scribbled in the inside cover of Amelia Earhart's journal? Why does the word appear in the middle of Glenn Miller's surviving music notation? Why was the word carved into the post of the last bed that Ambrose Bierce slept in before he vanished in Mexico in 1913? In the same way, why was "Croatoan" scratched on the wall of the cell that the notorious stagecoach robber Black Bart inhabited before he was released from prison in 1888 and walked out of history? Why was it written on the last page of the logbook of the ship Carroll A. Deering, when the ship ran aground with no one aboard on Cape Hatteras in 1921, *not that far from Croatoan Island?* What of New York Judge Joseph Crater, who stepped into a taxi cab in 1930 and was never seen again — and what of the word "Croatoan" seen scrawled on the wall of the restaurant out of which he had just walked? More frequently, didn't Jimmy Hoffa mention the Roanoke story in light conversation just hours before he walked into that car park?

What is the secret of Croatoan, and what is its connection to those born in the Americas, so that it follows them far from home? What takes these people out of the world? Where do they go?

Honest psychical researchers have found evidence that intelligent forces exist just outside our vision. Madame Blavatsky and her various followers have described them with, I think, some justification as "Devic intelligences." Whatever they are, it suits these forces to snatch people from the world, and for those with something of North America, that vast land of romance and violence and aspiration, the thing that seizes them and so rarely gives them back has some connection to the name "Croatoan." But what is that connection? What takes them away? Where do they go?

Story Hooks: Gone to Croatoan

• **Going Native**

If you haven't noticed, Mr. Nestel was a bit of a crank. Apart from the Roanoke incidence, the word "Croatoan" didn't pop up at all in any of the mysterious vanishings he mentions. It wasn't on Ambrose Bierce's bedpost, or on the wall of Black Bart's cell, and hell no, Jimmy Hoffa was never heard to opine on the fate of Roanoke Island.

Or at least it didn't in the real world. In the World of Darkness, maybe it did, maybe it didn't, but the article does demonstrate an important point: that symbolism and magic words have power, especially in the realm of the spirits.

Let's go back to the story of that Indian and the Spirit of the Island. Let's say that there was a Spirit on Croatoan Island, and let's say that it had the power to change people's shapes, but only under certain circumstances. Spirits often have circumstantial restrictions under which they can and cannot use their powers, or places they cannot go, or items or events that destroy them.

Perhaps — and this is only a perhaps — the spirit could not work until the community was tied to the land by having a member born there. Someone — Virginia Dare — made that land truly her home, and she was, as the first child born there, the focus of the colonists' identity. Suddenly, this was their land, and because of it, they belonged to the spirit that personified the land, which manifested through Croatoan Island. The Croatan Indians understood, but only inasmuch as they knew that the spirit existed, and they knew that they had to somehow co-habit with it or be forced to become part of the land in a much more permanent way.

Now imagine that the spirit of Croatan gained power through every disappearance it engineered, through every human who refused its arcane, complex deal and whom, thanks to that, it transformed into some part of the land. It is vast now; and its power extends across North America, and beyond, into the blood of everyone who makes that half-continent their home.

It can come to you at any time, in any shape, and before you vanish, you become compelled to speak its name.

A spate of disappearances cover the territory watched over by a group of hunters of any tier: a man is there one day, and he walks around a corner or steps into a car or takes a bus, or get on a plane, and bang, he's gone, transformed into a pigeon, or a squirrel, or a dog, or a bear, and he leaves behind him the name: Croatoan. And worse: anyone who sees him transformed must face the spirit, too and make the same deal, or be transformed on the spot. Hence the mass disappearance of the Roanoke Colony, and the vanishing of the crew of the Carroll A. Deering.

What bargain? That could be anything. It's not likely to be particularly horrible — the Croatoan spirit isn't really evil as such, just compelled to extend itself. Maybe the person has to never leave this one area, or travel to a remote area and live there. Maybe she must never speak of it; the mention of the name, its writing becoming the final trigger to a vanishing.

The secret to breaking the spirit's power may lie on that island, far away, but the problem is finding that spot, and finding the ban of the spirit before it comes to you and asks you to make a bargain you cannot possibly keep.

The Final Iteration

The age of exploration came to its inevitable close: we ran out of places to explore. We conquered the natural world. We put a collar around Gaia's neck and pulled the chain so tight we began to throttle her. Human endeavor reaches its final destination: humanity divorces itself from nature together (ask yourself: if the petrol ran out and the electricity stopped, how long could you survive?)

And with no connection to the natural world, humanity at large ceases to understand the animal side of our nature. Not that the shapechangers are any more in touch with the planet: no, they just understand the animal parts of themselves. But they're as selfish as the rest of us. And we understand them less than ever. We don't believe in them, don't expect them, don't know what to do when they come our way, teeth bared, claws raised, eyes, blazing. We're their food, and our dependence on the complicated paraphernalia of the modern and post-modern age has trapped us. The creatures that prey upon us don't need to hunt us in the same way anymore. We've engineered our civilization in such a way that we're locked into it, fenced in by our need for more cash, more TV, more gadgets, for petrol and electricity and food from supermarkets. We stopped being free range long ago. We're in a battery farm of our own devising, and all the monsters have to do is reach in and take their pick. Will we bite the hand that reaches into the cage? Is there any more we can do?

The Orang Pendek (1909)

From a journal, written in French and attributed to P. Thélème, Esq, found in a small private library somewhere in the English Peak District:

Digression: I am getting old. I suppose it must happen to most people, this acceptance of one's mortality, this understanding that you have limits, that you will eventually die. True, with me, it's been more gradual than with most, but still. I had honestly thought I was immortal. But I look in the mirror, and I have patches of gray at my temples. I see crows' feet around my eyes. My teeth aren't what they were. How long do I have, I wonder? Ten years? Fifty? Another hundred? Who knows?

This is of course a secondary concern at the moment. My primary concern is the difficulty of maintaining good hygiene and a satisfactory level of personal grooming when one is in the midst of the Sumatran jungle.

Situation: We are three days out of Kutaraja, and I am with Hans Niekerk, Karl van Moerik Broekman and our leader, William Gemeijns de Vries van Doesburgh, who complains if we call him van Doesburgh, or worse, Doesburgh, but who will just have to put up with it, because anyone who insists on the use of a five-part surname in the middle of the jungle is frankly being pretentious. Particularly when he hasn't even got the discipline to shave properly in the morning. Our common language on the journey is English, because it suits me to let my colleagues think that I can't speak Dutch.

Our guide's name is Wilham, or at least that is the name attached to him by my comrades. I have been unable to get his real name out of him. I think it suits him that his masters do not know what his real name is. This at least I understand perfectly.

We seek the Orang Pendek, the hairy man who walks upright and straddles the line between human and ape. A missing link, if you will. Broekman, a naturalist, wants to get a live individual or a carcass and take it back to Amsterdam, or London, or somewhere where he can show it to fusty individuals who will gasp and shower adulation on him for being clever enough to find another kind of ape they haven't seen before and listen to his point of view on human evolution. This, I have gathered from conversation, is that the Negroid peoples emerged from an ancestor common with the Gorillas of Africa, and the Asian peoples emerged from the Ourang-Outangs, and that the Caucasian people emerged from some other ape that is doubtless more intelligent and noble in every possible way, if I read him correctly. I tend to smile and nod when Broekman holds forth, and so he thinks that I agree with him implicitly.

Doesburgh is willing to pay for this expedition, presumably because he will have a rare specimen to put in a zoo, or on his wall. And Niekerk has a large and particularly unpleasant-looking rifle, which he spends an amount of time polishing and oiling that borders on the obscene. He is, despite his fascination with his toy, an otherwise decent sort, who almost treats Wilham with respect and kindness on occasion. A number of bearers and beaters join us with cages, snares, ammunition, supplies and all the usual equipment; Wilham translates for them and they have little to do with us. They carry the equipment and keep to themselves.

And me? I have nowhere else to go, and no monsters to fight. I thought this might divert me.

Development: We have been assured by Wilham that this area of the jungle is devoid of human habitation, for the Orang-Pendek refuses to exist in the regions where people live and hunt; however, at eleven o'clock this morning, Niekerk finds what looks like a knife. Despite Broekman's dire imprecations on the guide, Wilham insists that this is made by the Orang-Pendek. Which Broekman flatly denies, for the Orang-Pendek is an animal, and cannot make tools. Everyone knows that.

Development: I become aware that we are being watched; my discreet little friend having been called, I discover that we have attracted the attention of a troupe of Ourang-Outangs. I make note of this to Doesburgh, who is excited, for his zoo does not contain one of these creatures, and he had half-intended this expedition to seek out and find a family of these strange red-haired apes, should our primary purpose prove a failure. It's always good to have a secondary plan, isn't it?

Development: This morning we awake as usual to the finest of mornings. I leave the tent I share with Niekerk and perform my morning toilet. I become aware that the Ourang-Outangs are close by, watching me from behind the trunks of trees. They move from cover to cover, the better to see me. I sit and pay them no mind as I shave. Having made myself presentable, I look up, lift my hand and offer a cheery greeting. I cannot see how it will do any harm.

The largest of them is like a heavily-jowled old man, bearing huge plates of flesh on either side of his face and under his chin. He has shaggy red hair, and round eyes that glitter in the dappled light of the Sumatran morning. He raises a long hand, and the family shambles away.

Doesburgh and Broekman will later tell me that I imagined that he did that.

Development: We find more recently-made arrow heads. Doesburgh clouts Wilham across the back of the head, much to the open disgust of Niekerk. By mid-afternoon, the Ourang-Outangs are following us again. Doesburgh orders some of the beaters to get a snare ready; the process is long and for the servants at least somewhat frustrating.

I shall cut the account short: they catch an Ourang-Outang of smaller dimensions, one of the females, according to Broekman, which seems docile enough until, to their surprise, it breaks its bonds and, screaming, rampages through the column, coming eventually to Doesburgh, who roars at it like a man prone to getting what he wants; the poor creature, terrified out of its wits, turns and runs into the woods, only for Doesburgh to level his revolver at its back.

I tell him that this is unnecessary, and he tells me that I know nothing, and aims at the shape in the shadows, which turns its shaggy head just as he pulls the trigger.

Niekerk, Doesburgh and I pick through the undergrowth to find the carcass. Doesburgh gets there first and curses audibly. When I arrive, I see that he is standing over the naked body of a native woman, who has a neat bullet hole in her left temple, and the remains of her brain spread out on the forest floor beneath her. Niekerk goes to get Wilham, and Doesburgh berates him for allowing one of the bearers to get in the way of his shot. And he storms off.

I ask Wilham if the woman has any family, and if I can compensate them, or pay for the funerary rites, for this is a trifle for me in terms of costs. Wilham tells me she is not one of the bearers, and that he has never seen her before.

Development: The Ourang-Outangs are following us more persistently today, and with a less friendly aspect. They are at the same time more timid and more hostile. Their eyes bore into the back of my head.

Development: The weather changes, suddenly. The wind rises and the rain comes, although this is not the rainy season. We are obliged to make shelter here. The Ourang-Outangs are watching us. It is as if the rain is not falling on them. One might almost think they could do magic.

Development: Broekman comes to an unpleasant end. After three days of being trapped inside our tents against the driving rain, he chooses to go out, rain or no. We hear a scream, and then a repetitive commotion like loud cackling and screeching. We look outside; we see, thirty or forty meters from the perimeter of the camp, Broekman, lying face-forward over a fallen tree trunk. It looks as if he has tripped, but he is not moving, and he does not reply to our calls. Closer inspection reveals him to have fallen and to have impaled himself neatly through the heart on a protruding broken branch. We lift him off. Niekerk is in some distress; Doesburgh is annoyed, more than anything.

Having lifted Broekman from the branch, I note that the offending branch is not especially sharp, and hence Broekman must have propelled himself onto it with no small amount of force. It is not the right time to apprise my colleagues of this detail. The cackling continues. All around, the Ourang-Outangs watch us, and their teeth are bared. I could swear that they are laughing.

Development: The bearers abandon us overnight without telling us. Wilham leaves with them. Niekerk is nearly beside himself. Doesburgh is incandescent.

I am not going to neglect my personal grooming because of a detail such as this. Having washed, shaved and prepared my hair, I suggest to the other men that rain or no, we collect together all we can carry and strike back for Kutaraja.

Doesburgh disagrees: we have plenty of supplies, and that hence we sit out the rain.

I say: what if the rain does not stop? And I say that I do not like the attitude of the apes. Doesburgh scoffs and reminds us whose expedition this is. We stay.

Development: And only I am left alone to tell thee. The beasts attack before dawn. I emerge from the tent to see the apes tear Doesburgh's heart out with their bare hands.

Niekerk scrambles for his gun and barges out past me. I try to hold him back.

He doesn't stand a chance, has not time to even scream before his head and his body and his arms are flung in opposing directions. And now they are in a semi-circle and they are looking at me, as I sit here on my arse under the flap of the tent, with my head poking out, without having shaved or having prepared my hair. This is most embarrassing.

They are the creatures who have been following us, and yet they are not: they are a different shape, shorter than men and women, but with a different proportion, with arms only slightly longer than those of a man, legs slightly shorter, faces not so much those of apes as those of men and women wearing the masks of apes.

And I understand why no one has found the Orang-Pendek.

Here I would look my enemy in the eye and confront my enemy with evidence of his sin. Here I would spit hell-fire in his face. Here I would call down my familiar devil and have him gouge out their eyes. But what have they done? They have defended their home. They have avenged their sister. Were I them, I would have done the same. Our intention was to kill or capture them. They know this. And although I was not one of them, I came, I am complicit.

I am getting old. In the time of Robespierre or the time of Torquemada, I would have fought anyway. Instead, I flee. They do not chase; I do not know why. Perhaps I am to carry the message back with me: what you seek, you shall not find. As the rain stops, and I duck through the tangle, I feel more cheated than even Death has done these last five hundred years.

Story Hooks: Monkeywrenchers

• Other Animals

Not all were-creatures necessarily have to be wolves. Spiders, swans, snakes, ravens, rats, jaguars and apes have all numbered among the many forms into which people can become under the right circumstances. The shapeshifting orangutan shamans of Indonesia might not be right for every chronicle, but in the right place, a creature that can take the shape of a man, or vice versa, can be powerful and frightening. Animals have symbolic force. And different animals have different attributes that make them uncanny when they act like a human, and different symbols that they can bring to the table. A raven is a harbinger of doom and death (ask Edgar Allen Poe). A lion is strength and primal terror. A swan is grace and speed, and also the cold ruthlessness of a bird that can reputedly break a human limb with a single swipe of a limb. A snake is quiet danger, and poison, and the symbol of temptation and evil. Jaguars present native savagery. Rats eat filth and bring the plague. Some animals are more horrific than others, but even the most innocuous animals can be scary in the right place and time.

• Colonialism on Trial

Colonialism still exists. It's a different sort of colonialism, of course, enforced by economic might as much as military might, but it's colonialism nonetheless. The Orang Pendek — in the real world a bipedal

cryptid that they're still looking for in the Sumatran rain forests — wanted to be left alone, which has been the preoccupation with tribal peoples around the world for centuries.

Picture a sweatshop in one of the many Economic Protection Zones that exist in the Far East, in Indonesia, Thailand, China or elsewhere: teenagers work 18-hour days in slave conditions sewing together name brand training shoes, T-shirts and toys for Westerners, and get paid literal pennies for the privileges. They get herded into ghettoes. Their food is rationed. They get thrown out onto the streets if they talk or smile in the course of their work. Now picture that some of the teenagers forced to work there somehow discover that they can turn into spiders (or, if you're familiar with the monsters in **Werewolf: the Forsaken**, have their bodies invaded and their souls eaten by spider-like spirits). The spiders are hard workers, but their work has a lethal edge to it. People get tangled up in sewing machines; electrical lights short-circuit and electrocute a floor manager; and goods that go to the West develop characteristics that make them near-lethal. Training shoes poison their wearers; impregnated cloth dissolves the skin from people's feet.

Toys have lethal sharp edges. T-shirts supernaturally constrict. Hunters from Task Force: VALKYRIE or The Cheiron Group could find themselves seconded by their bosses to travel to the place of origin and find what's happened. TFV is inevitably influenced by the business lobby. Cheiron has partners in these factories. A consumer advocate from Network Zero might end up there, or a researcher from Null Mysteriis might be the only one who'll volunteer to go and investigate the phenomenon rationally on behalf of some government agency or another.

Getting into the sweatshop may or may not be easy — certainly, the owners, who sub-contract for a dozen massive brands — won't want to let Westerners see the full extent of the conditions. When the hunters see the everyday horrors the workers become subject to, what will they do? What *can* they do? When the *other* horror, the supernatural horror comes out, what then?

The Paramedic (2008)

Found on the computer of Austrian paramedic Christian Ankerl, dated two days before his disappearance but never sent:

From: Christian
To: marbleindexfrances@gmail.com
Subject: You will never believe this
29th April 2008. 01:15am

I must have dreamed this. We were on a call tonight and I think I saw a werewolf. Three werewolves. Four werewolves. Werewolves. I saw werewolves.

We were on a call-out. Car accident or something. We were first there, and yeah, there were three cars, in a heap, bang in the middle of this side street. And I hopped out the back of the car and I saw this thing in the middle of it all, like this huge hairy wolf-headed monster, bounding over the tops of one of the cars with an arm in his hand. And he was gnawing at it. Except he dropped it when he saw me. I kind of froze, like a rabbit, and then he started bounding towards me and I got right back into the back of the ambulance and yelled for Ben to start driving away, but he wasn't doing anything, and then I took a look out front and very nearly missed having my head ripped off by this big bloody arm that had come through the windscreen. And then the back doors of the ambulance tore open — there were two of them, there must have been two of them — and the thing from the pile-up was there, about to come in. I think I had a scalpel in my hand, because it was all I could find.

And the thing lunged forward, but it just stopped dead. It got yanked out backwards by the scruff of the neck by something that must have been just as big. I didn't look for Ben, or think about anything other than just getting out of there. Two of them were fighting behind the ambulance, rolling over and over in a big bundle of fur and claws and teeth, the gray one from the cars and a sandy brown one that must have been what saved me. And I backed around them and ran as fast as I could towards the front of the ambulance, straight headlong into another one, a reddish one that was gnawing at the stomach of what must have been the monster from the front of the ambulance, the one who put its arm through the windscreen. And the new monster — this one was white, with pink eyes — stared right at me, and lunged forwards, and I raised my arms, and it clamped around my left wrist and drew blood and then let go, and gave me this kind of "what are you waiting for?" look. And I ran. That was it, really. I found a phone box and called the police and sat tight for them to get there. By which time, the monsters had gone, and there were only people's bodies, in various states of dismemberment.

They were treating me for shock, and asking me what bit my arm. I couldn't say. I didn't know.

I've seen the movies. Am I going to turn into a werewolf now?

Story Hooks: Once Bitten

- **Tribal**

Although they don't generally know this or perceive it happening, the kind of werewolf that hunters are most likely to run into is not a normal human with a skin, a salve and a blood-signed contract with Lucifer. The most organized werewolves actually have their own underground society, with factions and wars. They're born half-human and when they change, they do it naturally and at will.

They vary in their attitude to humans. Not that you can divide these social lycanthropes into "nice" werewolves and "evil" werewolves. But it's pretty clear that some are more dangerous than others.

While violence has to come easy for a creature that can change at will into a nine-foot-tall beast-headed killing machine, clearly some groups of werewolves just want to get by and be left alone, while others are happy to kill and eat humans all the time. There's some sort of war going on, too.

Hunters might find themselves investigating deaths which turn out to be collateral damage in a turf war. Or they might find themselves hooking up with a group of seemingly like-minded individuals who are also trying to stop a man-eater from killing again, only to find that when it comes to the crunch, they're werewolves too, and they're not picky about who gets in the way when the fur starts flying.

• The Bite

In the movies, the werewolf's bite is supposed to transmit lycanthropy to its recipient (if he survives it). And it might really do that. While there are simply too many of the tribal, intelligent werewolves out there for an infectious bite to be realistic, there may well be one or two werewolves out there whose bite really is infectious. This is what might have happened to our Austrian paramedic: he wrote the email draft and for some reason decided not to send it just then. The following night, he saw the moon, felt a bit funny and knew no more.

Even if they aren't infectious, they're still dangerous: even if a werewolf in the World of Darkness isn't infectious, he still has the ability to track down by smell anyone he's ever bitten. A true werewolf never forgets the taste of a man's blood. Which is the other thing that might have happened: the werewolf bit the paramedic so that he could go and find him later, something that could easily happen to any hunter. He thinks he's got away, and thinks that the wound has healed... but one night, the monster comes to get him. Maybe he's one of them, now. Or maybe he's just food.

The Belt (2009)

Transcript of a British police interview, as retained by the European Operations Unit of Project TWILIGHT:

HAYDEN: Interview with Peter Stubb, conducted on [REDACTED]. Present with the suspect are DS Tim Paine, and myself, DCI Frank Crowe. The interview commenced at 4.28pm.

CROWE: All right, Pete?

STUBB: Peter. It's Peter. Always Peter.

CROWE: Sorry. Pete.

PAINE: DCI Crowe...

CROWE: What?

PAINE: Nothing.

CROWE: Good. So let's get on with it. Peter. I'm told that you gave a statement yesterday in which you confessed to the murders of Emma Bradbury, Bethan Cowles, Hannah Cole and Cheryl Lewis.

STUBB: That's right.

PAINE: Why confess, Peter?

STUBB: Because I did it. Because I need help. I need help. I didn't know what I was doing.

CROWE: You didn't know?

STUBB: I was a wolf.

CROWE: You were a wolf.

STUBB: That's right.

CROWE: You know there's a fine for wasting police time. It's a criminal offense.

STUBB: No. No. I did it. I'm a werewolf.

CROWE: Oh, piss off.

PAINE: DCI Crowe!

CROWE: What? What?

PAINE: Peter, you have to explain this. It's a little hard to believe.

CROWE: For the purpose of the recording, the suspect has just undone the top button of his rather nice Debenhams shirt.

STUBB: I turn into a wolf by night. A really big one. Size of a bull and about as strong. And I have claws like steak knives and massive feet. And I have huge eyes that light up everything. Like headlights.

CROWE: Like headlights.

STUBB: Is he just going to repeat everything I say?

CROWE: Watch it, sunshine.

PAINE: Go on, Peter.

STUBB: I know what I'm doing. I just can't control it. So when I see a woman — when I'm a wolf, this is, I don't do this when I'm a man — I need to eat her. So I do. And I wake up with a mouth full of blood, miles from home. Without any clothes on.

CROWE: Do me a favor.

PAINE: How exactly did you learn how to change into a... werewolf, Peter?

CROWE: I know this one. He got bit by a werewolf. It's like a disease, see.

STUBB: I have a magic belt.

CROWE: A magic..?

STUBB: It was given to me by my dad, who was also a werewolf — he's dead now. It's made of wolfskin. It comes from France. It's very old.

CROWE: And do you have it?

STUBB: No.

PAINE: So where is it?

STUBB: It's hidden under the bed in my mum's house.

CROWE: You still live at your mum's, is that right?

STUBB: That's right.

CROWE: Paine. Did you have the room searched?

PAINE: We did. Didn't find any belt, though.

STUBB: It was there.

PAINE: We didn't find it. Could anyone have moved it? Your mum?

STUBB: No. Maybe you should ask her, but...

CROWE: It was there. Except now it isn't.

STUBB: I don't understand.

CROWE: Did you kill those women?

STUBB: Yes. So who died first?

STUBB: The redhead was found first. And the newspapers reported that one first. But the blonde. The tall blonde. I killed her first. Then the brunette, then the other blonde, the short one.

PAINE: Is that—?

CROWE: Mm-hmm. All right. And how did you kill that first one?

STUBB: I used my teeth and claws. I held her down and she struggled. She struggled so. I tore and bit and scraped until she stopped moving, and then I ate her heart. I reached in and ate her heart.

CROWE: And then you drank her blood.

STUBB: And then I drank her blood, yes.

CROWE: Well, Peter, that's sort of funny, because Bethan Cowles' body was not missing internal organs, and hadn't been drained of blood. And trust me, I was there, and I know what a body drained of blood looks like. It isn't pretty.

STUBB: But I'm telling you—

CROWE: No, I'm telling you, Mr. Stubb. You didn't kill her.

STUBB: I did! I did! I killed all of them!

CROWE: All right, then. Let's talk about Hannah Cole.

STUBB: Which one—?

CROWE: The redhead.

STUBB: What about her?

CROWE: Where did you leave the body?

STUBB: By the side of the road, under a bush—

CROWE: She was stuffed inside a traffic light cabinet. All right, then. What about Emma Bradbury, the other blonde? Where did you take her to kill her after you got her out of the nightclub?

STUBB: The Kingsway multi-story carpark—

CROWE: Nope. The subway by the Evening Post offices. How about Cheryl Lewis? What did you do with her mobile?

STUBB: I threw it in the river—

CROWE: Nope. You crushed it under your foot. You did not kill these women, Peter.

STUBB: I did. I can remember it, as clear as day—

CROWE: DS Paine, have you done a drug test on this pathetic individual?

STUBB: I resent—

CROWE: Shut it. You did not murder those women. You are just doing it for the attention. I am not going to send you down for a murder you didn't do.

STUBB: I'm able to go—?

CROWE: I said shut it. So. Drug test?

PAINE: Waiting for the results.

CROWE: Drugs on him when he came in?

PAINE: Mushrooms in ziplock bags. Various herbs, also in ziplock bags. More than a dozen.

CROWE: That wasn't for personal use, was it?

STUBB: I have never seen that stuff. I swear—

CROWE: Of course you haven't. Paine?

PAINE: Peter Michael Stubb, I am arresting you for possession with intent to supply. You do not have to say anything, but it may harm your defense if you do not mention when questioned something that you later rely on in court. Anything you do say may be given in evidence. Do you understand?

Story Hooks: Faux-Wolves

• **Psychiatric Problems**

We've talked a little about people deluded into thinking they have become wolves, and who commit horrible crimes because they're deluded into thinking they're animals. But what of the poor individuals who haven't done anything wrong who believe themselves to be werewolves? Take Peter Stubb, for instance. On the one hand, he knows a detail of the case that's not been revealed to the public, and has a tendency to wake up naked and covered in blood miles from home. And he really does have these experiences. He dreamed about every one of those women.

He didn't do it. DNA evidence and scene evidence will exonerate him, even if DCI Crowe and DS Paine were ever in doubt of his innocence. So what's wrong with Peter?

Maybe he's just disturbed. He guessed a couple of things, but the rest he got from the papers (the photos of the four missing women have been plastered all over the national papers for weeks). He dreams about them and feels terrible about killing them, but he's innocent. A dupe. Hunters who run into an individual like this might feel they have to investigate. An individual like Peter Stubb could make for a whole story, or just a misleading sidetrack in a larger investigation. Characters might find him or someone like him, and feel they have to investigate his weird behavior, dreams and tendency to wake up naked, miles from home. It's always good to have one or two stories where the monster turns out not to be a supernatural monster, if only to underline that the supernatural is never commonplace. It upends players' expectations to have a non-supernatural rationale behind a series of events, and makes the supernatural seem that much more special.

On the other hand, these killings might be the work of a real werewolf (or vampire, or slasher), and Peter's insistent confession only muddies the waters, adding a level of confusion and delay to a case that was in some ways open and shut.

But on the other hand, consider this set-up: Peter really does own a wolfskin belt. The belt went away when he turned himself in. Peter's dreams are not from a natural source. The unfortunate man is being manipulated by some other force that is messing with his memories, creating hallucinations and even supplying the props. The belt did belong to Peter Stubb's father, but it's never more than a focus for a real werewolf to set Peter up as a patsy.

SIESTA EN LA PUEBLO DE LUNA Y SOL

AN EXOTIC MEXICAN VACATION THAT WON'T BREAK YOUR BUDGET

BY MATT MCFARLAND

El Gringo, after the fight:

A fly lands in my mouth. I bite down and feel it crunch between my teeth. Flies taste like shit, which is only right, I guess. I try and lift my arm, but it still won't budge. The bullet's starting to wriggle free. My foot has even started growing back, and the wounds are blackened. I should have believed my uncle when he told me about silver, but I guess I just always thought it was in the movies, it had to be bullshit.

The flies are going to town on my wounds. The nerves are still intact in places, so I can feel their little legs tickling. I'd call out for my uncle, but if he hasn't moved yet I know he's dead.

I start making a list to keep my mind off it. If I let my mind go to work, I'll lose my shit, and I'll be out here thrashing around on the ground missing a foot and unable to crawl.

I think of the people I'm going to find. There are five of them. Four were Mexican; the last one's a gringo like me. Only he's not the same kind of gringo. If he got pulled over out here, he'd say he's on vacation, and the cop would say, "*turista*" and then "It's okay, *señor*, never mind, have a good day." Me, I get pulled over and the cop says, "*Que pasó,* Gringo, why you driving so fast?" And then I give him a few bucks and he goes away. Guess there's not *that* much difference.

The gringo…wasn't their leader. They wanted me to think he was. They made sure I was watching him, and they suckered me in good, and then they…

I shift a little and bite down again. Crunch goes another fly. I can't think about what they did to us. I think about where they're from. They smelled like booze, but not smoke, no weed, no hookers. No scent of other people on them. They weren't from Puerto Vallarta. A weird smell on one of them, something doughy and thick, something I haven't smelled in a while… mashed potatoes. There are a couple of little *pueblos* near the city… what's the one with the little café that serves British food?

Luna y Sol. Sun and Moon. That's it. That's where they came from.

I look over at my uncle's body, and because anger would be too dangerous, I give way to grief. I start to cry, only I can't really move yet. Snot rolls out of my nose and down toward my

mouth, and I hock back and spit out of mouthful of blood. I feel a tooth come loose. That means I'm healing. That's good.

We didn't even hurt *one* of them.

I start crying again. My fingers twitch.

What did those fuckers want with my *foot*?

• • •

The cell, after the fight:

"Well, wasn't that a total clusterfuck." Miguel spat on the dusty ground. Anna was knocking back another shot in the bar, and Barry was sitting on the step, holding Jorge tight. Mamo was standing down the road a ways, smoking a cigarette. He had the bag in his hand, but Miguel knew better than to talk to him now.

Anna walked out of the bar. She wasn't feeling it yet, but pretty soon she'd be stumbling. She didn't weigh but 100 pounds soaking wet. "It wasn't supposed to be like that."

Miguel rounded on her. "No, it fucking wasn't. Jesus, Anna. Between you and these fucking *maricónes*—" Noting Barry and Jorge looking at them, he lowered his voice. "I told you I'd help you deal with the problem, not fucking kill people."

"We didn't kill a person."

"*Chale*," Miguel spat.

"*Así es*. We didn't. They weren't people. I thought you'd see that now."

Miguel spun around and walked into the bar. The bartender was asleep, and true to Anna's claim, hadn't so much as stirred since they'd been here. Miguel poured himself a shot and threw it back.

What *had* happened out there on the hill? He remembered gunplay, and Mamo doing… what Mamo did. But he didn't remember *people*, and that was scaring him. He remembered dogs, but that wasn't uncommon. The growers up in the hills usually had dogs with them to sniff out *rateros*. There had to have been people, though, because Mamo had pulled out his saw.

It wasn't Mamo's saw, though. Mamo's saw was discolored from use. This had been new and silver-shiny. Miguel spat again, this time at Barry's feet, and walked down the road. "*Órale,* Memo."

"Hey, man." Mamo stomped out his smoke. "Everything okay?"

Miguel shook his head. "What happened up there?"

PUERTA VALLARTA BARGAIN VACATIONERS' PARADISE
CHUCK'S VACATION HIGHLIGHT!

You don't have to spend a fortune to have an awesome vacation in Mexico. Forget Cabo and definitely forget Tiajuana....Puerta Vallarta is the new bargain vaction hunter's destination.

As tourism dropped off in the late 70s, the prices on hotel rooms and everything else dropped to where its now almost a steal.

Sample the local cuisine, bask in the sunlight, but whatever you do...don't drink the water. But serioulsy, if you have a delicate stomach, perhaps the Pueblo de Luna y Sol might be the place for you. Rather than your standard Mexican fare, they serve up good old fashioned meat and potatoes. And did I mention the full bar?

Trust this cheapskate, Puerta Vallarta will fufill all your beach and suntanning dreams as well as grow your appreciation of Mexico.

"*No sé,* man. Last I remember we were walking up there and waiting for two *gabos* to let Anna and the *maricónes* talk to them. And then there's guns going off and I'm cutting on a dude." He lit up again. Miguel winced; their mother had died of cancer three years ago, but it hadn't sunk in with Mamo.

"Where'd you get the saw?"

Mamo gestured toward Jorge. "*La mamon allí.* He said mine wouldn't cut the dude."

"So he wanted you to cut on him, even before we went up there?"

Mamo paused. Miguel looked for some sign of recall, something that showed that Mamo had known what he was getting into. Finally, he shrugged. "Don't know, man. I can't remember. The last day is just... I feel like I need to sleep it off."

"*Así es,*" his brother said.

· · ·

El Gringo, the hunt:

My fucking foot still hasn't grown back. I get it now. Silver *doesn't* heal. Doesn't matter, though. Uncle Robbie winged one of them before they took him down. I find the blood spatter, drying, but good enough for me. I lick it up, and sand coats my tongue, but I can handle that. I feel the guy's blood in my mouth, and I *know* him. I know he was scared when my uncle shot them, that he's scared most of the time. I know he's no warrior or hunter. And that only pisses me off more, because my uncle shouldn't have died from being shot by a pussy like this.

And then it's down the hill again, walking as a wolf, sniffing the air, looking for the scent. I don't let my thoughts distract me, but I wind up where I expected to: *Luna y Sol.* It's maybe about five in the afternoon. Siesta time. The sun's still bright, but people are snoozing. The *gabachos* up in their rented villas are swimming or drinking beer or napping. The folks down here in the village are resting up for the dinner crowds, such as they are. This is where white people come to vacation when they don't want to stay in Puerto Vallarta, and the folks who live here in town make a living selling shit to them, mostly food.

A lot of good scents in the air: ground beef, pork, chicken… smells like someone's making fish tacos, too. Most it's from lunch; no one's cooking yet. But wait — I smell potatoes. Tequila. And blood.

That restaurant where they serve the British stuff — I remember that. They have a bar, too. That's where I'm going.

Even killers gotta siesta, I guess. I hear gentle snores from one of the rooms. I chance a change up into human form — my foot hurts like a sonofabitch, and I'm naked, but no one's watching. I peek in a window and see the dude that Uncle Robbie shot crashed out on a cot. Another man is lying next to him. Gays aren't really welcome where I'm from, and down here, they call those people "*maricónes*" or "*putos*." I really don't care who people want to screw. At the moment I'm more interested in where the others are.

I could kill these two, I guess, but I'd hate to get stuck someplace I can't get out of. They know what I look like and they know I'm crippled. I couldn't outrun them easily, and this place is in the asscrack of nowhere. I don't know anyone in this village, I don't think.

I fall back to four legs and back up, to wait.

• • •

The cell, after the hunt:

"Mamo! *Mamo!*" Miguel was almost hysterical. Mamo coughed again, and a fresh mouthful of blood leaked out.

"We have to go," Barry said again. He hadn't said anything else since Jorge had died. "We have to go."

Miguel turned to him and screamed in Spanish. He had lost patience with the *gabacho*. Anna was gone, and Mamo…

"*Órale, hermano,*" he whispered.

"*No hable, Mamo,*" Miguel said. "*No hable ahora. Estará bien.*"

"*No mames, Miguel.*"

Miguel shut his eyes. His brother was right. That *thing*, whatever the hell it had been, had gutted him. It was a wonder he was still breathing, but judging from how he was choking, that wouldn't be much longer.

Barry crouched down. "Mamo, do you know where Jorge is?"

Mamo coughed. Miguel turned to Barry. "He's dead, *mamon*. He's fucking dead, alright? Him and Anna. That fucking thing killed them, and it's not dead yet."

"We've got to get out of here."

Miguel almost punched him, but Mamo motioned for him. "*Así es,*" he said. "Get out of here."

"Mamo." Miguel held him closer and sobbed. Barry stood up and walked away, not knowing what else to do.

Miguel joined him a few moments later, his chest and hands covered in his brother's blood. "Okay, let's go."

"Where?"

"Puerto Vallarta. We need to get away from this place. I… we can take Mamo's car. We get to Puerto Vallarta, you check us into a hotel, and then you buy us plane tickets to Los Angeles."

Barry looked shocked. "I can't take you back to L.A. I was supposed to come back with Anna and Jorge, and the sample. I was under contract, I can't—"

Miguel grabbed him by the shirt. "Listen, *maricón*. I don't give a fuck what you were 'supposed to.' I just lost my brother and my friend, and I am not dying out here because a bunch of *gabachos* decided to bring their white asses down here and start stirring up shit with the dealers in the hills."

Barry pushed him off. Miguel stumbled in surprise. Barry was stronger than he looked. "You think this is about drugs, you stupid wetback?" He pointed at Mamo's body. "You think he was shot? You didn't see that thing? That was a *werewolf.*"

Miguel shook his head. "*Chale. No es possible, gabo.*"

"Werewolf. *Hombre lobo.* What did you think we fought before, anyway? What did you think your brother chopped off? That's why we gave him a silver saw. That's why we shot the other one with silver." Barry opened his knapsack and pulled out a camcorder. "Want to see it again? Look — there's you. There's Mamo. There's the werewolf. See it?"

Miguel looked… but all he saw was a blur. It was big, sure, and it looked like it had hair, but… "No. I don't see it."

Barry put away the camera. "Not everyone does." He sighed. "That's one of the things we were trying to study, with folks like you and your brother—" He stopped short, but Miguel had heard.

"Like me and my brother, huh?" He took a step forward. Barry might be strong for a *maricón*, but Miguel was pissed. "Like us, *chicanos*?"

"No, no," Barry stepped back. "Just… your background. You've seen violence, that's all, and we thought—"

"Oh, okay. Like us, *callejeros*." He pulled out his piece. "I could shoot your gay ass right here and leave you in the dust, you know that? I could do that. And when they come see me about it, I tell the police, 'he's a worthless *maricón* and he tried to grab my ass,' and they never bother me. You know?"

"Look," Barry glanced around, but there was nothing on the streets of *Luna y Sol* but dust. The restaurants hadn't

opened. No cars, no cops, no people; just the dying sunlight and the flies, settling in to feast on Mamo.

"No, *you* look." Miguel cocked the gun. "We're going to Puerto Vallarta. You're putting me on a *puta* plane, and we are getting to L.A. And then you can take me to these people you work with and they can tell me why my brother had to die for this shit."

Barry nodded. "Okay. I'll do that. Let's get your br — your car."

• • •

El Gringo, after the hunt:

My foot still hurts, but I feel better. Tonight I'll hike back home and lay low a while. I'm pretty sure my foot will grow back, but I don't know. I never got hit with silver before.

I curl up and lay down under a table. I've killed two of them, and the psycho that cut my foot off isn't long for this world, either. The stupid fuckers actually went for siesta — they must've known I'd come for them? I'm not going to sweat it.

The woman's body is in front of me on the floor. Her head's behind the bar somewhere. She went down without a whimper, but the Mexican guy, the gay one, he put up a fight. But no silver — guess they ran out on Uncle Rob.

I barely remember killing him. I remember biting down, but that's about it. I remember someone screaming "Jorge, Jorge!" and figured that was his lover. I hate killing people in front of their families, but fuck 'em, that's what they did to me and Uncle Robbie.

The psycho dude burst right in, but by then I was thinking straight again. I remember him. I remember watching his eyes as I put my whole hand into his stomach. And I hate to admit it, but I'm *glad* the other one — I think they're brothers — got him out when he did. That means he died out on the street, in the heat and the dust, and that the flies are picking at him.

I don't hurt people often. I just wait here, between the *pueblos* and the farmers, between the cops and the growers. I've got my reasons, and these assholes wouldn't understand them. But I don't just attack people for no reason, and these assholes came at me like I was a monster.

I stand up and trot outside. I look down the block and see them. The one I gutted made it about 20 paces before he collapsed, and I can hear his brother crying. I smell the salt on his cheeks, and I smell my own blood from nearby… but not on them. They've got my fucking foot stashed somewhere around here. I sniff the air a bit more, and then I figure out where it is and where I need to hide.

I watch as they argue about what they're going to do. They think they're going to Puerto Vallarta. They think they're taking that psycho's car. But they don't know where I am.

I'm in the trunk. And they aren't making it to Puerto Vallarta. They're just making it out of *Luna y Sol*. I don't want to freak people out when they wake up from siesta, after all.

. . .

The cell, before the fight:

"You're sure it's just these two?" Jorge looked over the pictures. Barry touched his shoulder.

"Yes, I'm sure. It's just those two: Roberto Colón and his nephew." Barry held up a picture of a white man in his early 30s, smiling into the camera, his arm around a surprised-looking Mexican woman. "They just call him *El Gringo* out here."

Mamo and Miguel shot each other glances and tried not to laugh. "Why 'El Gringo'?"

Barry looked confused. "Because he's… white, right?"

"*Así es*," said Jorge. "But mostly they say *gabacho* or *gabo* now, *verdad*?"

"Right, *sí*," said Mamo. Under his breath, he muttered, "*se agringó totalmente*."

"*Y maricón tambien.*"

Anna set down her glass. "When?"

Jorge pointed to the pictures of the hillside. "I figure we follow them up into the hills. They walk slow, so we wait until we're out of sight of the highway, then we rush in, we take down the older one, and then take the sample from *El Gringo* here."

Miguel stood up. "What's 'take down,' *buey*? I don't remember saying I'd kill someone on this."

Anna shook her head. "We're not killing people. We just need the sample."

Miguel looked back at Mamo. These assholes were promising a lot of cash, but they were pretty clearly crazy, too. He dropped his hand to his waist and made a sign. *You okay with this?*

Mamo flashed one back. *Yeah, money's good.*

Miguel turned back to the other three. "Okay, how do we do this? Just fuck him up?"

Barry handed him a pistol. "Use this." He glanced at Miguel's face, and then hastily added. "You know,

threaten him. If he moves, shoot him." He pulled out a leather sleeve with something shiny in it, and handed it to Mamo. "When you get the sample, you need to use this."

"*Por que*?"

Barry opened his mouth, but Jorge cut him off. "Because you don't want his shit on your blade, *vato*."

"Okay, whatever. *Vato*."

Anna moved to refill her glass. Miguel stopped her. "Come on, *chica*. You need to be walking for this, right? It's gonna be a long walk up into the hills." She shrugged him off, but didn't reach for the bottle.

"What about after?" Mamo was looking at Anna. Miguel knew that he knew better than to make a play for her, drunk or not, but he'd want to go get laid after the job. He always did.

"After," said Barry, "we pay you, and Jorge, Anna and I go back to the States with the sample."

"Right." Mamo stood up and stretched. "I mean, *right* after. We just split up, or—"

"We come back here," said Anna. "Luis will be dead asleep. It'll be empty in town." She looked at the bottle, but Miguel shook his head and screwed the cap back on. "Everybody will be at siesta."

Mamo nodded. "*Órale*. Let's get to it."

. . .

The end of the hunt:

The jerk and stop of the car wakes me. I dozed off; guess I lost too much blood. Voices outside.

"Pop the trunk. I need to get my stuff."

Smell of grease. Smell of booze and blood. Gasoline. We're at a service station, probably that little one that Maria Velasquez' father runs.

I tense up. They can't know I'm in here, can they? They should barely even remember what happened.

Keys in the trunk. And… something else. Some metal-on-metal sound. Scraping, fingers alongside the metal. Gasoline smell gets stronger.

No.

Splashing liquid. Gasoline. Butane. The trunk opens. They're standing there. They knew.

The lighter flares up. My vision goes red, and all I know is *make them die*.

Siesta's over.

This chapter describes the various perspectives and agendas of the major hunter compacts and conspiracies towards werewolves and the mysteries of the spirit world, along with story hooks that can be used in any **Hunter** chronicle. In addition, you'll find several new hunter compacts and a new conspiracy known as Les Mystères, which draws its ability to hunt monsters from voluntary possession by spirits.

Cells

In general, a hunter cell only crosses paths with a werewolf when one of the creatures begins to hunt and kill in its neighborhood. Savagely mutilated victims turn up in darkened alleys or strewn across the grass of city parks, and the hunters are compelled to investigate before they or their loved ones become the next victims. They might decide to cruise the streets of their neighborhood or stake out the local watering holes, searching for clues to the killer's identity. If they are lucky, they might cross paths with the beast in its human form; if they are very, *very* lucky they might pick up on the monster's barely-leashed savagery and aggressive physical presence, and realize this is no mere serial killer they are dealing with.

If they are unlucky – or simply impetuous – they will confront the monster in its bestial form, perhaps catching it crouched over the body of its latest victim or cornering it in a copse of trees at the edge of a subdivision. At that point, they most likely only have a few seconds left to live.

A typical hunter cell – unaffiliated, ill-informed, poorly equipped and poorly armed – is at an extreme disadvantage against an individual werewolf, much less an entire *pack* of them. One on one, a human is no match for the speed, strength and ferocity of a werewolf, even assuming that the person is capable of functioning in the face of the beast's horrifying presence. Few direct confrontations with these monsters play out in the hunter's favor; if they survive, it's often by sheer chance, or because the creature inexplicably chose to spare the person's life. Sometimes part of a cell survives simply because they weren't there when the confrontation occurred, and they are left to glean whatever clues they can from the tragedy and figure out what their next move will be.

Hunter cells that learn to use patience, caution and stealth increase their odds immensely when dealing with a werewolf. In many respects, hunting these monsters is similar to stalking any other kind of super-predator: identify its hunting patterns, track its movements, locate its lair, if possible, and then pick a time to strike – preferably from a distance. The hunt at that point quickly evolves into a deadly game of cat-and-mouse; will the cell draw a net tight about their prey, or will they give themselves away and find the tables turned against them? If a hunter cell can choose to fight the monster on their own terms – picking the time, the location and the method of attack – their chances of success go up dramatically. No matter how keen their senses

"Millions of spiritual creatures walk the earth Unseen, both when we wake and when we sleep."

–John Milton, Paradise Lost

are, or how swift they can move, a silver-tipped rifle round fired from a hundred yards away is just as fatal for them as it would be for a human.

Unfortunately for hunters, werewolves rarely hunt alone. A pack of werewolves are often much more than a single hunter cell can handle, but patient and canny hunters can sometimes use a wolf pack's own tactics against them. With careful, long-term surveillance, a cell can search for weak links among the pack members and look for opportunities to isolate and attack them one by one. In some cases it might even be possible to turn members of a pack against one another – the savage urges of the beasts aren't just directed at humanity, after all. Of course, every night the hunters patiently lay their snares is another night that the werewolves prowl the streets and stalk human prey. How long can a cell maintain its resolve as more and more of their friends and neighbors fall prey to the beasts? In the end, it all comes down to who has the more predatory instinct – something that humans possess every bit as much as the monsters themselves.

Fortunately for hunter cells, they are typically far more likely to encounter spirits and spirit-possessed humans than they are a pack of savage werewolves. City slums and decaying housing projects attract malevolent forces like lodestones. Hospitals, prisons and rest homes grow thick with the energy of suffering souls and fragile, desperate minds. Though spirits can be frightening and even dangerous to humans if they grow powerful enough, they are often bound to a specific location or haunt. This allows the hunters more control over how and when they choose to confront such entities, which gives them a significant advantage. If an encounter gets out of hand, most times the cell can retreat from the area and come up with a different strategy for attacking the problem.

Mortals possessed by spirits present an entirely different set of challenges. While not as deadly as werewolves on an individual basis, they can be superhumanly strong, swift, and resilient. The spirit-ridden human can sometimes draw on the spirit's knowledge and experience as well, making them much more capable than they might otherwise be. Above all, the possessed aren't tied to a specific location; the body itself provides the anchor that the spirit needs, so the Ridden host can move easily among the crowds of a city or the church congregations of a small town. Perhaps most dangerous of all, no two spirits are ever exactly alike; just like people, they have their own set of motivations, goals and hungers, and their own powers, strengths and weaknesses. What works well against one spirit might only strengthen another, and unwary

hunters who rush in too quickly might find themselves facing an adversary they are ill-prepared to deal with.

Compacts

Compacts possess significant advantages over isolated hunter cells when dealing with the threat of werewolves or malevolent spirits; though they don't have the wealth of information, manpower and resources that the larger conspiracies can call upon, they are on the whole better informed and equipped than a typical cell. Despite these advantages, however, compacts have their own drawbacks and disadvantages that complicate their efforts: a lack of true, centralized leadership breeds inefficiency, competition for resources, and conflicting agendas that complicate an already desperate struggle against the forces of the night.

Given their unique histories and methodology, no two hunter compacts approach the threat of werewolves and evil spirits in the same way. The hunters of The Long Night view werewolves as harbingers of the apocalypse, which must be excised from humanity with fire and silver. Conversely, the scholars of Null Mysteriis or the underground video jockeys of Network 0 view shapechangers as subjects of academic and media scrutiny, seeking to unravel the mysteries of their existence and spreading the truth to whomever will listen.

Ashwood Abbey

The hunters of Ashwood Abbey are no strangers to hunting werewolves – in fact, their compact can trace its origins directly to a werewolf attack that nearly wiped out the progenitors of the group in 1855. As a result, a good "wolf hunt" is considered to be the height of fashion for cells across Europe and the United Kingdom, often drawing interested participants from all over the continent. It's considered *de rigeur* to take the ears of a dead werewolf as trophies – some send the shorn pieces, packed in salt, to the late Reverend Ogilvy's estate, but few hunters outside the UK follow the tradition. It's rumored that some wealthy members of the compact go so far as to completely skin the human bodies of dead werewolves and lay them out as trophy rugs in their private libraries or sitting rooms, but no one who's sober is willing to admit the fact.

Not that such opportunities are common – all too often, a wolf hunt comes up empty-handed, as the hunting party (emphasis on party) grows too large and unwieldy to effectively run the prey to ground. Sometimes the werewolf turns the tables on the hunters and picks off the more careless members of the party, while other times the monster simply drops out of sight altogether. When a hunting party succeeds in bagging a shapechanger it usually happens because the monster foolishly tries to confront the hunters all at once; the members of Ashwood Abbey are hedonists and libertines, but they can also afford the best firepower and all the silver bullets they can carry. Such confrontations are bloody, chaotic affairs, and they almost always end badly for the werewolf.

Not all members of the Abbey go in for hunting parties. Some prefer to see themselves as the "Great White Hunters" of centuries past, going into an area known for werewolf activity and stalking their prey with patience, cunning, and large-bore rifles. They are also perfectly willing to use a werewolf's friends and loved ones as bait if necessary to draw the monster out – when you're hunting a creature that is far and away the deadliest predator on the planet, there can't be any room for scruples or regrets.

An even smaller clique of Abbey hunters takes a different, more dangerous approach: stalking shapechangers in their human guises and seducing them before putting a bullet in their brain. The game of wits and passion between hunter and hunted can quicken the pulse of even the Abbey's most jaded members, and the moment of revelation, when the monster realizes he or she has been deceived – is truly something to savor. Complicating the issue somewhat are occasional by-blows produced by these relationships. Though none of these bastard children have become werewolves themselves – at least, not as far as Abbey members are aware – the prospect is enough to make the compact's leaders frown on the practice.

The pursuit of spirits holds less interest for members of the Abbey. A haunted castle or monastery makes a great site for a week-long debauch, but spirits themselves don't offer much in the way of entertainment for the hedonists of the compact. Ghosts are so single-minded and unimaginative, so *pedestrian* – why bother with such common fare when there are so many more interesting creatures roaming the world? Cases of possession are another matter entirely, of course, because that usually presents the hunters with a physical form they can interact with. Rumors abound that a cell in France dallied for more than a year with a murderous spirit known only as "Jean-Pierre," who possessed working-class laborers in Lille and took out its urges on their host's families. The cell reportedly made a game of it, hunting Jean-Pierre down, killing its host, and letting the spirit loose to find another body before starting the chase once more. Had the spirit not run afoul of a cell from the

Malleus Maleficarum several months later, the game would still be going on today.

In the United States, a number of cells in and around New York have taken to flirting with spirit possession on a much more personal level. They seek out haunted sites or search out suspected cases of possession, then use a variety of methods to try and invite the spirits into themselves for a brief period. Hunters that have flirted with possession claim it's a mind-altering experience, but for many libertines of the compact such excess carries things just a bit too far.

Story Hooks

• Jenkins seemed like a decent sort – knew all the right people, took all the right drugs – and he told the most titillating stories about the wolf-girl he'd stumbled onto in Kensington, of all places. He spun the most delicious tales of her seduction, teasing out the beast a single step at a time and separating her from the rest of her pack. He'd even gone so far as to arrange a lavish party at his family's estate in the country, inviting members of the Abbey from all across England to share in the upcoming hunt. But then something went wrong. Old Jenkins stopped coming to the club on Wednesdays – and more worrisome, he stopped sharing stories about his ongoing conquest. Now the fellow seems to have disappeared entirely, and his bank accounts have been cleaned out. Bad enough if the girl caught on to his games and tore Jenkins apart; what if the seducer has become the seduced, and the fool has "gone native" with his she-wolf? There are rumors he's been spotted at his family's chateau in France; time to chase those rumors to ground and see whose side Jenkins is really on.

• Reports are coming out of Romania that a construction company building luxury villas at the foot of the Carpathians has suffered inexplicable acts of sabotage; heavy equipment has been stolen or outright destroyed, and workers have experienced the eerie sensation of being stalked through the forest on the way to and from the work site. All this began when the company stumbled upon a circle of old, moss-covered *menhirs* in a secluded hollow at the edge of their work site. Someone high up in the company must be a superstitious sort, because a great deal of money has been spent to bring in a team of specialists to remove the stones and transport them to some museum or other. For now, the site is virginal, pristine. Imagine how the beasts will respond to a debauch around their sacred stones! Time to

clean the old elephant gun and find the best drug dealers in Bucharest.

• Tales are told of a 15th-century bordello in Rome, where the noble patrons came in the dead of night to partake of men and women whom the proprietor swore were possessed by "licentious spirits devoted to Satan himself." It would be easy to dismiss the tales but for the payment the proprietor demanded – not gold, but the blood and flesh of a maiden. Evidently the skills of the whores and catamites were wondrous indeed, for the bordello's patrons killed so many young servant girls to sate their lusts that they attracted the attention of the Inquisition. In the end, the agents of the church sealed the doors of the bordello and burnt it to the ground – with the proprietor and her possessed workers still inside. Rivers of gold flowed into the Vatican's coffers as the guilty nobles paid staggering bribes to keep from burning at the stake, and eventually the matter became just another footnote in the church records. But now, almost a hundred years to the day that the Inquisition burned the house of sin to the ground, the apartment buildings situated on the site are reportedly suffering a plague of bizarre sex crimes and violent assaults on young girls living there. Have Satan's whores returned to earth once more? Naturally, it behooves us to find out.

The Long Night

The Tribulation Militia is locked in a constant, twilit struggle with the legions of the Devil himself, struggling to save the human race from the fires of Armageddon one bloody night at a time. Lucifer's minions assume many forms to lead the faithful astray: demons wearing the flesh of beautiful women or charismatic men, or witches claiming to fulfill the needs of the flesh at the cost of one's immortal soul.

Even the living dead can be seductive and beguiling, luring the innocent to their doom with alluring faces and false promises of immortality. Their illusions and deceits force hunters of the Long Night to tread carefully and contemplate the righteousness of every action they take.

By contrast, there's nothing ambiguous about werewolves and their ilk. Shapechangers are vicious killers who prey upon the flesh of the innocent and virtuous, driven by the Devil's own appetite for destruction. That kind of black-and-white conflict is something that the Tribulation Militia lives for, and pursues with righteous zeal.

To most hunters of the Long Night, a werewolf is a man or woman who has willingly entered into a pact with Satan. The Great Deceiver grants these damned souls whatever earthly reward they desire, but in return the Devil transforms them into ravening beasts when it suits his purposes. As far as the Tribulation Militia is concerned, these monsters have to be put down like rabid dogs, without hesitation or mercy. The Long Night pursues a shamelessly scorched-earth policy regarding shapechangers, fearing that unless they employ extreme measures to extinguish every trace of the mortal's iniquity, it could continue to tempt others into corruption. To some radical members of the compact, that means not just killing the werewolf, but any member of the shapeshifter's family and friends that might have had reason to suspect who or what the werewolf was. If innocent lives are lost in the process, it's regrettable, but at the end of the day God will know His own.

Of course, not everyone subscribes to this extreme fire-and-brimstone policy. Some members of the compact take a more compassionate view, insisting that if God's grace is to have any meaning at all, then *any* sin, no matter how grave, can ultimately be forgiven if the sinner accepts Christ as his savior. This has caused considerable friction between outspoken believers in both parties, and led to several angry confrontations in the field. Unfortunately, every attempt to force a shapechanger to admit his sin and reject the Devil's gifts has only ended in disaster, which only furthers the convictions of the compact's extremists. Rumors persist of a church-affiliated cell deep in the Appalachian Mountains of the United States that is enjoying some success in gradually redeeming the souls of a handful of remorseful werewolves. To date none of the hunters involved are willing to come forward with details, for fear of repercussions from the compact's more extreme members.

The matter of hauntings and spirits – particularly cases of spirit possession – present a much thornier problem for the Long Night. There is much debate within the compact as to the true nature of ghosts or spirits – are they lost souls, somehow interrupted in their progress to judgment, or are they merely demons in disguise? Whenever possible, members of the Tribulation Militia try to confront these spirits and banish them from the physical world. Sometimes that means blessing a haunted house, or in extreme cases burning it to the ground – but the members of the Long Night prefer to confront spirits directly if a means can be found. In the case of spirit possession, the hunters will try to find a way to exorcise the spirit if possible, but their resources and experience in such matters isn't as extensive as the Malleus Maleficarum. In many cases, all the hunters can do is beg God's forgiveness and free the host of its captor by destroying them both.

Story Hooks

• Every year, right around harvest time, a handful of children disappear from their homes in the small town of Culter, West Virginia. The disappearances always occur on the nights of the full moon, and in each case the victim appears to simply leave his or her bed and walk off into the forest, never to be seen again. Residents tell tales of an Indian curse cast upon the town a century past, while others speak of an abandoned mine far up the mountain side that lures adventurous children to their doom. Still others speak of strange rituals performed out in the deep woods under the light of the moon, and savage howls that echo from the hollows at midnight. It's clear that Satan's minions are at work in the town of Culter, and it's incumbent upon us to scour their evil away with fire and sword – and uncover the hidden sin that has brought this curse down upon the people of this God-fearing town.

• Signs of the Great Beast are everywhere – but in the deep woods around Owensboro, Kentucky, the beast has taken physical form and is stalking the town's teenage boys. A few months ago, a troubled young man named Eddie Matthews was found wandering Country Road #7 with a terrible bite on his shoulder. Matthews claimed he was attacked by a "huge wolf" that had stalked him through the woods after his car broke down on the way to his girlfriend's home. A week later, Matthews disappeared, and shortly afterwards the killings began. All of the victims were members of Matthews' high school, and all of them knew the young man to one degree or another. Locals report that Matthews had always been a disturbed and violent boy, and fellow students told the press that he had shown an increasing fascination with the occult prior to his disappearance. Did Matthews make a deal with the Devil and gain the Mark of the Beast? If so, he must be stopped before more innocents suffer at his hands.

• Jebediah Stone claims to be a prophet and a servant of the Lord, and his ministry has drawn men and women from all over the country to his sprawling compound in the Nevada desert. His day-long sermons are closed to outsiders, but there are claims that when the Holy Spirit is upon him, his eyes burn like fire and he speaks in ancient tongues. Stone reportedly heals the sick of even the worst afflictions. The crippled are made to walk, the blind to see and the mute to speak. But when they emerge from the desert and return to their daily lives, something goes terribly wrong. The souls that Stone reportedly saves become obsessed with bloodletting and violence, taking out their urges on whomever crosses their path. Recently, a string of brutal torture-homicides in Dallas were traced to a man who Stone reportedly cured of cancer a month before. In police interviews, the killer refused to answer to his given name, and when pressed by investigators he began to curse them loudly in Latin, Hebrew and what may be ancient Egyptian. Whoever – or whatever – Stone is, he is clearly a false prophet sent by Satan to lead the faithful astray, and must be stopped at all costs.

Loyalists of Thule

The Loyalists of Thule know more about werewolves than they let on – which isn't all that surprising, really, considering how their years of painstaking study were perverted by the Nazis when they rose to power in the late 1930s. As most members of the Thule Gesellschaft were being scattered to the winds by Heinrich Himmler's Gestapo, one of their most senior members – an occult scholar by the name of Konrad Sanger – sought power and prestige in service to the Nazis by inflating the egos of high-ranking members of the party and helping refine rationales for Aryan genetic supremacy. Nazi propagandists drank deep from Sanger's wellspring of knowledge regarding the hoary Master Race of legend, which was bad enough. Later, however, as World War II began and Hitler started to build his Thousand-Year Reich at bayonet-point, Nazi scientists learned of some of the other secrets contained in Sanger's library: namely

his lifelong study of shapechangers and their fearsome powers. At first Sanger was reluctant to share this hidden knowledge, until his family was arrested by the Gestapo and sent off to a labor camp to ensure Sanger's complete cooperation. Horrified, the scholar turned over his precious books and consulted with Nazi geneticists to produce some of the most horrific eugenics experiments of the war. Records of the werewolf super-soldier project were lost at the end of the war, and Sanger himself committed suicide in Berlin in early 1945, but it is known that hundreds of prisoners were shipped from Eastern Europe to a research complex in the Aachen forest and subjected to horrible experiments to determine if they carried the genetic traces of lycanthropy. After three years of horror, the project was shut down as Allied troops approached Aachen, and the research facilities were reportedly destroyed. No one knows what became of Sanger's extensive occult library; some believe it was destroyed during an air raid on Berlin (prompting Sanger's death), while others think it fell into Soviet hands at the end of the war. Regardless, the Sanger affair created a stigma that the Loyalists of Thule are still working hard to erase, and as a result the majority of the compact's members go to great lengths to conceal their dealings with shapeshifters and keep what they learn a closely-guarded secret.

The Loyalists of Thule developed an abiding interest in werewolves through their extensive studies of the spirit world and dialogues with what they believe to be ancestor-spirits from lost Atlantis. Through these dialogues (many of which survived the war only as hand-written transcripts), the organization's scholars learned a great deal about the ways in which the spirit world interacted with the physical world – and gradually realized that werewolves somehow existed in both realms at once. This fascinated the scholars, because they believed the path to the Ultimate Source lay in plumbing the memories of ancestor-spirits, and they theorized that the werewolves could teach them many valuable secrets about creating alliances with powerful beings in the spirit realm.

Unfortunately, the werewolves were less than receptive to the compact's overtures. Numerous attempts at contacting the beasts proved futile, and more than a few ended in disaster. The shapechangers were wary and unpredictable creatures, and mistrusted the hunters' motives from the start. For years, the members of the compact tried various means to win the trust of a number of werewolves they'd kept tabs on; sometimes they would shield the shapechangers from other hunter cells, or divert the attention of the authorities if they drew too near. Later, they offered to share their own library of occult lore with the werewolves, only to have their store of knowledge dismissed out of hand. It was only by accident that a cell in Brussels stumbled upon information valuable enough to interest the shapechangers. The scholars were investigating reports of masses of rats rising at night from the sewers beneath the city and infesting a number of office buildings within a single square mile of the city center. When the cell shared this news in passing with the werewolf they occasionally communicated with, the shapechanger grew extremely curious. Over the next four weeks, the scholars continued their studies of the rats, and provided their findings to the werewolf, who later summoned his pack and destroyed the creatures beneath the light of the full moon. The shapechangers shared little in return, but from what the scholars could infer from the werewolf's actions, the rats were themselves a kind of shapeshifting entity that sought to weaken the barrier between the physical realm and the spiritual realm. Since then, the Brussels cell has continued to provide information to the local werewolf pack concerning strange animal activity in the city, and then studiously compiled whatever scraps of knowledge the werewolves let slip over the course of their investigation. (At the same time, the compact has devoted considerable effort in locating other rat-shifters elsewhere and trying to open lines of communication with them as well.) So far, interactions between the compact and other shapechangers have been sporadic, and of mixed success, but the scholars remain optimistic that their hard work will one day bear fruit.

The Loyalists of Thule also aggressively study and attempt to communicate with denizens of the spirit realm, from the ghosts of dead mortals to more esoteric entities such as nature spirits. Some members of the compact advocate a more forceful approach in dealing with these spirits, insisting that if they could find a means to entrap them they could advance their store of knowledge by leaps and bounds compared to the current process of séances and summonings. The approach is gaining more and more converts within the compact, though to date the scholars have no practical means of reliably uprooting a spirit and containing it.

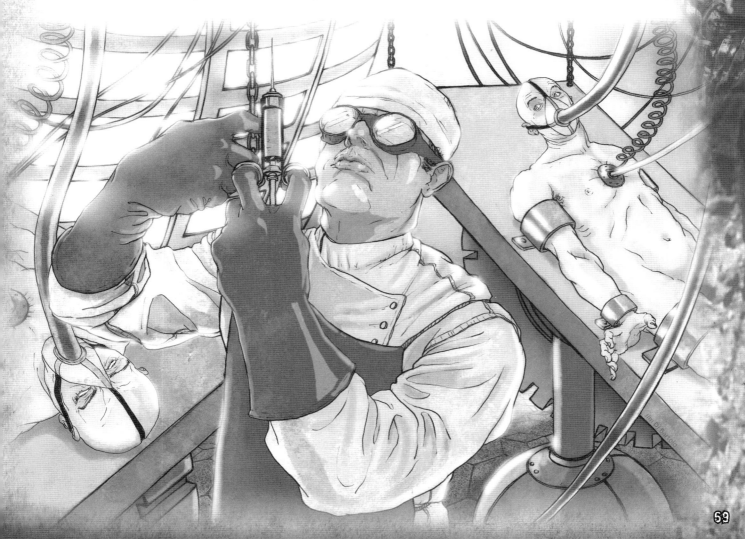

Story Hooks

• Recently, a cell of scholars in Bavaria reported that a rare book dealer in Regensburg had sent out a discrete announcement to his patrons regarding a series of slim, leather-bound volumes reportedly discovered hidden in a basement of one Helmut Dietz, a man rumored to have been a Colonel in Hitler's feared S.S. during World War II. The volumes apparently contain strange symbols and occult incantations that, according to the marginalia, originated in "lost Atlantis." One of the members of the Bavarian cell managed to get a look at the books, and believed them to be part of the lost library of Konrad Sanger, a former member of the Thule Gesellschraft who left the order to join the Nazi party and was believed to have been a member of Himmler's infamous "Werewolf" super-soldier project in 1945. The cell managed to break into the dealer's shop and steal the volumes, but before the books could be sent to Munich all five of the members mysteriously disappeared. When the *polizei* searched the home of Wilma Beyer, the cell's leader, they found the place torn to pieces. Written in blood on one wall of the flat were the words: *Aachen Forest*. Supposedly, the research facilities for Himmler's Werewolf Brigade were somewhere near Aachen. What does it mean?

• A cell near Rouen, France sent a surprising report last month regarding an unexpected meeting with an individual who claimed to represent a coalition of shapechangers known only as "the Pure." The gentleman, who went only by the name of Gerard, told the cell members his masters were interested in forming an alliance of sorts with our organization in the interests of sharing information about what they termed as "renegades and criminals" of their people. According to Gerard, the Pure offered to share information on other races of shapechanging creatures in return for our records on werewolf activities across Europe in the last fifty years. As a gesture of good faith, we want you to carry a small amount of information on this disk to Rouen, where Gerard will provide you the location of a "nest" of shapechangers supposedly hiding in Marseille. Investigate the veracity of Gerard's information and report back to us at once.

• During the 1950s, a member of our order named Joachim Bader was successful in making contact with an ancient spirit who identified itself as a Rmoahal priest named Vicurga, who lived in the latter days of Atlantis. Over the course of five days, Bader was plunged into a cataleptic state, wherein he transcribed page after page of occult lore that could possibly provide once and for all the truth regarding the Ultimate Source. Unfortunately, Bader's health gave out before he could finish Vicurga's Testament, and since then our elders have waited for the proper alignment of cosmic forces that would allow a repeat of Bader's experiment. The alignment will occur in just a week's time; we've already taken the liberty of purchasing tickets and lodging for your cell in Hamburg. A man named Thulmann will meet you at the airport with further instructions.

Network 0

The successful filming of a werewolf's transformation remains the Holy Grail for many hunters tuned in to the Secret Frequency. Pictures of huge, bipedal beast-men aren't any more convincing than the Patterson-Gimlin Bigfoot footage, nor are grainy digital shots of enormous wolves prowling the streets of Philadelphia. People have any number of ways to explain away images like that – but a recording of a human being changing into a nine-foot-tall fanged monster? That's something else entirely.

Unfortunately, the members of the compact have had precious little success in catching a shapechanger in the act. Werewolves appear to go to great lengths to hide their existence from mankind – a fact that continues to baffle Network 0 members who have personally encountered the creatures – and those who have managed to witness the transformation claim it happened too fast to capture on camera. At this point, senior members of the compact have concluded that the only way to pull off such a feat would be to get a willing participant – a werewolf who would agree to come into an underground studio somewhere and transform himself in front of a dozen cameras. As yet, the network hasn't had any success in locating a volunteer.

When it comes to ghosts and other spirits, however, the Network has recently enjoyed considerable success. After years of effort documenting and recording instances of paranormal activity and having it disputed and ignored by the masses, a groundswell of interest in the supernatural has grown within the mainstream media. Suddenly, paranormal investigators are getting a level of respect they've never known before, and clients are coming out of the woodwork to cleanse their home of a "haunting." Unfortunately, this sudden popularity has done much more harm than good to the compact's efforts, for only a tiny fraction of the investigations turn out to have any merit. Many cells spend so much time chasing down false leads that they don't have the resources to investigate legitimate spirit activity when it occurs. On the positive side, however, the steady influx of money from would-be clients allows many of the compact's cells to purchase higher-quality equipment in anticipation of the time when they encounter a true, documentable case of spirit activity.

Story Hooks

• There's a story making the rounds about a broken, blood-stained camcorder showing up on the doorstep of a small sheriff's department near Roanoke, Virginia. Upon reviewing the camcorder footage, it appears to show a group of hikers getting lost up in the mountains nearby and being stalked, *Blair Witch*-fashion, by creatures that one of the deputies described as "some kind of damned beast-men." The authorities were unable to identify anyone appearing in the footage, and supposedly they couldn't determine where the footage was taken, although rumors persist that the sheriff knows more than he's letting on. The whole thing is being passed off as a publicity stunt for an upcoming indie horror film, but so far, no one's come forward to take credit for it. If we could get our hands on the camcorder maybe we could discover the truth.

• Normally, being approached by the FBI is the very last thing you and your cell members would ever want – but this time the Feebs aren't trying to confiscate your tapes or shut down your site. It seems they had set up a series of surveillance devices in a townhouse in Philadelphia and picked up about 14 minutes of extremely disturbing audio: a group of men and women who speak in eager whispers of stealing into the bedrooms of the home's occupants and torturing them to death on the night of the new moon "for the glory of He Who Must Not Be Named." The problem is that the home was under visual surveillance at the time, and the agents are certain that *no one was in the residence at the time of the recording*. The Feebs have had every one of their specialists go over the recording, and none of them can prove it was faked. Reluctantly, they've turned to you for help. The new moon is only three nights away.

• For the last three months, you have received a CD in the mail each week that contains poor-quality video of a young man in his 20s who is filming himself in what looks like a bare, dingy basement room. The first videos are simply confessionals: the subject speaks fearfully of terrible dreams and sudden, violent urges. His parents have him in therapy, but he's stopped taking the medication they gave him because it makes him a zombie. Later, the subject talks about a hunger for fresh blood, and fantasizes about "the feel of my teeth in some asshole's throat." As the videos progress, the subject's dreams appear to spill over into his waking hours; he hallucinates visions of huge wolves who seem to stalk him from the shadows wherever he goes. The most recent video was the most disturbing of all. Lasting less than 30 seconds, it showed the young man, naked and covered in blood and filth. His expression was distant and haunted, and his voice had a rough, bestial edge to it. *"They're dead. I woke up this morning and they were all dead,"* he says to the camera. *"There are pieces of them in my bed. I think… I think I ate parts of them. And you know what? It feels good."*

Null Mysteriis

The scientists of Null Mysteriis have been struggling to unlock the secret of lycanthropy for decades, spawning a wide range of theories that continue to be hotly debated by cells across the world. Some insist that lycanthropes are victims of a rare genetic disease that transforms their bodies in the absence of solar radiation. Others agree the basis for the phenomena is genetic, but is a combination of recessive traits that unlock a sort of "primal template" in the human body and regress it to a more feral, monstrous state. Still others insist shapechangers aren't even human at all, but a parasitic race that has existed secretly among true humans for thousands of years. Until the compact can obtain verifiable genetic material to study, the debate about the origins of werewolves will continue unabated.

The tendency of werewolf flesh to revert to baseline human after death continues to confound the scientists of the compact. Numerous experimental methods – from dropping severed tissue into liquid nitrogen to keeping the flesh charged with a low-level electrical current – have proven fruitless. Whatever causes the transformation does not appear to obey known laws of chemistry, biology or physics: a realization that both excites and troubles the members of Null Mysteriis. After repeated failures to gather material from werewolf attacks or discover useful data from dissections of recovered bodies, members

quantified, it is believed that tools can be created that can reliably detect, communicate with, contain – and destroy – any spirit the compact encounters. What the compact will do with such a revolutionary discovery remains to be seen, and the possibility has touched off yet more lively debate among the hunters. Should the compact share its knowledge with other hunters worldwide in hopes of ridding the world of malevolent spirits, or should it conceal the knowledge lest someone find a way to abuse it? Could it potentially use such technology to explore the spirit world as no mortal has ever done before, or should it use it to isolate the aetheric realm from the physical

of Null Mysteriis have concluded that the only way to unravel the truth is to capture a healthy werewolf and perform a detailed vivisection. So far, most of the compact's cells have balked at such a measure, even in the interests of science, and the few who are willing to undertake such a plan have met with no success. If and when a Null Mysteriis cell succeeds in capturing a live werewolf – and holding him for any length of time – many members of the organization believe they will have reached a fateful crossroads in the existence of their compact. Those with any kind of conscience dread the coming of that day, for they know that sooner or later it will arrive.

In the meantime, the compact continues to study paranormal effects at spiritually active sites around the world, focusing primarily on how spirit energy interacts with the physical world. A number of eminent members of the compact have published papers that attempt to define "aetheric convergence factors" and "electromagnetic inference patterns on the human brain," and many of the members of the group believe they are on the verge of a breakthrough in measuring the energy exchange between spiritual and physical objects. If this crucial transfer of energy can be observed and

world forever? So far, no consensus has been reached among the rank and file, and there is every possibility that one will never arise – instead the compact might fracture into a half-dozen splinter groups, each pursuing its own agenda independent of the others. The history of the Vigil provides ample evidence of such schisms occurring in other hunter organizations, and some members of Null Mysteriis fear the fruits of their greatest achievement might one day shatter their loose-knit compact beyond repair.

Story Hooks

• If you hadn't been screwing around with your camera, you'd never have caught it. You were waiting for the train at Grand Central and started snapping shots of the rush-hour crowd using the modified Kirlian attachment that you'd been working on for the last few months. You were curious to see what sort of effect the crowd would have on the individual auras of the people themselves – but what you got was far stranger. Half a dozen women in the crowd had small, ghostly figures standing at their sides – with some image enhancement software it became clear they were the figures of children, wearing clothes that seemed to date from around the early 1900s. The spirits seemed to be clinging to the hands or the skirts of the women, their blurry faces turned upwards as though asking a question or making a plea. The next day, two of the women were on the morning news. They had come home from work, made dinner, and poisoned their young children with insecticides. Were the spirits harbingers of death – or did they cause these mothers to kill their own children? You plan on returning to the station with your camera to see if you can learn more.

• The prevailing opinion among many members of the compact is that lycanthropy is a genetic disorder brought about by a combination of recessive traits that work together to cause unprecedented mutations in an individual's body. For decades, members of the compact have attempted to isolate these genetic markers, using blood and skin samples taken from alleged werewolf attacks, but without success. Now, however, a hunter named Anna Beth Carter believes the best chance for collecting a useful genetic sample is to collect material from a human on the cusp of transformation. Carter believes it's no coincidence that the lore surrounding werewolf transformations peg the time of the first change during adolescence – when the human body is already undergoing a riot of physical and hormonal changes. If samples can be drawn from a young man or woman within a week of his or her first change, the subtle genetic markers that cause lycanthropy might be easier to identify. Carter has even produced a list of names cross-referenced from juvenile court records and school disciplinary reports that provide possible candidates for the process. Any one of these kids might be a potential werewolf – all you have to do is watch them closely and be prepared to move when their first transformation occurs.

• One facet of the werewolf phenomena continues to baffle members of your compact. On more than one occasion, victims of werewolf attacks are found in locked rooms that could only be secured from the inside, yet aside from bloody paw prints and claw marks, no trace of the killers are ever found. In every case, a reflective surface is found at the scene – and in more than one instance, a trail of prints leads to the mirror (or basin of water) and simply… stops. One member of your compact, a man named John Theissen, has developed a radical theory to explain this mysterious ability. Some werewolves, he theorizes, have taken their ability to shapeshift to its logical extreme – altering their composition at the atomic level and transforming themselves into pure energy! This allows them to effectively teleport from one location to another. What's interesting about this theory isn't so much what it says about lycanthropes, but how it applies to spirits as a whole. If a werewolf can change its energy state and become a spirit, can a spirit's energy state be altered to give it a physical form? Thiessen has created a device that he believes will be able to alter a spirit's energy state – just for a split second, but enough to be measureable – and now he just needs a cell of hunters to find a haunted site and test it.

The Union

The hunters of the Union honestly don't give a damn what werewolves actually are, or where they came from. In fact, as long as the beasts keep their noses out of the neighborhood, most Union members don't much care what they're up to, either. When you're working twelve-hour shifts just to make ends meet and there's talk of layoffs, your father's got cancer and your kids are flunking school, you've got a lot bigger things to worry about most nights.

The Union takes care of business when they have to, and tries to keep body and soul together in the meantime. Their encounters with werewolves have been brief, bloody and often indecisive; most often the shapechanger decides that the neighborhood is simply too dangerous and moves on, and the hunters can't afford to pursue the matter further. A beast that refuses to back down and tries to stake a claim on its new territory had best be prepared for a serious fight. If there's one thing that Union hunters and shapechangers can agree upon, it's the need to protect one's turf. If you aren't willing to fight for what you've got, then you damn sure don't deserve to keep it.

Some of the most vicious and brutal battles fought between hunters and werewolves have been waged by Union cells who refused to see their streets become a hunting ground for a pack of flesh-eating monsters. By the same token, however, more than a few documented instances have occurred of Union cells that have reached a détente of sorts with werewolf packs that take up residence in their neighborhoods. One such occurrence happened in the Bronx back in the 70s, when a small cell of hunters known as the Ironmongers worked out a truce with a pack of shapechangers in the face of an even greater threat: the endemic gang violence that gripped the neighborhood in those days. So long as the werewolves focused their hunts on the guys selling heroin and mugging old ladies on the stoops of their homes, the hunters gave them no trouble. The arrangement held together for almost five years, until two members of the cell were killed in an unrelated encounter with a vampire that was stalking the area and the rest of the group went their separate ways. On other occasions, in other cities, Union hunters have found common ground with werewolf packs over such things as family, territory, and law and order. Other compacts have excoriated these cells for turning a blind eye to the presence of monsters in their midst, but the members of the Union reply with a shrug. People who don't have to put food on the table can pound their chest and talk about holy crusades all they want. Every day a Union hunter spends in the hospital is a day they aren't bringing in a paycheck. And if they wind up dead, who is going to take care of their families?

Union cells take the same approach with spirits and haunted places in their territory. If there is a way to deal with an angry spirit that doesn't involve directly confronting it, they'll do it every time. Houses with dark reputations burn to the ground, or they're bulldozed to make way for a park or a new housing complex. Ghosts who linger with unfinished business might get a helping hand so they can move on and leave the living in peace. Members of the Union take each situation as it comes, and find the most practical way to deal with it.

The straightforward, down-to-earth attitude of the Union comes up short when faced with a threat from a possessed human. Most times, a spirit in control of a human body can't be persuaded, threatened or reasoned with — they've got nothing to lose, and an appetite for evil that they'll do anything to feed. When that happens, there's little thought spared for the poor schmuck who's been taken over by the spirit. The spirit

has to be stopped by any means necessary, and if that means hitting the thing with a truck or dousing it with homemade napalm and flicking a Bic – well, that's just life in the big city, you know?

Story Hooks

• It took a lot of time and effort to raise money for the new community center in your neighborhood – you did your part and then some, because your construction company did most of the framing for the place – but it was all worth it, because local leaders think it could really make a difference for the kids in the neighborhood. Except that none of the kids will go near the place. They did at first, but within a week, the number of the kids at the center dwindled to almost nothing. Not long afterward, volunteers at the center began to complain about strange occurrences: lights going on and off, doors opening and closing, strange groans rising from the basement. The director of the center blamed the occurrences on shoddy construction, but you know for a fact that ain't right. Something is haunting the place – but what? The center is only two months old. Time to get with your people and start looking for some answers.

• There's a hunter who lives across town – a stand-up guy with a good bunch of people working with him who's done a lot to clean up his neighborhood over the last year. Sure, he tends to break stuff first and ask questions later, but what do you expect? Earl's no genius, but the guy knows right from wrong, and unlike some other people you know, he's not afraid to kick ass and take names when he needs to. The last you heard from Earl, he and his guys were looking into whoever was cutting up hookers down on the south side; you figure he must have stumbled onto something important, because he hasn't been posting on the forums for a while now. Then yesterday Earl makes a post out of the blue, calling for help. Except it isn't Earl making the post – it's Earl's young son Bill, using his dad's login. It seems that Earl went away with his guys for a couple of days, then came back in the dead of night without telling anyone. He won't leave his workshop in the basement, and chases away anybody who tries to come down and talk to him. He's working on something down there, something that smells like rotten meat. Now you think you need to get across town and see what's gotten into Earl.

• For weeks your home town has been plagued by a series of brutal killings that have left the local

police baffled. The attacks seem as random as they are vicious; drifters, joggers, churchgoers – nobody is safe. People leave their homes after dark and are found torn to pieces the next day. Naturally, every hunter you know is out cruising the streets, looking for who or what is causing this, but so far the killer seems one step ahead of you. As the bodies start to mount, the more organized your local chapter gets, until finally one of the town's cells has the balls to use one of their own members as bait to draw the monster out. After a couple of false starts the plan works – and the cell pays the price. Three dead, two in critical condition, and the son of a bitch gets away. But the sole survivor catches a glimpse of the killer as he flees the scene: a huge, shaggy beast that transforms from one step to the next into a naked, blood-smeared teenage boy. If that wasn't bad enough, the hunter recognized the kid – in this town everybody pretty much knows everybody else. Problem is, the kid's parents are *hunters* – members of your own damned chapter! Now you get to find out how deep the ties of loyalty run.

Conspiracies

Conspiracies possess the most material advantages when dealing with werewolves or malevolent spirits; their hunters are more numerous and generally better informed about their prey, and they have access to better and more specialized equipment than any typical cell or compact. At the same time, however, most conspiracies suffer from bureaucratic inertia and rigid policies that prevent their hunters from improvising or adapting a response to unique situations. Conspiracies are very powerful, very successful hunter organizations, but the older they get, the more ossified their outlook becomes – and some of these organizations have been hunting werewolves for hundreds or even *thousands* of years.

Aegis Kai Doru

The hunters of the Shield and Spear are among a shapechanger's most implacable foes. Their conspiracy swore an oath millennia ago to punish the werewolves and their ilk for bringing about the fall of Paradise itself. Though the exact reasons for the oath have since been lost to time, the organization continues to honor its spirit with ferocious zeal. In this day and age, with werewolves and other shapechangers growing increasingly rare, it is considered a high honor and a mark of special favor to be given the opportunity to join in a hunt against these monsters.

Though the Aegis Kai Doru has lost a great deal of their arcane knowledge over the centuries, they remain possibly the most knowledgeable hunter organization in the world regarding the nature of shapechangers and their abilities. They are familiar with werewolves, wererats and werespiders, and are somewhat knowledgeable about how these creatures interact with the physical and spiritual realms. The organization even has in its possession a number of very powerful spirit fetishes taken from slain Uratha over the centuries, which are stored in a Labyrinth of their own at a secret location somewhere in Greece.

For many years, the elders of the conspiracy studied these tools and weapons in an attempt to find a way to use them against their makers, but their efforts were in vain. Now, the group is content to simply lock them away in the darkness and keep them out of the hands of their foes.

Access to the conspiracy's store of knowledge about shapechangers depends upon a member's status in the group. At the lowest level, Aegis cells are provided enough knowledge to know how to recognize shapechanger activity when they encounter it, and who in the organization to report it to. The evidence is

then evaluated by more senior members of the group, and if the cell has proven its abilities on other hunts in the past, they will be provided with more specific information about their prey: habits, abilities, weaknesses, etc. – and given permission to hunt the monster down. If the hunt is successful, the cell's status increases, and they are likely to be called upon again if another shapechanger is discovered in their area. In this way, each region contains at least one highly experienced and knowledgeable cell that is capable of hunting powerful werewolf packs, or offering assistance to less-experienced cells when necessary. These high-

Jim Di Bartolo

status cells may also draw upon the conspiracy's store of powerful magical artifacts if the situation warrants it, further adding to their capabilities.

The Aegis Kai Doru's implacable war against the shapechangers has generated friction within the ranks over the years. Some hunters in the group have questioned the merciless nature of the oath, when the creatures that were truly guilty of the crime no doubt died off centuries ago. A 16-year-old boy who has just suffered his first transformation scarcely knows what he is, much less has any knowledge of a mythical paradise that fell before the dawn of recorded history. Why does he deserve to die for the crime? Rumors exist, some no doubt aprocryphal, of Aegis cells that spared the lives of certain shapechangers if it was clear that they had committed no crimes against the innocent. The conspiracy's elders go to great lengths to quell these rumors, and often warn the rank and file that any violation of their sacred oath will be dealt with by the harshest means available.

Compared to their unyielding war against the shapechangers, the Aegis's perspective on spirit possession and haunted sites is much more flexible and enlightened. The conspiracy understands that there was once a time when the physical and the spirit worlds interacted much more freely than they do at present, and so they understand somewhat the need to keep both forces in balance for the good of the world. They are generally respectful of sacred sites, and in fact they make some effort to tend such places in areas where the organization has a strong presence. By the same token, the group recognizes the threat that a spiritually corrupted site presents to a human community, and they have a number of different approaches to deal with the problem. The Aegis elders possess occult tomes that contain a number of potent rites of exorcism, and if the opportunity presents itself, the group will sometimes dispatch an Aegis cell to cleanse a haunted site of its inimical spirits. If the spirits in question aren't potent enough to warrant the effort of an exorcism, the group will sometimes take direct action to alter or cleanse the physical site – burning an old building, destroying personal articles that a spirit could use as an anchor, etc. Supposedly, the conspiracy also possesses rituals and magical items that are capable of binding spirits and trapping them in special reliquaries made of lead and glass. It's believed that this process was perfected as recently as the 14th century, when Aegis elders acquired certain occult items from the Church and modified their properties to suit the conspiracy's ends. Originally, these reliquaries were simply prisons meant to entrap demonic forces, but supposedly the Aegis elders found a way to use these lead chambers to interrogate – and even tap the power – of the spirits imprisoned within.

Story Hooks

• Your cell has received an unexpected communiqué from Athens: Gilbert Royce, one of the most respected senior members of your conspiracy has gone missing. Royce was an eminent researcher, responsible for taking care of many of the organization's most potent relics – and one of the few who knew the location of the hidden Labyrinth containing the conspiracy's captured werewolf fetishes. Upon discovering his disappearance, the Aegis elders immediately did an inventory of the stored fetishes and discovered that one had been stolen. The fetish is a short staff of carved oak, wound with leather cords and decorated with feathers and turquoise beads. The top of the staff is capped with the bronze carving of an eagle's head, and a crackling nimbus of power surrounds the strange item. Upon checking Royce's credit card records, the elders discovered that 12 hours ago he purchased a one-way plane ticket to your hometown. What is Royce up to? What does he want with the fetish? And does this have anything to do with the recent incidents of werewolf activity in the area?

• Your elders have informed you that an Aegis cell near your city requested urgent help in dealing with a family of four that have apparently become possessed by an entire pack of evil spirits. Three of the spirits seem subservient to the fourth, a foul, demonic being that inhabits the body of the family's youngest son. From what the cell has been able to determine, the three lesser spirits lure victims into their home, where the master spirit stuns or poisons them and drags them into the basement. Once they disappear down the basement stairs, the victims are never seen again, and the cell estimates that at least two dozen people have disappeared in the last two weeks. Your cell is being sent in to help, but the elders have given you very specific orders about what to do with the master spirit: they've given you a book containing a complicated spell of binding, and a small, seemingly delicate box made of lead and thick, faceted glass.

• Your cell just barely survived an encounter with a very powerful werewolf – a drifter who stole like a shadow into your town and spent more than eight weeks hunting the elderly residents of your neighborhood. More than two dozen men and

women died before you were able to corner the beast and put an end to its reign of terror. Once the thing was dead, you discovered a strange leather bag clutched in the naked man's scarred hand. If you had to guess, you'd say the bag was made from *human hide*, and its tied shut with a cord woven from braided human hair. Strangest of all, the skin is warm to the touch, and seems full of something soft and yielding that moans ever so slightly when touched. You were trying to think of some foolproof way to destroy the thing when you get a call from your elders in Athens. They want the bag. Now. Plane tickets are waiting for you and your cell at the airport. All you have to do is deliver the bag to your superiors. What could possibly go wrong?

Ascending Ones

The Cult of the Phoenix exists to defend humanity from the evil that hides in their midst; but not everything that is inhuman is necessarily evil. Every follower of Islam knows that the *djinni* themselves can be good Muslims if they choose to accept that Allah is the one God, and Muhammad is His Prophet. Good Christians know that angels can become demons, but demons can also become angels. And the Ascending Ones have believed for a long time that werewolves are among the most fearsome kinds of *djinn*, the most brutal of demons.

The Ascending Ones have fought countless bitter battles with shapechangers since the cult's origins in ancient Egypt; their potent Elixirs can lend them the speed, strength, and acuity to battle with a werewolf on something close to an even footing – or failing that, they can create potions that can boil a shapechanger's blood or steal the vitality from his limbs. But as many times as the cult has had to hunt and kill one of the changing breeds, there have been other times when the Ascending Ones succeeded in reaching a peace of sorts with these monsters – and on rare occasions, members of the cult and packs of werewolves have fought side-by-side against far greater and more terrible evils. The cult's practice of *Sulha*, of individual diplomacy between contesting factions, has served them well in many encounters with shapechangers, building a rapport with these creatures that none of the other hunter organizations can lay claim to.

Though the Ascending Ones still know very little about how shapechangers relate to one another, they know enough to deal with each creature or pack on an individual basis, and then come up with a response that's appropriate to the situation. When a cell becomes aware of a werewolf or other shapechanger at work in their community, their first inclination is to attempt to communicate with it and learn what they can about the creature's intentions. If the werewolf is looking for a territory to claim as its own, the cult might agree to respect the creature's hunting grounds on the condition that it refrains from harming the innocent. In this way, the monster becomes a member of the community – something that speaks to the core of most cult members' Islamic beliefs – and the two groups develop a foundation of respect that they can build upon later.

If the werewolf won't listen to reason, or refuses to abide by the cult's agreement, then the Ascending Ones won't hesitate to protect their neighbors in a more forceful manner.

The rapport that some cultic cells have built with the changing breeds has given the Ascending Ones a number of insights into the disparate cultures of the were-creatures. The cult senses that there is an ancient and terrible rift that exists between the werewolf "tribes," and they are aware that werewolves, werespiders and wererats are bitter enemies of one another. Attempts to use the practice of *Sulha* to intermediate between the three breeds have met with disaster, though there have been a handful of cases in Europe where werewolves have asked members of the cult to act as intermediaries between feuding packs. Such a task is fraught with danger, and more than once has ended in terrible tragedy, but the individuals involved believe the potential benefits greatly outweigh the risks.

The cult has enjoyed far less success when dealing with the spirit world. Though the Ascending Ones have managed to create certain Elixirs that allow their members to perceive and interact with spirits in the physical realm, they lack the practical means of combating them except in the most simple and direct fashion. Where possible, most cult members attempt to communicate with spirits and try to resolve whatever unfinished business that is keeping them anchored to the physical realm, but that approach doesn't always pay off. Some spirits linger simply because they can, or because they want to torment the living. Against such threats, the conspiracy is no more or less capable than any other hunter cell. The cult has dealt with numerous cases of human possession in the past, and inevitably such encounters lead to the destruction of the human host. It's said that there are some elders among the Ascending Ones that are working to create an Elixir that could eject a spirit from the body of its host, but so far they've had no success.

Story Hooks

• A senior member of the cult has contacted your cell with strange and wondrous news: he claims to have created an Elixir that allows a human to transmute his *corpus* into pure spirit, allowing a hunter of strong will to cross over into the spirit realm for a time. Being a prudent sort, he requests your cell to observe the first, extended test of the Elixir, and naturally you feel obligated to help in any way you can. A few days later your cell gathers with the elder at his sanctum and watches as he drinks deep of a strange, quicksilver-like fluid. For a moment, nothing happens; then the elder's eyes roll back in his head and he undergoes a kind of seizure. Before you can act, the elder's tremors cease and his eyes open once more. For a moment, it seems as though he doesn't know where he is, but then he bows to you and your friends and manages an embarrassed smile. He says that clearly he's made an error with the formulation of the Elixir, and begs your forgiveness for dragging you out on a fool's errand. You look into the elder's eyes… and realize that whomever you are talking to, it's not the man you were speaking to a few moments before.

• A string of vicious murders have dominated the headlines in your home town – entire families attacked in their homes and torn limb from limb, as though by a wild animal. Strange sightings of huge dogs or wolves on the city streets can only mean one thing – a werewolf, or pack of werewolves, are on the hunt in your community. On the surface, the actions of the monsters appear unforgiveable, but your contacts in the police department report some strange discoveries in the homes of the victims: secret rooms inscribed with strange runes, stains on the hardwood that are discovered to be old blood and signs of pervasive abuse on the bodies of the slain children. There is clearly more here than meets the eye; are the werewolves vicious murderers, or are they fighting another, more terrible enemy?

• For more than a month, a wild battle has been raging on the streets of your city. Eyewitness reports tell of huge, hairy man-sized creatures tearing at one another with tooth and claw, or slashing and stabbing with massive, rune-marked blades. A feud between packs of werewolves would normally be none of your affair, but this battle has spilled over into the public eye, and therefore you and your cell are compelled to step in and put a stop to it one way or the other. If you

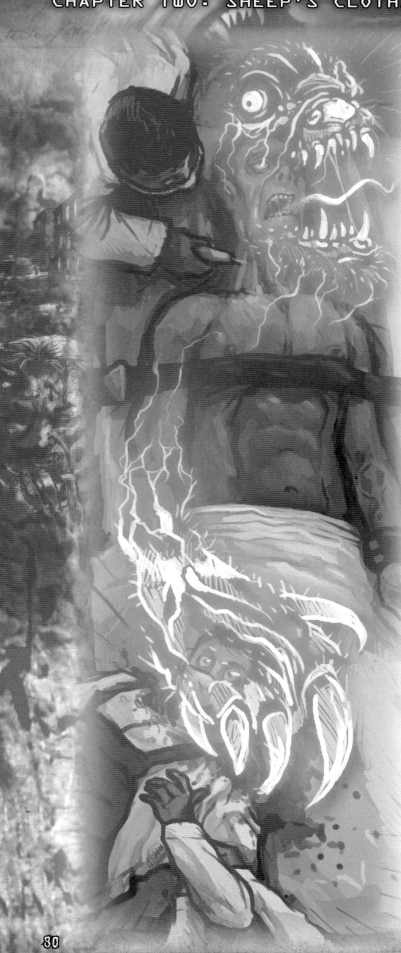

can find one pack or the other, perhaps you can attempt to mediate between the packs and convince them to take their battle elsewhere.

The Cheiron Group

As far as the pharmaceutical and medical researchers at the Cheiron Group are concerned, werewolves are worth their weight in gold. Shapechangers are a veritable cornucopia of potential miracle drugs and surgical implants: a werewolf's regenerative capability alone would revolutionize the field of medicine if a means could be found to duplicate its properties. Werewolves don't suffer from infections, rarely get sick, process toxins at an incredible rate and can alter their physical form at will. Any one of these abilities would be the discovery of the century, and werewolves contain all these potentialities in one extremely volatile package.

Unfortunately, the researchers have had almost no success in synthesizing any of these incredible abilities to date. Transfusions of werewolf blood work no better than human blood. Skin and organ transplants have an almost 90% rejection rate, and the transplants that *do* take are no different than those of a human. Extensive brain scans and complicated vivisections have revealed no clues as to how a werewolf alters his shape – much less where all the extra mass comes from. Countless theories and hundreds of experiments later, the researchers of the Cheiron Group have nothing to show for their efforts except for a lot of outwardly human corpses and three dozen employees on permanent disability.

Not that this stops the conspiracy from continuing their efforts. The answer is just out of reach, but they inch a tiny bit closer to it with every failed effort. Or so they would like to believe.

And so, despite decades of frustration, the Cheiron Group puts a high premium on locating, tracking, and capturing werewolves for future study. Field teams are quickly dispatched to any location, anywhere in the world where there has been a reliable report of werewolf activity; often these agents masquerade as members of the US Center for Disease Control in to gain access to police and medical records of any victims, and to use law enforcement resources as stalking horses to locate and identify any likely suspects. Despite all the years spent studying werewolves, the only reliable advice the Cheiron Group has for its agents when trying to capture one is to *try and confront the monster while it is in human form.* The researchers know for a "fact" that while a werewolf is wearing its human guise, it's just as vulnerable to attack as any other person: if long-term surveillance indicates that the werewolf has loved ones or family members that the agents can get to, then so much the better. Of course, if the agents miscalculate and the werewolf sees them coming, then all bets are off. Sometimes the agents possess the right kind of physical augmentation to survive a werewolf attack, but most often the results are pretty gruesome.

The number of werewolves captured by the corporation in the last 20 years remains a closely-guarded secret. It's popular knowledge among the rank-and-file that only a chosen few among Cheiron's field operatives are tapped to try out experimental surgical implants drawn from werewolf bodies. Supposedly the corporation has had some success with mitigating the intense fear response these creatures provoke in humans, and supposedly Cheiron has had some success in synthesizing useful properties from werewolf blood, but the actual results are also highly secret.

In recent years, Cheiron has also invested considerable effort into studying the phenomena of spirit possession and the effects it has on the human body. The R&D department is extremely interested in learning how the spirit is able to force its will on the human host, and how it is able to make the host's body perform supernatural feats of speed, strength, and stamina. If the corporation can figure out how this phenomena works, the senior researchers believe it could open up a whole new range of physical enhancements without the need for so much invasive and risky surgery. Field agents who are familiar with the project also can't help but be aware of the potential to completely override the conscious will of the human involved.

Story Hooks

• You've been contacted by the company to come in for a "routine checkup," which means that the R&D department has come up with a new implant or enhancement they want to field-test on a young, healthy employee. When you wake up from the surgery, the incisions in both of your legs are already nearly healed – and you're absolutely ravenous for all the warm, raw meat you can get. The docs have conducted a bone marrow transplant using marrow taken from a recently captured werewolf – somehow they used direct cerebral stimulation on the monster to keep it in its transformed state while conducting the operation, and the theory is that if they got the werewolf marrow into your bones quickly enough, it might take hold. Unfortunately, the docs aren't exactly sure what effects the transplant might have, but there's no time for extended study. The

beast they kept in wolf-form and operated on tore off its restraints, bit the heads off the two orderlies in the room, and is now on the loose somewhere in the building…

• Police in Sacramento have taken a 20-year-old woman into custody and accused her of the cannibalistic murders of eight fraternity brothers at the University of California. According to police reports, the woman lured each man back to her apartment over a four-day period, tore out their throats with her teeth, and then feasted on their hearts and livers. Supposedly there were strange symbols painted on the walls of her apartment using the victims' blood. The company wants you and your team to get to Sacramento, bluff your way past the cops and take custody of the woman. A team of medical researchers is prepped and awaiting your arrival at the company's research facility in Bakersfield.

• Don Blake is a senior field agent for the Cheiron Group; he's smart, experienced, and he's got half of a dead man's brain in his head. According to all the rumors, that hunk of dead brain matter lets Blake see the monsters for what they truly are, and not feel even a twinge of fear. He's put that piece of moldy gray matter to good use, hunting down bloodsuckers, werewolves and sorcerers for more than three years. But last week, something went wrong. Blake and his team went after a guy up in Jersey who was kidnapping postal workers in Fort Lee and eating their organs; upper management figured Blake would be dealing with a werewolf, but it turned out the guy had been possessed by something he'd dug up while renovating his basement. Well, Blake managed to track the killer down and put a bullet in his head – but then he let out a scream and hit the floor. His teammates bundled him into the van and were on the way to the hospital when Blake suddenly woke up, drew his gun and shot his buddies dead. The cops found the van a few hours later, but Blake was nowhere to be seen. Now the company wants you to head up to Jersey and find Blake – and whatever is hiding inside his head.

The Lucifuge

Blood will out. The members of the Lucifuge know this. If the blood of demons or monsters run through your veins, there's no point trying to escape it. Sooner or later, it will rise to the surface; it's the choices you make afterwards that matters.

The 666 agents of the Lucifuge know what it's like to wake up one day and discover there's a monster hiding beneath your skin. Unlike many of their Satanic kin, they have chosen to use their powers to fight the evils of the world – and if the sons and daughters of the Dukes of Hell can deny their evil lineage, it's not much of a stretch to believe that shapechangers can do the same.

The Lucifuge has fought its share of battles against werewolves and the other changing breeds, but unlike many other hunter groups, they don't automatically assume that an individual shapechanger is irredeemably evil. As with other monsters, the Lucifuge will spend time and effort observing a werewolf – to the extent they are able – and attempt to determine if the creature's actions are evil, or if perhaps the monster is acting in the pursuit of some higher goal. Of course, this isn't always obvious from outside observation, and some agents are bold enough to try and communicate with their quarry before passing judgment.

Ironically, most werewolves have an extremely hard time seeing the Lucifuge as anything other than servants of darkness. They can sense the hunters' diabolical nature somehow, and instinctively perceive them as a terrible threat. And attempting to communicate with the shapechangers via a demonic servant doesn't much help matters, either. If the hunter is lucky, his servant will be able to escape in one piece. At worst, the little imp will be trapped by the werewolf and used to work its way back to the hunter who sent it.

As a result, a great gulf of anger and mistrust exists between werewolves and the Lucifuge, despite the fact that both sides could possibly stand to benefit a great deal by talking to one another. Many Lucifuge hunters decide they can't afford to risk approaching a werewolf, and simply act on whatever circumstantial evidence they uncover about the monster's actions. A few determined hunters continue to try and approach the shapechangers, but very few such attempts have been successful. Usually the hunter in question is lucky to escape with a (mostly) whole skin.

The hunters of the Lucifuge devote far less energy to dealing with ghosts or the spirit realm; only 666 hunters are active worldwide, and more than enough evils exist in the physical realm to deal with. Spirit possession is another matter entirely, particularly in the case of demonic possession. Lucifuge hunters are typically highly proficient at exorcising malevolent spirits, and many will try to subjugate an exorcised demon into serving them.

Story Hooks

• You've heard reports that something is killing werewolves in the city of San Francisco; some-thing huge and powerful that leaves the withered bodies of the shapechangers wrapped in bloody silk and hung from the corners of tall buildings like some kind of massive spider. Whatever the monster is, it's claimed at least four werewolves over the space of a single week. According to surveillance reports of werewolf activity in the city, that leaves only three shapechangers left alive, and they've currently disappeared. It's possible that this situation might present a chance to finally build some trust between the Lucifuge and the werewolves in the city, if you can find the surviving shapechangers and offer the assistance of your cell. Of course, if this monster is capable of killing four werewolves in single combat, God only knows how much help you and your team are going to be.

• In the storm-ravaged city of New Orleans, an elderly member of the Lucifuge has been working for the last 10 years on a very special sort of genealogy project. Tracing the bloodlines of Lucifer's children is nothing new to your conspiracy, but in this case, Henri Laveau has dedicated his time and effort towards tracing the family lines of known werewolves that have been encountered in his home state. What he discovered was surprising; cases of lycanthropy occurring again and again in specific bloodlines going back more than 200 years. If true, it suggests that there is some truth to the idea that lycanthropy is genetic – perhaps making them distant cousins to you and your brethren. Unfortunately, shortly after reporting his findings to your superiors, Laveau's home in the Ninth Ward burned to the ground, and the scholar disappeared. You're being sent to the Big Easy to find Laveau if you can – or failing that, his journals. The Lucifuge is eager to learn the truth of Solomon's assertions, and what that implies for the rest of Satan's brood.

• There's a demon loose in the city of Atlanta, hunting down every agent of the Lucifuge it can find. Four hunters are already dead, their hearts torn from their bodies and their corpses burned in a kind of spontaneous human combustion. In each case, a message was left behind, burned into the surface of a nearby wall: *the childer of Abdiel shall know the face of their father and despair.* As far as the Lucifuge knows, there is only one child of Abdiel's line left, and that is you. They're sending you and your cell into the city to draw out this creature of Hell and find out why Abdiel has sent it to Earth to destroy his progeny.

Malleus Maleficarum

For centuries, the witch hunters of the Malleus Maleficarum have fought a secret war against Satan's minions, pitting themselves relentlessly against witches, warlocks, vampires and skinchangers. At the time of the conspiracy's origin in the 16th century it was widely believed that werewolves were wicked souls who worshipped the Devil and transformed into monsters by the light of the moon to feed on the blood of the innocent. The monsters that the Church's hunters encountered in those years did little to dispel that myth. Papal records of that time mention numerous, savage encounters with flesh-eating monsters roaming the forests of Europe, and there was a period in the mid-1600's when Hammer cells were present at no less than a dozen werewolf trials across Germany, France, and Belgium. Countless members of the church perished in desperate battles against "covens" of shapechanging "witches," battling the fearsome power of the werewolves with faith, fire, and silver. In those early days, when the Inquisition still held much of Europe in its iron grip, entire families perished at the stake if one of their number was believed to be a skinchanger, and such was the devastation wrought by the agents of the Church that there were no recorded instances of werewolf attacks on the continent for more than 200 years. Even today, European werewolves view the agents of the Church with an equal mix of hatred and dread, and when the two sides meet, no quarter is asked and none is given. Shapechangers as far away as Asia or North America believe that they can expect no mercy from the hunters of the Malleus Maleficarum; the only options are to fight or to flee, and most choose the former.

Most modern members of the conspiracy are no more enlightened than their forebears as to the true nature of werewolves or other shapechangers; papal lore recounts the savage nature of the monsters and their mindless cruelty, and new inductees are told all the old tales before setting out to hunt a skinchanger. From the perspective of the Church, this indoctrination is to prepare the hunters for what they are about to face, and to steel their faith against the monsters' savage aura. The werewolves, for their part, can recount long litanies of atrocities perpetrated on their ancestors by the agents of the Church, and the tribes of the moon neither forgive nor forget the crimes their kin has suffered. Now, after hundreds of years of bloodshed, the two forces are locked in a death-grip. The struggle will not end until one side or the other has been wiped from the face of the Earth.

The hunters of the Malleus Maleficarum are equally implacable when it comes to instances of spiritual possession or malevolent hauntings. Though it's official policy for mainstream Church officials to petition the Vatican for permission to perform an exorcism or a spiritual cleansing upon a person or a home, the Shadow Congregation has a special dispensation from the Pope to perform these rites if the cell is in unanimous agreement that such an action is required. If none of the members of the cell are part of the clergy (an all-too-common occurrence in modern times), the cell can petition the Vatican on a case-by-case basis for the authorization to contact a local member of the priesthood and request him to perform the rites instead. If the priest is unwilling to aid the cell, the hunters can use their papal authority to compel him to cooperate, though this naturally leads to dangerous complications in an already risky endeavor.

If an exorcism isn't an option, a Hammer cell may appeal to the Vatican for dispensation to confront and destroy a possessed individual instead. Such requests are rarely refused, but the cell must go to great lengths to provide a convincing case for such an execution, and demonstrate that innocent souls will be in dire peril unless extreme action is taken. The Church insists that these bureaucratic rituals are vital to spare the souls of their servants from corruption, but modern hunters frequently chafe under the time-consuming restrictions. More than one cell has taken matters into their own hands and been excommunicated from the conspiracy as a result.

Story Hooks

• Nearly every member of the Malleus Maleficarum knows of Father Reynard Simon, a renowned hunter of werewolves who has served the Church and your conspiracy with faith and courage for more than 25 years. After being seriously wounded in a battle with a werewolf pack outside Caen, Fr Simon was forced to put down his sword and his Bible and take up the pen instead. For the last five years he has researched Church records regarding werewolf encounters – and then, without warning, he simply disappeared from his apartments at the Vatican. For several weeks, Church officials and his fellow hunters search Rome and the surrounding countryside for signs of the esteemed priest – and then a cell in Edinburgh reported seeing Fr Simon on the streets of the city in the company of a man suspected of being a werewolf! Now, you've received orders to travel to Edinburgh at once to find Simon and discover the cause of his strange behavior. And God help any werewolf who gets in your way.

• Word has reached the Church of miraculous events occurring at a small church outside Mexico City. According to the local bishop, a young girl named Consuela entered the church a few days before, displaying clear signs of stigmata. When questioned, Consuela claimed she had been sent by the Virgin Mary to heal the sick, and begged the priest to send out a call for those in need of healing. Reportedly, the child has performed more than 20 confirmed miracles: healing the blind, the infirm, the crippled and the mute. In return, Consuela asked each person she healed to "keep her in their prayers" – and now each and every one of them has fallen into a deathly coma inside their homes. The Church fears this is something far more sinister than a holy visitation. You're being sent to find out the truth.

• You're awakened in the dead of night by a call from an official at the Vatican; a cell of witch hunters in a nearby town had been called in to deal with a case of suspected demon possession at an institution for troubled children. After careful investigation, the leader of the cell reported that the situation warranted a priest and the performance of not just one exorcism, but *six* of them. A priest was hurriedly located and the hunters entered the home to perform the rite. Eight hours later the leader of the cell reported to Rome that the rites had been performed successfully, and the crisis had been averted. But then, four hours after the call, the Vatican learned that police had been called to the institution and discovered every one of the children dead, their throats cut and their blood splashed across the walls. Inside the institution's small chapel, the police found the bodies of seven adults; every one had been expertly skinned. The police believed the murders had been committed more than eight hours before they arrived. If so, who made the call to the Vatican, and what has become of the things wearing the skins of your fellow hunters?

Task Force: VALKYRIE

As far as the Men in Black are concerned, shapechangers represent one of the greatest – if not *the* greatest – paranormal security threat facing the American homeland. Some hunters argue that this just demonstrates Task Force: VALKYRIE's deep ignorance of the supernatural world, but the field agents who have survived a werewolf attack don't believe a word of it. Any creature that can operate in any environment, pass undetected among normal humans and change into a nine-foot-tall killing machine virtually at will is something that gives most VALKYRIE agents chills. Never mind the fact that these creatures can heal damn near any injury in seconds *and* travel unseen from one physical location to another.

As a result, VALKYRIE monitors law enforcement and domestic intelligence data feeds on a constant basis, alert for indicators of werewolf activity across the country. Police or news reports of savage, unexplained murders – particularly in remote or rural areas – will raise an immediate red flag, and a field team will get a call within 48 hours of the event. Where possible, VALKYRIE will give the job to a team that already has a lot of experience in dealing with shapeshifters, but the timing and location of an incident doesn't always make that possible. At the very least, the investigators are given a thorough brief on the capabilities of a typical werewolf, and every effort is made to make sure they're equipped to survive an encounter with one. This can include silver rounds for their issue sidearms, silver buckshot for tactical shotguns, scent neutralizing spray, and even experimental gear like hormone-balancing auto-injectors to help fight off the worst effects of a werewolf's terrifying aura. Of course, if the creature in question turns out to be a different kind of shapechanger – or another sort of monster entirely – the agents can quickly find themselves up the proverbial creek without a paddle. The fact that this happens with disturbing frequency leads many experienced field teams to pass on the offers of equipment and go into the investigation with only their wits and a few basic tools to assist them.

During VALKYRIE's early years, considerable effort was devoted to try and capture one or more shapechangers for medical and scientific study. It's known that in the late 40s at least three werewolves were captured during covert operations in Nazi Germany, but casualties among the capture teams was so high that the practice was abandoned. Files of the subsequent examinations still exist, but with the medical technology of the time, little useful data was obtained. Since then, the organization has managed to build a fairly useful database on werewolves and other shape-changing creatures, pulling facts from team debriefs and witness interviews that go back more than 50 years. Most of the information in the database is very specialized: estimated speed and strength, estimated regenerative capacity, known weaknesses, and so forth. Task Force VALKYRIE knows next to nothing about what shapechangers are and how they interact, but they've got a pretty good handle on how to hunt and kill them.

In the case of purely spiritual threats, Task Force VALKYRIE is hamstrung by characteristic governmental short-sightedness. The wording of the organization's mandate empowers them to deal with "tangible threats to the safety and security of the United States and its citizens," which is often interpreted too literally by field supervisors to mean that ghosts and other *intangible* spirits fall outside the agency's remit. Field teams frequently conduct investigations of haunted sites, but other than collecting EVP's and digital Kirlian footage, most times that's as far as an investigation is allowed to go. Once a person is possessed by a malevolent spirit, the agents can take action against the threat, but until that point their hands are often tied. Even then, VALKYRIE's response is typically limited to dealing with the possession itself, and the possessing spirit all too often escapes to find another victim later.

Story Hooks

- Recently, you've heard rumors from other field agents that Task Force VALKYRIE has had a rash of encounters with werewolves all across the United States. From what you've heard, possibly as many as fifteen shapechangers have been killed in five separate raids – an unprecedented number in such a short amount of time. No one knows for sure how the conspiracy has gotten such solid intel on the werewolves all of a sudden, but there's speculation that there's a traitor among the shapechangers who has proved willing to betray his fellows for an unspecified price. Now, you've received orders from your field supervisor to take your team to the Black Hills of North Dakota, where you'll meet a contact code-named Fenrir. Fenrir is supposed to hand over a CD containing actionable intel on a number of werewolf packs operating in the northwestern US. Who is the source, and

what's his motive for selling out the shapechangers? And what might happen if the werewolves discover what Fenrir is up to? Worse, could this be a trap?

• Over the last forty-eight hours, six teenage kids have gone missing in St. Louis, Missouri. In four of the cases, the kids' parents were savagely murdered, and it looks like we could be dealing with a sequel to the Harvest Moon slayings in Oregon back in the early 80s. This time, however, we've got better information technology than the Oregon State Police had at that time. Surveillance video from a truck stop outside St. Louis shows four of the teens buying sodas in the company of two unidentified adult males. Eyewitness testimony indicated that the individuals were riding in an old Dodge van, and they were heading south. At this point they could be in Louisiana or northern Texas; we hope to know more by the time you and your team are on the ground in St. Louis. We've got every reason to believe we're dealing with a pack of juvenile werewolves and two or more adults who may be acting as mentors or ringleaders. We need to find out where these kids are going, and why – and then we need to take them down before they can hurt anybody else.

• Homeland Security and the CIA have been keeping tabs on a US citizen named Barry Knowles, a white supremacist and a member of the White Dawn militia group in Iowa. The White Dawn is a group that advocates armed overthrow of the US government and mass slaughter of blacks, Jews, Hispanics, and other minorities to a supposedly Aryan "deity" known as Juhukar. Knowles is considered a radical even among the white power movement, but his bloodthirsty dogma has gained him a small but dangerous following. Twenty-four hours ago, Homeland Security agents felt like they had enough evidence to arrest Knowles on charges of illegal arms dealing. He and three followers were pulled over outside Boise by ATF agents, and in the ensuing gun battle Knowles' soldiers and four ATF agents were killed. Eyewitness reports and dashboard video footage of the shootout clearly show Knowles being shot more than 12 times by ATF agents, but the militia leader seemed oblivious to the wounds. Despite being shot multiple times, Knowles managed to flee back to his compound in rural Idaho. We want you and your team to get out there and get some answers before the ATF surrounds the place and things get out of hand.

THE BEAR LODGE
THE MOST DANGEROUS HUNT

Some hunters take up the Vigil out of fear, panicking at the thought of beasts coming out of the night. Some face monsters out of responsibility, determined that their loved ones should never fall to creatures that place themselves above mankind. Some derive their hunt from their need for knowledge, for the secret truths behind the world.

The Bear Lodge hunts and kills monsters for no greater reason than to prove that they can.

In the face of ever-tighter restrictions on big-game hunting and stringent laws against killing endangered species, it's getting harder for hunters to really prove themselves, to face animals that are their equals and emerge victorious. The Bear Lodge has always gone after the most dangerous prey, and they haven't really changed — but instead of lions, tigers, and wolves, they choose to face something far more dangerous. Every lodge-house has a spot for a werewolf's head on their wall, and every hunter dreams of putting the last silver bullet into an inhuman beast.

History

The Bear Lodge can draw a straight line back through individual monster hunters to the end of published records. Though their assumed history impresses new members, and in some cases inspires individual members to go the extra mile, they lived in a time without a Bear Lodge for them to join. The first recorded meeting of the big-game hunters that would found the Lodge was back in 1901. Hunters from across the United States met in the otherwise unremarkable town of Glasgow, Montana, to discuss their experiences hunting strange creatures.

"WAIT! I NEED HIS EARS TO PROVE MY KILL."

Though some hunters described their encounters with civilized creatures living in cities and towns, their tales paled compared to those of Don Edwards, a local man. Edwards had set out with five companions to hunt elk in the woods. Instead of their prey, they encountered a scene of carnage — both elk and mountain lions torn apart by some powerful beast that had consumed the hearts of its kill. Rather than returning to town for supplies, Edwards and his companions followed the bloody trail. After half a day's tracking, they found their quarry — three beasts that in the poor light Edwards first mistook for giant wolves. When one turned to face them, the hunters recognized the light of intelligence in its eyes — and it recognized them. They could see the razor-sharp teeth in its mouth as it leapt at them. Edwards was the only one who had the wherewithal to fire his rifle. A lucky shot caught the beast in the temple and brought the other hunters to their senses. Concentrating their fire, the beast fell. The rest of the pack descended on the hunters, tearing them into bloody chunks. Giving in to the primal fear stirring in his gut, Don Edwards ran for his life. Somehow, he avoided the creatures and made it back to town. Returning with more people to look for survivors, he found nothing but blood and bone — and the body of a strange man riddled with bullet holes. The others dismissed Don's tale as the result of a hunting accident and too much whiskey, but he knew the truth. The dead stranger had the same eyes as the feral beast he'd hunted.

Though many other hunters told their tale at that first meeting, Edwards' story struck a chord in the assembled hunters. They all knew that something stalked the wilderness, something that scared even them. Rather than admit it, they established the first Bear Lodge, a hunting lodge half an hour's ride from Glasgow. Though they didn't advertise as such, word spread that hunters looking to track a werewolf or other mysterious creature could find support at the Lodge. Soon, hunters flocked to the area. Some had grown tired of hunting game, others wanted to prove their manhood by facing the most dangerous prey.

Those few members of the Lodge who survived brought back tales of black magic and shapechanging beasts. Rather than running in fear, the hunters coated their knives with wolfsbane and loaded their guns with silver. Over time, hunting parties from the Bear Lodge grew better at killing werewolves. They insisted that an experienced hunter accompany every group venturing into the wilds, and that their hunters use silver weapons. Unusual for a hunting lodge, members attached no shame in running from a superior foe, especially given the high likelihood of death common around werewolves.

In 1946, four veteran hunters founded a second Bear Lodge in Washington State, with the blessing of the Montana lodge. Over the next ten years, five more Bear Lodges opened across the rural United States, including one in southern Alaska. The last established Lodge opened in 1959 near Candle Lake, Saskatchewan, and remains the only Bear Lodge outside of the United States. Members of one Lodge are members of every Lodge, and can travel freely between sites. Even when miles from an established Lodge, members must look out for one another — though individuals may prefer to work alone, the upper echelons know that no hunter stands a chance against a werewolf on his own.

Time has changed the Bear Lodge. While once members connected through mail and telephone, the organization now maintains a secure website for members — including forums where members can ask for help from other hunters without concern for physical location. Many hunters discuss tactics and equipment on the site, while others share their experiences in the field. Having the Bear Lodge present helps remind a member of what she faces, even against the terrible fear that wracks her mind and warps her memories. Only members of the Lodge can access the website, other visitors see nothing more than a page offering field journals and equipment reviews by a team of experienced hunters.

Despite their decentralized nature, a hunter still has to prove himself as a member of the Bear Lodge, and that involves a hunt. Most members have already had some experiences of the supernatural world, though a few come in cold and have to learn on the trail. Regardless, a group of hunters meets at one of the Lodges, arms themselves for werewolf, and sets out into the night. The new member must see a werewolf as what it is — a bestial hybrid of wolf and man — and the party must then kill their foe. The new member then takes a trophy from the body — usually a finger or an ear — that's kept in the Lodge as a record of their membership. Those who don't succeed in killing a werewolf often don't survive, and those who do brush the whole event off as a bad trip, or a particularly vicious bear attack.

Less favorably, the original Bear Lodge in Montana is all but gone. Constant werewolf attacks forced the last hunters to abandon the building in 1987. Only members of the Lodge know of the building's existence, and every time they've mounted an expedition to reclaim the original Lodge, they've become the victims in a werewolf's hunt. Some members believe that any expedition achieves little more than goading the werewolves to attack, while others believe that the archived transcripts of early hunts and images of man-beasts are worth the risk.

The Enemy

Hunters who belong to the Bear Lodge dedicate themselves to hunting werewolves above everything else. While some hunters encounter vampires and yet stranger things over the course of urban hunts, those creatures don't really count. In the mind of the Bear Lodge, the prey's the thing. They're out to prove themselves better than anything that nature can create, with only human ingenuity — and human engineering — on their side.

Despite their reliance on human conveniences, hunters belonging to the Bear Lodge have picked up a lot of tricks from werewolves over the years. Some members spend years studying wolf packs in the wild to get a better idea of how they can hunt successfully — and how their prey might think when animal instinct suppresses human thought. Like a wolf pack, a cell of hunters belonging to the Lodge first observes their prey from a safe distance. Almost like an animal, each hunter uses the terrain, daubing mud and animal shit on his body to mask his scent. From there, he watches and waits, studying the pack for days or even weeks. Though following a pack of werewolves is incredibly dangerous, he needs to isolate the weakest member, the focal point in the pack. Once he's done that, he can strike. Initiations into the Lodge take place with an experienced hunter who has already identified a weak werewolf.

Once he has selected his target, the hunter needs to strike when it's alone. Sometimes, the rest of the pack will depart on a strange errand — or even vanish entirely — leaving the weakest behind. Other times it's up to the hunter to manufacture a distraction, whether by destroying some of the pack's territory or even sending in a cell of unaffiliated hunters for the rest to play with. Though this last tactic is more than a little cold, it's also incredibly pragmatic: if the other cell is lucky, there's another dead werewolf. Even if they're not, the attack on the weakest member gets traced back to the other cell, drawing suspicion from the Bear Lodge.

When the weakest werewolf is alone, the hunters strike. At least one member captures the hunt on video, and the most experienced hunter reassures the others against the primal terror that even the weakest werewolf can bring forth. If possible, the hunters bring the werewolf into a killing field — an area that they've had a chance to prepare with snares, pits, and other means of holding the werewolf in place. Using range to their advantage, they can strike the werewolf down in a hail of silver bullets. Even when they haven't had a chance to prepare the ground, Bear Lodge hunters use range to their advantage, along with modern transport that can outpace even the fastest werewolf.

Some members of the Lodge have discovered werewolves inhabiting urban areas along with the wilderness. Much as they do in the wild, they follow their prey and attempt to isolate the weakest, but they don't have to worry so much about stealth. A human can follow a werewolf all day in the city without taking any special measures — any good crowd is perfect for hiding in plain sight. Cells who operate in cities often maintain a stronghold used exclusively for drawing werewolves, where sensory overload can help them bring down the greatest prey of all.

Away from werewolves, the Bear Lodge turns a blind eye. While some members will go after vampires, seeing them as a different challenge, others would rather avoid the creatures of the night — or even work with them.

A few hunters choose dangerous human prey in addition to supernatural beasts, but they've got to be careful. When he does, the hunter's got to choose his targets carefully. He selects his prey based on demonstrated acts of brutality and inhumanity — the same as if he were hunting a vampire. A child molester who snatches children off the streets and constructs deathtraps for parents who try to follow him is a greater threat than a serial killer who strikes only when his targets are drugged or asleep or a vampire who never kills. The majority of Lodge members still look on the practice with suspicion. Once a hunter starts killing things that might as well be people, it's a small step to losing respect for his prey. Losing that respect is the hallmark of a slasher, not a hunter.

Hunters

You'd been hunting in the same woods for nearly 20 years when you first saw it. At first, it looked like another group of hunters, but then they brought out what looked like old elk-skins and put them on like a new jacket. They were eight feet tall when they stood up, with hideous horns growing from their heads. You got a shot off, but they didn't notice even if you hit. They chased you, and you ran like hell. Only later did you find that you weren't the only one to see something weird while hunting.

Ashwood Abbey: I led a hunt for a group of these guys a couple of months back. They wanted a werewolf, obviously knew their shit but didn't have the first idea about the wilderness. They helped out, not like most fair-weather hunters, but they just wanted to trap the beast, so they could kill it slowly. Now, I've never tortured an animal before. But they asked me to join in and, well, I'm taking them out again next week.

Null Mysteriis: I used to hunt with a group of scientists a while back. They gave me a real challenge: could I help them watch a werewolf in the wild? They thought there was some big difference between wolves in the cities and in the forest. I got them in close, and they just watched. One of them had a video camera. Three hours we were there and nothing happened. They even paid me a bonus to leave the thing alive.

Malleus Maleficarum: I've seen one of these guys in action, actually out in the wild. He had this idea that werewolves were men with the souls of beasts, damned things, and he was hunting a whole pack at once. The freakish thing is, when he stopped to pray, things really started going our way. Until he let his urge to be a martyr get the better of him. One of the beasts tore his head clean off, and I ran like hell.

The Cheiron Group: A guy from a medical company gave me a call last month. Didn't beat around the bush, he wanted me to get him a werewolf. One thousand bucks for the body of a confirmed werewolf, and I shot enough film to prove my kill to them. I've no problem with freelancing for them, and I know that a few others do the same, but I don't want to know what they use the bodies for. And I know I'm not going to take them up on the ten thousand for a live capture. I'm not stupid.

You're not yet 18 years old, but you feel much older. Your father and your granddaddy took you out hunting as a birthday present, pressed a gun into your hands, and showed you how to track animals. You found the wolf-tracks on your own and thought it'd be a good idea to follow them. You never wanted to pull the trigger, but then the wolf gave you no choice. It grew almost as big as a pony, with great jaws ready to crack your bones. You pulled the trigger once, and then ran. The others had silver bullets. When they'd put the beast down, they had you take a trophy and welcomed you into the family secret.

Other people might not realize it, but you know which way the wind's blowing. When the United Nations takes control of the glorious U. S. of A. you've got a whole family who'll be waiting for them. You've seen their shock-troops, the infiltrators they've sent in to ruin the country. Holdovers from Nazi experiments, you wouldn't wonder, men who can turn into beasts. One tried getting into your compound. He made it past the razor-wire, but tripped an alarm. You got in touch with some people, who recommended that you join the Bear Lodge. They don't know the truth, but they have some good tactics.

You barely set foot outside the city limits all your life, but you're still a hunter. You graduated from picking on kids with a slingshot to sniping bums with an air-rifle from your fire-escape. You learned parkour before it was cool, and prowled the streets. Then you saw it: a huge black dog, some kind of wolf throwback, tearing the throat out of some city businessman. You ran that time, but you weren't stupid. The very next day you bought a gun and went online. Some guy you met on an "urban hunting" forum turned out to know the guy you watched die, and he put you on to a hunting lodge that could help you out.

Motivations

Hunters of the Bear Lodge have no problem agreeing on how they should hunt their prey. The real dividing point is the reasons that a hunter has for continuing. After all, most people who face a werewolf wouldn't go out looking to repeat the experience.

Sportsmen hunt werewolves to prove that they're the best at what they do. The challenge, the burning fear running through their veins when they first see the monstrous creature, the strange memory blackouts after the hunt — all these things are badges of honor, a mark that the hunter has gone up against something truly unnatural. Some seek out werewolves and other supernatural creatures, hoping to bag the big trophies, while others see the hunt as the apex of their personal development.

Trappers don't believe in needless danger. They may hunt other animals for sport, but they hunt werewolves to keep people safe. As such, they're mostly interested in recording the best ways to defeat a werewolf, and some make all kinds of strange deals to get more information. Others fall back on experiments, luring werewolves into areas full of traps designed to test different methods. Most of the hunters hoping to retake the Montana Lodge belong to this group.

Vigilantes hunt werewolves out of a sense of justice. Werewolves kill people, and vigilantes kill werewolves. Maybe they've caught a glimpse of the uncaring, monstrous world and need to fight back, or maybe they're out for vengeance. Some vigilantes patrol urban areas, taking on all manner of killers — including crazed slashers and bloodthirsty vampires. A few even refuse to kill werewolves who haven't murdered people, but those hunters (and the prey they let go) are very rare.

Status

Standing in the Bear Lodge is based purely on how many werewolf hunts a member has survived. While some would prefer a ranking based on kills, the Lodge as a whole hold to the idea that any encounter with a werewolf is enough — providing the hunter didn't just shit himself and leave his fellows to die.

• You've been on a hunt and seen a real, live werewolf. While you probably didn't do much by way of helping to kill it, you did take a trophy

and your name's in the Lodge's records as a full member. If nothing else, you can get in touch with other members and share stories of what works and what doesn't. You gain a dot of Contacts among the werewolf-hunting experts of the Lodge.

••• You've been on several hunts and have seen things that you'll never forget — no matter how much you want to. The Lodge believes that you're ready to lead the hunts that initiate new members. Your exposure to the supernatural fear of werewolves has dulled your reaction to it slightly. You're affected by Lunacy (p. 163) as if your Willpower were one dot greater than it actually is.

••••• You've hunted impossible creatures and come close to death more times than you can imagine. Only now can you really admit to what you have seen, only now do you know that you faced a beast put on this world purely to hunt — and you know what it really means to be its prey. Your study of your foe gives you the Unseen Sense Merit applied to werewolves. If you already have the Merit applied to werewolves, you can apply it to any one other kind of tangible supernatural creature.

ILLUMINATED BROTHERHOOD
THE PSYCHONAUTS

Monsters stalk the world, preying on humanity. Witches snatch people away for blasphemous sacrifices. Feral beasts lurk in the shadows, waiting to spill human blood. Mysterious creatures sabotage exploration into the deep seas. Some people say the world's sick, or that it's cracked and broken. Madmen suggest that the legions of Hell are present on Earth, drinking blood and cracking bones.

The Illuminated Brotherhood knows that something's wrong, but not what they can do to make it right. Rather than running to dusty tomes of occult lore or the theories of bleeding-edge parapsychology, they plumb the depths of the human mind. A member of the Brotherhood plumbs her own psyche in search of the truth, hoping to plug into the planetary consciousness to explain what he's seen. Whether he makes it or not, the next morning he faces the same twisted world, but with the hollow knowledge that next time, he might come back with the Truth.

The more she seeks the truth, the more a member of the Illuminated Brotherhood comes face to face with creatures and events that send her right back to her psychedelic-induced visions. To an outsider, she's trapped in a vicious cycle of addiction, but in her own head she's inching closer to the truth, and she might find it after just one more encounter.

History

The first recognizable Illuminated Brotherhood started in the early 1980s as a result of an attempt to recreate the Marsh Chapel Experiment, an experiment to determine if psilocybin could facilitate religious experiences at a significant church service. Rather than dividing the participants into two groups, the new experiment was designed to test the effectiveness of various hallucinogenic drugs in facilitating religious experiences.

Unfortunately, the experimenters didn't know one core fact: a disturbingly high percentage of their test subjects were in fact people with close ties to the spirit world, mediums who had infiltrated the experiment to, frankly, gain access to the mind-opening and mind-altering drugs. The presence of so many mediums combined with the drugs in use lead to disaster. Powerful spirits crashed through the barriers between flesh and spirit, taking random participants in the service as physical bodies and shattering their minds. The nightmare lasted for six hours, and later became the subject of a cover-up by local and Federal authorities — and the final nail in the coffin for psychedelic experimentation.

A handful of people who survived the service started meeting up. They started out as a support group, trying to work out what had happened when the rules of the world turned out to be little more than guidelines. Inside of a year, they'd come to the conclusion that the bizarre events had some link to the experiment. A few of the survivors banded together and made their goal clear: whatever had happened was related to the psychedelic nature of the experiment, and it must be reproduced. The best way to find the truth was through similar entheogenic experiences. Calling themselves the Illuminated Brotherhood, members sought out the truths only accessible through psychedelic experimentation.

By 1992, the Illuminated Brotherhood had spread to colleges across the United States, but its members were no closer to the truth. The original members had drifted far enough away that the group had no real leadership. The future seemed set: the Illuminated Brotherhood was becoming little more than another group of stoners with no idea of their own mortality and one too many Timothy Leary books. That all changed when members began reporting encounters with strange creatures. In unrelated incidents across the country, members swore blind that they'd seen men made of spiders or women who feasted on the

brains of the homeless. A few members, those who'd gone the furthest into their own minds, felt creatures calling to them from beyond the physical world.

Knowing that anyone outside the group would blame a member of the Brotherhood's repeated use of hallucinogenic drugs for her suddenly encountering creatures from folklore and the darkest pits of Hollywood's imagination, the Illuminated Brotherhood turned inwards. The sudden rise in supernatural events could only mean one thing: they were getting closer to the truth. Some people joined the Brotherhood after encountering the supernatural, believing that the group offered understanding and a chance to find out what really happened. Other new members had prior experience with psychoactives, and had encountered the shadowy truth when pursuing a new experience.

Regardless of how they came to the Illuminated Brotherhood, there's no shortage of young people who've encountered the supernatural and who burn with a need to find the truth. Slowly, the focus of the group has shifted — the entheogenic experience is a useful explanation for what's going on, but every twisted killer and animate corpse provides another bit of the puzzle. Members of the Brotherhood get hooked on the hunt, on that ephemeral feeling that they're so close to understanding, that the next hunt will bring the truth. It's the same feeling as waking up after a mushroom trip — you touched minds with God and learned a part of the secret truths, but you don't quite remember what they were. Next time, you'll remember. Next time, you'll find the key.

Next time, you'll die.

There's no other way to put it. The mortality rate in the Illuminated Brotherhood is very high. Psychedelics don't teach people how to fight. Even when it comes to obvious creatures from folklore, members of the Brotherhood don't know any more than they learn from bad monster movies. Most members make up for their lack of training by being young. The misguided energy that makes a college kid sleep on the grave of a notorious killer runs through everything they do — in many ways, the Illuminated Brotherhood are too dumb not to get involved with the supernatural world. Many members are still young enough that they don't have a sense of their own mortality. The hunters who die obviously weren't thinking clearly. They made a dumb mistake. Underneath all this bravado is a clear message: it was the hunter's fault. Nobody dies if they're prepared.

I've seen things you couldn't believe.

GROUP SUPPORT

Some critics — including some ex-members — say the Illuminated Brotherhood hurts its members more than it helps them. In the end, they've got a point. Members of the Brotherhood push each other to greater and greater risks — like the college kids pushing each other to experience the weirdest and worst acid trip they've ever done. Unlike those students, members of the Brotherhood stand a very real chance of death every single time they hunt

On the other hand, the Brotherhood does help its members in its own strange way. Even other hunters would have a hard time believing them, given the group's propensity for hallucinogenics. Everyone needs someone to fall back on, even if her support group just pushes her into greater and greater risks.

The Enemy

As a group, the Illuminated Brotherhood focuses its Vigil on spirits, often subconsciously. Unfettered from the mundane world by the entheogenic experience, the human mind is free to create, to add resonance to the spirit world — and to be shaped by that world. While a few members are natural mediums, and others have the life of a medium thrust upon them, many members never directly interact with the spirit world. Quite the contrary: the spirit world wants to interfere with them.

It's hard fighting creatures of the night when nobody believes they exist. It's far harder when you can't see them at all. The Illuminated Brotherhood doesn't have any means by which its members can affect spirits. While a few achieve the ability through dedication to entheogenic experiences, most hunters face an opponent they've only heard about that can alter the world around them. Getting a spirit's interest is much like living a bad trip that won't go away by waiting.

Members of the Illuminated Brotherhood don't hunt alone. Having a group around gives the hunter a chance to work out what's really happening and what's just in his head. While the Brotherhood doesn't know much about spirits, they often have a better understanding of how an area feels — and therefore its resonance — than other hunters. When under attack from a hostile spirit, a member of the Brotherhood often looks for a way to alter the resonance of the area to defend himself.

Not every encounter with spirits has to be antagonistic. In many cases, the Illuminated Brothers go out looking for places where the walls between worlds are thin. In such Loci, the hunters deliberately open themselves up to the creatures beyond. The affects of the world around the hunters give them clues into the spirit world and the alien denizens underpinning the world. The Brotherhood hopes that by studying the reactions of the spirits they can find scraps of the truth. Many members push each other, starting out with Kirlian photography and Ouija boards and moving on to consuming hallucinogens at a Locus. A few even push themselves further, inviting spirits to possess them, though such hunters often don't last long.

When it comes to more physical threats, the Illuminated Brotherhood prefers to investigate rather than confronting the beasts head-on. From studying the strange creatures that lurk in the shadows, a member of the Brotherhood can see what happens when a specific spirit takes a human body as its own. A bestial spirit in human form can twist the body, while an alien aspect of hunger looks like the archetypal vampire. Even among the different types of possessed creature there are plenty of differences. The current theory among the Brotherhood is that these differences are due to each hunter who encounters such a creature perceiving it through a filter based on his own subconscious expectations.

Hunters

You're one of the oldest people remaining in the Illuminated Brotherhood, one of the only founding members left. In a society that seems to refresh its membership every four years, that's rare. Unlike other members, you're seriously into consciousness manipulation — continuing the experiments started by Leary, though you have to remain an impartial observer. You've had a hard time getting funding, but at least the Brotherhood keeps you in willing test subjects.

You got into the Brotherhood for the drugs. Not because you need them, but because you've always seen strange things. Your grandfather goes on and on about being the next shaman, but you don't believe a word of it. Something weird's going on, and you wish you knew what — that's what the Illuminated Brotherhood is for. You want answers, but so far all it's got is more questions.

Some people can't deal with the world around them. A werewolf killed a woman right in front of you, tore her body in two, and all you could do was watch.

STEREOTYPES

Ascending Ones: I had a contact who could supply a particularly effective variety of DMT. He never told me exactly what was in it, and I didn't want to know. One dose knocked me into orbit, and I finally understood the world, the strange creatures beyond, everything. It all fit into place. Not like normally, where you just get this feeling of it making sense — this time it actually did. Unfortunately, I puked up the memory along with my lunch. I wonder what happened to that guy. He sure seemed to know more than he let on.

Les Mystères: You want weird and dangerous? These guys have it in spades. There's these groups all over the country, all different, all busy recruiting shamans or wise-men or people who can talk to the saints. Turns out they're after people who can talk to the alien space gods in the guise of some weird religious shit. I watched one of their rituals through a window, and they invited the spirits to possess them. Yeaaaah. No. I'm no fan of anyone who wants to turn himself into a monster.

Null Mysteriis: I was casing out a place, somewhere that I'd heard was special to a bunch of werewolves. Nice and quiet, then these guys just showed up out of nowhere. They didn't ask questions, not even why I was there. They just started taking photographs and setting up some science project right in the middle of the site I was watching! Once they were done, they headed out without ever speaking to me, like I was some kind of amateur. One of them did look over at me, and he nodded like I was right where he expected me to be. Freaky.

The Union: Sometimes, these guys can be a real asset. Watching and trying to understand is all well and good, but sometimes a beast wants to eat you, and a gang of people who can swing a wrench and mean it make good backup. If you end up working with them, it's a good idea not to tell them about the drugs — most members that I've worked with are big on the whole "community protection" thing, which includes getting drugs off the streets.

The primal fear clutched your heart and kept you rooted to the spot. You told everyone who would listen about what you saw, but you couldn't remember anything beyond the fear. Only a few people took you seriously. They took you out of yourself, let you remember what happened for a few minutes. You remember that fear, that clarity — that *rush*. You had to have it again.

You weren't cool enough or rich enough to get into a fraternity, but you stuck around, watching from the fringes. When the pledges had to spend the night in a graveyard, you went along too. Everyone bedded down on a grave. How were you supposed to know that your chosen resting place held the body of a multiple murderer? Terrible nightmares plagued your sleep — then you woke up to see one of the pledges taking a bite out of one of the slumbering ones. You ran back to the college, and straight into the arms of the Illuminated Brotherhood.

Movements

The Illuminated Brotherhood divides itself into groups intended to support members in their specific area of interest. These divisions give hunters a chance to discuss their experiences — and share new dares — with people whose Vigil closely matches their own.

The **Children of Leary** focus on expanding their minds and studying the entheogenic experience as the key method of finding truth in the world: they don't go out to hunt monsters or spend their nights in haunted houses; instead they plumb the heights — and depths — of their own minds. Just because they don't go looking doesn't mean the Children don't encounter monsters, quite the opposite. Strange and horrifying creatures dog their footsteps, but alone among the Illuminated Brotherhood the Children of Leary can't tell when they're real.

Hunters who belong to the **Spirit-Seekers** spend their days tracking down rumors of occult locations — the house where a serial killer brought his victims to slaughter them, or a site where people have experienced alien abductions. They push each other to find strange places and spend the night. Some cover their enthusiasm in pseudoscience, setting up recording equipment and hoping to catch a spirit or ghost on camera. Others prefer to experience the site through altered states of consciousness. When they do find a Locus (p. 174), Spirit-Seekers invariably draw the attention of spirits in the area. While they can study some without drawing attention, other times they must face creatures they can't see or touch.

Perhaps the most conventional hunters among the Illuminated Brotherhood, the **Watching Eye**, concern themselves with spirits and ghosts who take on human bodies. The real effects of the spirit world

TRUTH IN A PILE OF COWSHIT

Hallucinogens (like the mushrooms that sometimes grow in the aforementioned heaps of cow-flop) can work in the World of Darkness to open one's mind to the hidden worlds of spirits and ghosts. That may mean offering a glimpse into the state of Twilight (non-corporeal existence in this world) or into the spirit world (a secondary plane of existence outside our own, where inscrutable entities manipulate material reality from beyond that veil). Assume that less potent hallucinogens (LSD, mushrooms) offer the former, whereas truly potent entheogens (ayahuasca, DMT) offer the big glimpse into what werewolves call "The Shadow."

Within the Illuminated Brotherhood, the hunters make heavy use of "spirit guides" or what are jokingly referred to as "trip advisors:" mentors within the group who stay sober while a younger member goes on an entheogenic "journey." The mentor in theory is a positive force that keeps the young hunter from experiencing a bad trip. Of course, more than a few have been outed as salacious Svengalis, manipulating the naïve for their own gain or amusement.

are best observed when it interacts directly with people — possessing them and turning them into monsters. The Watching Eye believes monsters are the result of spiritual possession, and their appearance as the classic "monsters" from Hollywood movies and folk tales are the result of "semiotic ghosting" — the world changing slightly to benefit from people's perspective.

Status

For all that the Illuminated Brotherhood talks about being egalitarian, it still has a fairly strict hierarchy. Members gain respect for divining scraps of the truth behind the world, whether through gathering information or through expanding their mind with hallucinogenic drugs.

• You've felt the presence of spirits in the world, and you've had first-hand experience of the Brotherhood's experiments in consciousness al-teration. You gain the Parapsychology specialty in either Occult or Science.

••• You're starting to get an idea of what you're up against, and just what the stakes are. You've encountered enough of the strange sides of the world that you can feel you're getting close, but the truth remains elusive to you. You receive the benefits of the Unseen Sense Merit applied to Loci. If you already have the Merit, you expand your area of expertise to spirits in general. If you already have the Merit as applied to spirits, you gain no further bonus.

••••• You've seen the hidden face of the world, and whether you want to or not you can't un-see it. You gain the Merit: Natural Medium. If you already have this Merit, you instead gain two dice on the roll to resist spirit influences.

TALBOT GROUP

THE REDEEMERS

Most hunters are driven by tragedy to do battle with the night; they have witnessed unspeakable horrors or saw loved ones die at the hands of monsters, and so they try to save others from a similar fate. They seek out the monsters where they live and kill them by any means necessary. For these hunters, the Vigil is a war with only one possible outcome: the elimination of every monster on the face of the Earth.

The men and women of the Talbot Group see things differently, because many of their loved ones *are* monsters. Their Vigil is one of desperate, often violent interventions and chilling therapies: drugs, surgeries and isolation cells deep in the forests of the Pacific Northwest. First and foremost, these hunters seek to save the monsters from themselves, even at the risk of their own lives.

The cure is out there, and they won't rest until they find it.

History

Residents of the Seattle-Tacoma area in the early 1980s remember the Harvest Moon Massacres, an unprecedented spree of killings at area schools and homes that left a total of forty-eight people dead over a three-day period. Eight high-school seniors, from communities as far north as Mount Vernon and as far south as Olympia, apparently suffered what authorities later described as "spontaneous psychotic episodes" and went on a rampage, killing anyone who crossed their path. Despite a swift and overwhelming response to the attacks, local authorities seemed powerless to prevent them – and worse, failed to capture or kill any of the perpetrators involved. In each case, the attackers vanished without a trace, leaving a gruesome trail of mutilated bodies in their wake. The

resulting investigation, including a massive manhunt that involved local police, federal agents, and members of the Washington National Guard, failed to turn up any clues as to the attackers' whereabouts, or offered anything but speculation to explain the violent outbreaks. The families of the victims and perpetrators alike were left with nothing but questions and the lingering pain of their loss.

Most of the parents of the attackers – those who survived – ultimately left the Washington area to try and rebuild their lives elsewhere, but a determined few refused to give up the search for answers. Foremost among them were Paul and Isabelle Talbot, two prominent Washington doctors whose son, Andrew, was one of the first and most violent of the eight attackers. Their quest to find their missing son and solve the riddle of the mysterious rampage attracted national attention during the mid to late 80s. While Isabelle paid large sums to private investigators and traveled up and down the western seaboard chasing reports of possible sightings of her son, Paul campaigned tirelessly for greater psychological screening of troubled teens in the public school system, and eventually created a counseling program that was adopted by the Seattle Board of Education in the late 80s. During this period, the two also co-wrote a book called *Modern-day Demons*, chronicling their experiences during the massacres and the observations afterward. The book became an instant bestseller, and gained the Talbots a degree of fame and moderate fortune that would pay even greater dividends later on.

The couple might have faded into quiet obscurity after the publication of their book, if not for a second tragedy that occurred in mid-1989. Isabelle Talbot had traveled to Santa Fe, New Mexico, to meet with a pair of private investigators who believed they had found Andrew living at a homeless shelter in the city. Neither of the Talbots had much reason to hope at that point; they had lost count of the many false leads and mistaken identities they endured over the past few years. Isabelle left Seattle on a Thursday, and expected to return on Saturday at the latest, having put yet another false sighting to rest. When Saturday came and went without any word from her, Paul became concerned. By Monday, he made a frantic call to the Santa Fe police, who went to Mrs. Talbot's hotel room and found a scene of unspeakable carnage. Blood and torn pieces of flesh and bone were everywhere; it took two weeks for pathologists to determine exactly how many victims were present at the scene. Isabelle Talbot was found in the bathroom, suffering from severe injuries across more than 70% of her body. Despite massive blood loss, Mrs. Talbot clung tenaciously to life. She was eventually able to identify the other victims as the two private investigators who had summoned her to Santa Fe. When questioned about her attacker, a sedated Isabelle repeatedly described a towering, furred beast, with savage talons and massive jaws. Sometimes she referred to the creature as a monster – a beast sent straight from the depths of Hell.

Other times, when she was a bit more lucid, she insisted her attacker was Andrew, her missing son.

There were no other witnesses to the attack, and the police had no credible leads. Paul Talbot rushed to Santa Fe to collect his wife, and had her transferred to Seattle, where she faced years of surgery and physical therapy to recover from her wounds. The horrors Isabelle witnessed in Santa Fe would change the Talbots' lives forever.

While Paul Talbot continued to explore ways to counsel and treat severe adolescent aggression, Isabelle Talbot chose a different course entirely. She rejected science in favor of spiritualism, immersing herself completely in the lore of the Native American tribes that once inhabited the region. Their tales of the spirit realm and its inhabitants offered a chilling explanation for what had happened to Andrew and the other lost children during the Harvest Moon Massacre. The more Isabelle delved into Native American myth, the more convinced she became that her son had been possessed by a malevolent spirit, a flesh-eating demon that transformed Andrew's body into a towering, fanged monster. Through her researches, Isabelle came into contact with other individuals who shared similar beliefs, and in her zeal to prove her theories – and perhaps find a way to save her son – she created a sort of loose network of contacts along the West Coast who helped search for evidence of spiritual influence in their communities. At first, Paul viewed his wife's growing obsession with concern and no small amount of embarrassment, but he chose not to interfere, believing that she had to find her own way to come to peace with the loss of their son. For his part, Talbot's counseling program was showing signs of success, and gathering a considerable amount of local interest. It was at this point that Mr. Talbot was approached by Dr. Robert Courtland, a behavioral psychologist who had plans to found a school and counseling center that catered specifically to the needs of adolescents and teens with severe behavioral problems. Courtland had already lined up the funding for the school from a number of wealthy donors, and hoped to enter into a partnership with Talbot and incorporate his own treatment programs. The partnership led to the foundation of the Talbot Group, a non-profit organization dedicated to counseling, rehabilitating and educating troubled youths. The first school was established outside Seattle in 1992.

Meanwhile, Isabelle and her peers continued to amass and collate information about supernatural phenomena from Vancouver to San Diego. Over time, when compared with case histories of violent crimes and other bizarre behavior, certain patterns began to emerge. Certain geographical areas were more likely to produce phenomena than others. The same could be said for certain people with similar psychological and social profiles. When Isabelle compared these findings to her husband's case histories of severe adolescent aggression, she discovered a number of startling similarities. In nearly every case, the most severe cases of adolescent violence occurred in what she termed as "spiritual hot zones."

Now that she had a working theory to explain her observations, Mrs. Talbot had to go out and find the evidence to prove it. Though physically frail after her attack in Santa Fe, Isabelle remained a force to be reckoned with. She gathered her companions and began a Vigil of her own, searching for signs of spirits and spirit possession in Seattle-Tacoma and beyond. The first few years were marked by numerous false starts and failures, and more than one brush with mundane, human danger. But then, in 1995, she and her hunters had a breakthrough. On a summer night near Jackson Heights in Los Angeles, Isabelle came face-to-face with a man possessed by a spirit of pure, unalloyed murder. The encounter left three members of Talbot's group hospitalized, two in critical condition, but to the hunters it was considered a signal victory. They had seen a glimpse of their enemy at last. Now they had to develop the means of dealing with them.

For the next several years, Isabelle's hunters grew more experienced, more knowledgeable and more organized. Cells took shape in Washington, Oregon and California, mostly focused on observing and collecting data on spirit phenomena. Cells tried different ways to clean out or "redeem" a spiritually-infested area, and in a handful of cases they attempted exorcisms of possessed individuals. There were numerous failures – some disastrous – but over time the group achieved an increasing string of successes. It was during this period that the Talbot Group began to encounter the "wolf-people."

The "wolf-people" – Talbot insisted that they not be trivialized with the Hollywood term "werewolves" – clashed with the hunters a half-dozen times from 1995 to 1998. Sometimes the creatures issued curt warnings to keep clear of a hot zone, while other times they resorted to pure, bestial violence to get their point across. Several of Talbot's hunters were killed, and others grew too frightened to continue their activities, but the rest persevered. They tried to gather information on these elusive creatures wherever they could, and eventually the group came to the consensus that the wolf-people were possessed by elemental nature-spirits, driven into human bodies by the encroachment of human civilization. It was the only logical explanation why the creatures were found in such large numbers inside cities and urban areas. The hunters also concluded that there was no way to meaningfully interact with the spirits – they were too unpredictable and dangerous to communicate with, much less help. The one attempt to corner and exorcise a wolf-person happened in Portland, Oregon in early 1999, and ended in disaster. Not one of the hunters involved survived.

Isabelle made the wolf-people her primary focus of study, developing theories as to their origins and development. From her studies she concluded that possession occurred early in the victim's life – during the teenage years or early adulthood at the latest – and the longer the person remained possessed, the more difficult the spirit was to exorcise. If they could get to a victim early enough, there might still be a hope of saving them from the awful fate that befell her son. Her ideas dovetailed fatefully with the growing success of the Talbot Group.

By this point, Paul Talbot was no longer a skeptic – Isabelle had exposed him to too much evidence of spiritual activity for him to comfortably deny it. When she proposed her radical program for treating the most troubled, violent youths in his program, he was initially resistant, but eventually he allowed Isabelle and a group of her most experienced hunters to observe several of his patients and determine if any showed signs of possession. To Paul's surprise, a significant fraction of them did. It explained their most violent compulsions, their resistance to meds and their startling, almost inhuman ability to manipulate those around them. Being a doctor and a compassionate man, Paul Talbot felt he had no choice but to explore his wife's suggestions for a cure.

Of course, the idea of exorcism as therapy wasn't something that the general public would support, so the Talbots understood that their experiments would have to be conducted in secret. Fortunately, the Talbot Group was in the midst of constructing a "nature campus" near the expansive Olympic National Park. This was quickly repurposed as a facility for the most troubled members of the group's small number of patients, where Paul, Isabelle and eventually Dr. Courtland could experiment with ways to identify and remove the spirits plaguing some of these youths. The next step, as far as Isabelle was concerned, was to begin searching the West Coast for youths marked by wolf-spirits and try to get them into the program for study.

The task turned out to be easier than either of the Talbots expected. Traumatized parents were all too willing to accept a generous offer of inexpensive treatment for their violent and extremely troubled children, and within a few years the campus was nearly at capacity. The problem, as the Talbots found, wasn't gaining access to the kids; identifying with any certainty which were wolf-touched and which weren't. The nature of possession was far more subtle than any other the hunters had encountered. The first time they knew they had one of the possessed in their care was when the girl went through her first transformation, nearly escaping and killing everyone in her part of the residence hall. Had she not already been under a heavy regimen of mood stabilizers and anti-psychotic meds, the Talbots could well have had a bloodbath on their hands. In time, they were able to manage the girl's episodes with the proper levels of medication, and she became the group's Patient Zero. Since her first change, Emily Langford has cooperated with the Talbots to the best of her ability, trying to describe the nature of her affliction through a haze of extremely powerful pharmaceuticals. She has even been instrumental in identifying other wolf-touched patients brought into the campus; as of 2008, the Talbot Group has a half-dozen young wolf-people under their care.

So far, a cure for their possession continues to elude the Talbots, but the couple remains optimistic. After almost 16 years, the Talbot Group has evolved into a full-fleshed compact, funding hunter cells up and down the West Coast and supporting their efforts to examine, identify – and where possible, eradicate – spiritual "hot spots" that threaten their communities.

The Enemy

The hunters of the Talbot Group focus primarily on spirits and their haunts – called "hot spots" in their terminology (see Loci, p. 174) – and go to great lengths to try and save the possessed from the beings that control them. Much of the time and energy of an individual cell is focused on research and field observation, honing their skills at identifying likely hot spots and looking for signs of possession among members of the community. They stay abreast of police reports concerning outbreaks of serial criminal activity – anything from rape and murder to a rash of strange thefts or vandalism. Most times the activity can be traced back to simple criminals, but occasionally the trail leads the hunters to one of the spirit-ridden.

When confronted by signs of spirit activity in the area, the first step these cells take is to identify the source of the spiritual energy – the hot spot – and look for ways to cleanse or "rehabilitate" it. Years ago, this practice was pretty much a matter of trial and error, but time and experience have provided the compact with a useful body of knowledge to draw on when dealing with these sites. They've learned, for example, that fire and running water both have powerful cleansing properties, and that in most cases the most expedient way to deal with a hot spot is to burn it to the ground. In other cases, they try to enlist members of the community to clean out trouble spots or find ways to repurpose them, bringing in other psychic influences to combat the negative spirits lodged there. In many cases, this is enough to weaken a spirit's grip on its human host, forcing it to relinquish its hold. In cases where it doesn't, the hunters must address the possessed individual directly. Some cells prefer to try and exorcise the spirit – no mean feat with a willing host, much less an unwilling one – while others will try to communicate directly with the entity and attempt to negotiate for the host's release. Physically confronting a possessed individual is the last resort of most Talbot cells, but sometimes it's the only way to stop the spirit's rampage.

As the compact becomes increasingly successful in dealing with spirits and haunted sites, they have come more and more into conflict with the wolf-people, who seem to have an almost territorial possessiveness of some areas. In nearly every case, encounters with the creatures have gone badly, owing in part to the monsters' fearsome abilities and the hunters' own reluctance to kill what they see as an innocent victim of spirit possession. As these encounters have grown more frequent, however, some cells have begun taking steps to defend themselves, carrying silver bullets and improvised napalm to deal with potential attacks.

The Talbot Group continues to search for wolf-touched children along the West Coast, and the senior members of the compact work hard to convince the parents of these children to commit them for counseling and therapy at the Olympic campus. In some cases, when the child in question has run away from home, a hunter cell is sent to find the lost child and "rescue" them from whatever situation the kids have fallen into. Sometimes these rescues put the hunters in far more danger than they bargained for.

Hunters

You've been a community activist for five years, ever since you moved into a part of the city overrun with gangs, drug dealers, and petty thieves. Your neighbors stayed locked in their homes at night, and had to duck the stray bullets that came through their walls as the gang-bangers went at one another in the street outside. You've worked with the police, set up a

STEREOTYPES

The Cheiron Group: This is what happens when paranormal science becomes corrupted by corporate greed. There's so much we could learn from their studies, and vice versa, but how can we trust that they won't use our data to turn a profit somehow? It's tragic, and at times it's downright obscene.

The Long Night: Extremists and religious vigilantes whose scorched-earth campaign against victims of possession typically cause more harm than good. While it's true that there are some spirit-ridden humans that are too far gone to save, these hunters rarely bother to draw the distinction. All too often the violence they inflict on their victims – and occasionally the victim's family – leaves a spiritual stain that takes years to dissipate, and can draw even more spirits to the area over time. And they call *us* misguided.

Network 0: These guys understand the need to get the truth out there, where others can benefit from the knowledge and try to make a difference in the world. We're happy to share whatever we learn in the hopes that others will take notice, and we learn what we can from the contributions of others. We're all too happy to work with them when we get the chance – we just wish they were a little more discerning in what they chose to broadcast sometimes. Just a bit more scientific rigor would keep half of those grainy "bigfoot" videos from taking up so much bandwidth.

Task Force: VALKYRIE: Good God, what a bunch of jack-booted thugs. They shoot first, ask questions later (if at all), and cover everything up afterwards. Or worse, they scoop up innocent people and drag them off to some undisclosed location and try to make *weapons* out of them. The last thing you want to do is to get their attention. If you get in their way you'll just disappear.

The Union: For a group that calls itself the Union, these guys often seem like anarchy in action. No real leadership to speak of, no comprehensive organization or methodology – most of their online forums and mailing lists contain way too much noise for the limited amount of signal they provide. Don't get me wrong – their hearts are in the right place. But all too often they go off half-cocked, and somebody gets hurt. Worse, they are often too headstrong to listen when we try to offer a little bit of our hard-won experience.

and the Internet for ways to root it out. That's how you found the Talbot Group, and you've been working to reclaim your neighborhood ever since.

You're a social worker who has spent much of your career trying to save troubled kids from themselves. Some of them come from broken homes, others are victims of abuse who have become abusers in turn, and still others are simply kids with disabilities who don't know how to deal with a world that frustrates and humiliates them at every turn. And then there are some kids who simply go bad; no rhyme or reason, no obvious triggers for their behavior – just an inexorable slide into violence and self-destructive behavior that often ends in tragedy. Many times, those kids are the hardest ones to handle. One in particular still haunts you: a young girl, bright, beautiful and charming, with a loving family and a world full of prospects – until her junior year, when she began getting into fights at school and cutting at her skin with whatever sharp edge was available. No amount of counseling seemed to work, and the violence continued to escalate. Then, one night, you got a call from the police; the girl had run away from home, leaving behind the bodies of her parents and her two siblings. The helplessness and frustration you felt nearly drove you over the edge. In desperation, you started your own search for answers – and that's how you learned about the Talbot Group.

Your big brother ran away from home when he was 16; by then he and your parents were fighting almost every night. It was bad enough when your dad was sober, but when he was drunk the blood would really start to fly. The police came to the house all the time, but no one would admit to anything. You still re-

neighborhood watch and cleaned your share of parking lots and sidewalks, but nothing ever seemed to help. It was like there was a cancer in the heart of the neighborhood, seeping through the air and corrupting everything it touched. Something foul and invisible that lurked in the hallways of the apartment complexes and rose in poisonous clouds from the steam vents on the streets. And then one night you saw it – just a passing glimpse, a leering, insubstantial shadow that hovered over the body of a young thug lying in a pool of blood outside your house. That's when you realized there were forces that could poison people's minds that were far worse than booze, or meth, or smack, and you started to search the libraries member the helpless looks on their faces as they'd leave each time, knowing that sooner or later they'd be back again. One night things came to a head. Your brother had been kicked out of school for breaking another kid's arms, and your dad finally had enough. He went at your brother with his heavy leather belt. Your brother took one hit and *growled* at your dad, then grabbed him by the throat and threw him across the room. The look of rage in your brother's eyes made your blood run cold. If you hadn't gotten in his way at that point, your dad might not have survived. That was when your brother ran, and you haven't seen him since. In desperation, you turned to the Internet for help, and heard about the Talbot Group. Since then, you've learned much more about your brother and what he might have become than you ever wanted to know.

You've been a reporter for the local paper for a couple of years, covering the crime section and spending a lot of time listening to police scanners and hanging out at night court. In two years, you thought you'd seen it all; until one night the police radio came alive with confused shouts and calls for help. A patrol car had come upon a grisly scene: a homeless guy down by the river, gutted like a steer – and a huge, hairy beast crouched over the steaming guts with blood dripping from its muzzle. Intrigued, you rushed down to the riverside as the cops tried to give chase, and you listened as the pursuit led them from one end of the city to the other. You followed along on the radio, hearing the cops call out directions and street names, until you realized the thing was doubling back, returning to the scene of its kill. When you got to the murder site, the body was already being loaded into the back of an ambulance, but you got your camera ready, just in case. Moments later, a terrible howl echoed down the darkened streets, and a hulking thing leapt from the shadows into the midst of the paramedics. For a few moments the creature was revealed in the flashing lights of the ambulance, and the sight caused your brain to reel in horror. When the sense of shock faded, the beast was gone, having collected the body of its victim before disappearing into the night. All you had to show for it was a blurry image captured on your digital camera and a vision that haunted you every time you closed your eyes. Until you posted the picture on the Internet and received an e-mail from a pirate broadcaster in Eugene who hooked you up with the Talbot Group.

Methodologies

While the members of the Talbot Group are in agreement that supernatural hot spots and spirit possession are hazards to human society, the members of the compact are divided as to the most effective method of dealing with the problem. This has led to the evolution of three distinct methodologies, two of which have developed only within the last few years.

Exorcists follow the original philosophies of the compact and believe that that spirit infestations – whether in an area or inside a single individual – represent a kind of sickness that must be expunged for the good of society as a whole. They burn down the homes of dead serial killers or nursing homes closed for investigations of abuse, and track down the spirit-ridden men and women who prey upon innocent victims in their communities. Victims of possession are sick and deserve compassionate treatment, but sometimes the cancer runs so deep the only cure is death itself.

Redactors have been exposed to supernatural hot spots and possessed individuals and drawn the conclusion that the problem isn't the spirits, but the people themselves. Spirits have always been a part of the physical world – Native American lore is full of examples of the interactions between humans and the spirit realm – so, logically, there is some flaw within the possessed that draws the worst sort of spirit-energy to them. These hunters are much more likely to use violence when dealing with possessed individuals, believing that no amount of exorcism or site rehabilitation is going to help – these poor souls will just draw another spirit to them as soon as they've shaken the current one off.

This methodology was championed in large part by Dr Courtland, Paul Talbot's long-time partner. In the late 90s, he was made aware of the group's paranormal activities, and eventually he became an active contributor in the efforts to rehabilitate the wolf-children under the group's care. Courtland believes it might be possible to treat "possession susceptibility" with a combination of medication and surgery to remove key parts of the subject's brain. So far, Courtland hasn't been able to put his theories into practice, but they are increasingly gaining support among other redactors.

Conciliators are a very recent – and some say radical – development among the members of the Talbot Group, and include some of the most senior and experienced hunters in the compact. These members of the compact have interacted with Emily and the other wolf-children being treated by the group, and they wonder if perhaps it might be possible to make use of their special abilities to protect mankind from the worst excesses of the spirit realm. These hunters put their theories to practice out in the field by attempting to negotiate and enlist the aid of

It's not you.
I know that.
It's the thing
hiding inside you.

spirits, rather than immediately assuming them to be inimical. Many other members of the compact look on the conciliators with considerable skepticism, but recently their theories have won over Isabelle Talbot, who likely hopes to use their methods to reach out to her missing son.

Status

Over the past 10 years, the Talbot Group's organization has evolved into a fairly strict hierarchy that determines the level of access its hunters have to the compact's information and resources. This is partly a matter of simple resource management; the organization's assets aren't limitless, and the Talbots want to ensure the most experienced members are guaranteed to receive whatever tools they need to carry out the Vigil. At the same time, the Talbots are wary of revealing too much about their rehabilitation efforts at their wilderness campus, fearful of knee-jerk reactions to their radical methods and afraid of drawing the attention of wolf-people who might be compelled to rescue the children under their care.

• You've been involved in a few case studies of hot spots in your area, and have had at least one run-in with a spirit or a possessed individual. Having proven yourself as a capable hunter, you've been given access to the compact's case files, forums and local network of cells. You receive one dot in Contacts and one dot in Allies among the supernatural experts of the compact.

••• You're a seasoned investigator and spirit hunter who has cleared out a number of hot spots and confronted your share of possessed individuals. It's possible you've even crossed paths with one of the wolf-people and survived the experience, and the compact views you as a trusted and valued member. Your exposure to the spirit world has granted you the Unseen Sense merit in regards to spirits, and you gain another dot of Contacts among the wolf-hunters of the compact.

••••• You've ventured into some of the most haunted places on the West Coast and lived to tell the tale, and hunted more possessed humans than almost any other member of the compact. Your body bears scars from run-ins with the wolf-people, and you're one of the few who can claim to have actually slain one in self-defense. Your exposure to the wolf-people has dulled the natural horror that humans experience in their presence. You're affected by Predator's Aura (Lunacy, p. 163) as if your Willpower were one dot higher than it actually is.

LES MYSTERES
THE SPIRIT EMISSARIES

The *bokor* looking over the ruins of New Orleans from her temporary home. The Pentecostal snake-handler who speaks the Lord's words and keeps his congregation safe. The witch-doctor who takes evil spirits into himself and consumes them to protect his people. The girl taking part in a Len Dong ritual, hoping for the strategist who defeated two Mongol invasions to save her corner of Saigon. Every society has someone standing on the edge, not fully part of the community but not an outsider; someone who people turn to for help when other channels fail. Those people are Les Mystères.

A Mystère has to stand apart from society. Nobody wants to get too close to someone who trucks with angels and demons or all manner of strange spirits, but that suits her just fine. By standing on the edge, she has more time to work with the alien spirits, setting out bizarre gifts in return for unspeakable favors and nursing the strange creatures that come into the world. It also gives her a chance to take the fight to creatures that would gladly see human and spirit both torn asunder and thrown back to a time before fire and the wheel. All manner of creatures prey on humans, but none threaten Les Mystères more than werewolves.

Anyone can be a Mystère. There's no formal training, no shadowy organization backing a hunter with resources and secret information, and certainly no badge and gun. All a prospective has is her knowledge of spirits—whether she thinks them angels, demons, or even alien visitors. Over time, she'll come to the second thing that sets her apart: the understanding that she must walk a road of balance, using spirits to further the ends of men just as much as she uses people to appease the spirits. Les Mystères are little more than a support group, a collection of covens and bands of shamans and spirit-talkers kept together by phone, email, and word of mouth. Each Mystère helps others not out of obligation, but because they've got nobody else. For every one who commands a measure of respect there's 10 people who can't walk down the street without people getting out of their way. Loneliness and isolation drives them to each other. It also drives many Mystères closer to those empty spaces where people deliberately don't look; the spaces where monsters lurk.

Les Mystères isn't an organization in the sense that most hunters would recognize. They don't have the single unifying ideal of most compacts, and unlike most conspiracies they don't have a unified goal. Each cell of Mystères stands alone, recruiting new members and training them in their particular method of forcing their will on the spirits. One cell holds to traditional Yoruba Voudou, while another practices Pentecostal Christianity and encourages snake-handling and speaking in tongues. A third cell, radical even for Les Mystères, counsels the survivors of alien abductions and shows them how to draw on the strange energies of their former captors. They're linked by little more than word of mouth, sharing information and indeed working together because nobody else understands their strange duty.

No matter how she perceives the spirit world, a Mystère feels the immaterial urging her towards places and people cursed with darkness. A group of alien abductees finds a cheerleader in the woods without a drop of blood left in her body. A Pentecostal minister gets his hands on an ancient blade that drinks the souls of the people it wounds. A *bokor* comes face to face with the unquiet dead, out for revenge against the Loa's servant because he refused to protect them. Some Mystères voluntarily spend their lives in service to their community. Others don't share their dedication to a group of people. Those Mystères drift away from human contact slowly, spending more of their time with spirits and strange creatures, but they don't choose to drift away from family and friends. It just happens, until the only time a Mystère talks to a normal person is when they want something from her — or she wants something from them. Whether it's something mundane, like the Mystère ordering takeout, or something more significant, like a woman needing revenge on a cheating husband, every dealing a Mystère has with normal people comes in the form of a transaction. Socializing and casual chat die off in favor of the trade. After all the Mystère can do strange and terrible things with the help of the Loa, but anything she does comes at a price.

This trade carries over into dealings with spirits. Every deal with a spirit is a transaction of some kind. In many ways, it's the only way to have an honest deal with a spirit — and it's the only way to stop a Mystère making deals with spirits that leave her with great and terrible powers. A measure of fear and a good dose of respect never hurt anyone, but dealing in trades helps a Mystère know his place. The only proper place for someone with a Mystère's power is in service to the people around him.

It's that sense of duty that unites the disparate cabals and covens that make up Les Mystères. They've got a duty to other people and to each other, a duty that won't end until the Mystère is dead or the spirits stop answering her calls. As time moves on, the traditional groups who recognize the importance of a Mystère are dying out. People leave their families, moving to new cities where they never really know anybody. The curse of long working hours and constant connectivity means that most people only really know their apartment super and his work colleagues. A few Mystères try to nurture the seed of kinship in the people around them, but ultimately it's a selfish urge — if the hunter can get the people working together, he'll have an easier time manipulating them to the benefit of the local spirits. Whether he uses the influence of a local church — especially an evangelical church — or by setting himself up as a medium, bringing people a touch of the spirit world, he does what he can. Most of his efforts are doomed to failure, but he tries anyway.

Les Mystères reserve a special hatred for werewolves. Unlike other monsters, the half-beasts have a close connection to the spirit realm, yet they abuse their gift. Rather than understanding that the real world and spirit world are interlinked, the beasts try to destroy an area's spiritual harmony by keeping flesh and spirit apart. The spirits beg the Mystère to act. Often, the werewolves don't realize the implications of what they're doing. Occasionally though, a Mystère comes across a pack that knows full well what they're doing and what they're hurting. The creatures think they're doing the right thing by policing

THE TRUTH

Everything that Les Mystères know is true. They just don't know the extent of that truth. Most cells of Spirit Emissaries believe they hunt werewolves because of the threat the beasts pose to the spirit world. The truth is far simpler — the spirits drive each Mystère to fight werewolves, a fact that she later reconciles with her sense of duty until the spirit doesn't have to goad her any more. How much of her other actions are down to the subtle manipulations of spirits and how much is up to the Mystère herself can vary. It is worth noting that a Mystère isn't ever actually possessed by spirits — she draws them in herself, using her own force of will. No Mystère would go along with a spirit's suggestion without getting something in return.

Despite the wild and varied misinformation from spirits, Les Mystères do talk to each other — they are, truly, a confederation of cults. Comparing and contrasting stories allows them to resist the wilder claims of many spirits. Their one blind spot is the truth about werewolves. Spirits the world over, whether they claim to be angels, saints, or Loa, tell a version of the same story — how the werewolves want to tear the worlds of flesh and spirit from each other. When every spirit that deals with a Mystère tells broadly the same story, it's hard to find evidence against it. Some hunters do, whether by interrogating unsuspecting spirits or actually opening a dialogue with their enemies. Though they can recruit the help of their local cell, the other cells and groups that make up Les Mystères would never believe them. Whatever the source, wandering wise-folk among the Spirit Emissaries know one thing for certain. Something sparked a war between the shapeshifters and the immaterial a long time ago, and spirits hold grudges for a very long time.

creatures of the night. It's the oldest duty anyone has.

History

For as long as people have gathered together, Les Mystères have watched over them. Secular spiritualists trace their workings back to the earliest priests and shamans of animistic religions, while others prefer to trace their line back to the spirit-talkers of their own faiths. Anyone who works with angels or speaks with the voice of a prophet and receives only condemnation in return is likely to be a Mystère in spirit if not in fact.

Throughout history, these people did the work of spirits and saints and angels to keep the people around them safe. Some of them became renowned as great heroes among their people, while others were condemned as witches. As time marched on, these tales of great people become first myths, then children's stories. Though individual spirit-talkers did great work, people thought them unique. No fellows came to their side when true evil woke from within the bowels of the earth. Nobody told them that what they did was good.

For thousands of years, the Mystères stood alone. In many ways, they still do.

As a distributed organization, it's hard to isolate the beginning of Les Mystères as anything more than unrelated cells of shamans. Most historians put the origins of the group in West Africa, among the Yoruba people. Individuals who could make direct contact with the Orishas started sharing information between each other, and trading rituals by which they could bring the Orisha and Aye into themselves to save their people from the darkness without. Over time, they shared ideas and rituals — always in secret — with others, including the Fon and Ewe peoples. Slowly, they built a network of support for each other, weeding out those who could invite the spirits into them from the other practitioners — and from the few who had stranger talents.

the border between flesh and spirit, never caring for the very real harm they're doing by tearing the world away from its spiritual roots. They even claim to have the blessing of the moon-spirit — when they can be bothered to talk to a hunter. Far more often, the only response a Mystère gets involves fangs and blood and bone. A very few werewolves understand the damage that their fellows cause. Sometimes they seek out Les Mystères, or a Mystère discovers two packs in bloody combat. These renegade werewolves reject the moon-spirit, forsaking the blessing of a powerful patron to save the rest of the spirit world from their power-mad cousins. Though a hunter can't ever fully trust a werewolf, a temporary alliance with a rebel beast might just tip the balance against other monsters.

Standing with one foot outside the mundane world, Les Mystères see hunting monsters as just one part of their duty as the medicine-men and wise-women to the world. But in a world full of monsters, it's the most important part of that duty. Despite varying beliefs and often conflicting means of venerating the spirits, Mystères from different cells work together to hunt the

RIDDEN?

If you have Werewolf: The Forsaken, these guys sound like spirit-ridden. And, in a way, they are. The rules don't quite apply the same way (unless you want them or need them to, of course), for the hunters of this conspiracy do not allow the spirits to remain in possession of them. In fact, it's less about full-scale possession and more about a kind of spiritual symbiosis.

When ships came and took many members of the unofficial alliance to the New World, the group expanded throughout the Caribbean, Haiti, the Americas, and all the other places where Africans were taken from their homes to another land to be sold as property. Unable to identify the priests of the Loa, authorities in Haiti prosecuted the *bokor*, the wandering priests who worked for hire and served groups of slaves and the Loa both. The persecution spread to New Orleans and through the rest of Louisiana. The traveling sorcerers kept to the traditions of their ancestors, training each other when their paths crossed and seeking out others who could talk to the Loa. The ocean was no boundary to these new spirit-talkers, as they sent seemingly innocent messages along with the crew. From a small collection of like-minded practitioners in West Africa, the network spread outwards. Though they had never needed a name before, in the New World they called their network Les Mystères, "The Mysteries," describing as much their relationship with outsiders as their ties to each other. (In this way, it became a greeting between like-minded practitioners: "Do you know the Mysteries?" "I know the Mysteries.")

Though originally only slaves brought from the Fon, Ewe, and Yoruba peoples needed *bokor*, Les Mystères expanded to cover the priests and sorcerers of other groups of slaves and free blacks both. Soon, they encountered people in North America who could talk to the Loa, though these men believed that they spoke with "angels" or "saints." Though pressures of the time ensured that meetings between Negro Mystères and their Caucasian protégés remained secret they still happened, and small cells of Christian Mystères joined the ranks. From there, they spread to small mystery cults in the salons of Europe. The world at that time would've been scandalized to know of the extent of Les Mystères. Fortunately for them, it was nearly impossible to trace the network back. Scattered groups contacted each other, individual cells talking to each other without the knowledge of any other members of the group.

Over the years, Les Mystères found members from around the world, connecting with cells who were already members in all but name. Vietnamese practitioners of Dao Mau (Len Dong goddess venera-tion that involves spirit possession), Native American spirit-talkers, witch-doctors of African tribes, confused teens who knew that the talk of spirits really disguised the actions of saints and angels, priests who abjured demonic "spirits" to serve their congregation, and Pentecostal ministers who called the presence of God into themselves. Members of Les Mystères cared only that prospective members had the special touch necessary to invite a spirit to Ride them — and that they do so with respect.

The expansion of Les Mystères led many members to some stunning realizations about the world. While anyone who communed with spirits for long enough knew about werewolves, the despicable beasts who would erect a wall between flesh and spirit, the Spirit Emissaries learned of other threats. In the Deep South, elitist white vampires came in the night, certain they could drink a black man dry and nobody would care — if they could bring themselves to sup his blood. In Eastern Europe, rough-hewn Reanimated walked the wilds and looked at the humans they so crudely aped. In Vietnam and China, bizarre mystics claiming a heritage beyond the sea took sacrifices to power their bloody magic. Watching from the outside, Les Mystères saw what was going on, and they coerced the spirits into giving their aid. Though being Ridden was originally a tool for members who sought the insights of gods, the temporary fusion of flesh and spirit soon became one of the only weapons against the dangerous creatures who lurked in the shadows.

Despite sweeping changes in the world, from the Civil Rights movement to the end of Apartheid, Les Mystères hasn't changed. With every new route of communication they've found people who walk the fine line between spirit and flesh — and forged new links in the now worldwide network of Spirit Emissaries. Without a central authority, or even an idea of how many Mystères exist worldwide, no one cell can try to seize control. Instead, the organization is little more than a loose confederation of cults, covens, and like-minded people who happen to share the experience of being Ridden. Many wouldn't have it any other way. An organization would distract them from the people and the spirits that need their help — and the monsters that they must hunt.

Syncretism

Individual cells of Les Mystères hold to a wide range of beliefs and practices. It's hardly surprising — a revivalist preacher won't think of vodou rituals save to condemn them as the Devil's work. While every cell knows their way is the right way, and that they know the truth about the alien spirits that help them, each cell also accepts that other Mystères with other beliefs know things that they don't. Mystères thus face different beliefs head-on, speaking in terms that both parties will understand — while mentally translating the conversation into the "right" form. While the alien abductee might look like a godless hippy to a Pentecostal preacher, they both likely have things they can learn, just as a wandering *bokor* could have yet more knowledge. Les Mystères don't have a shared

that where differences of faith get in the way of understanding, those differences get put aside. Unfortunately, that custom's not a hard and fast rule. While lively debates are fine, some cells have severed their connection over religious disputes. In rare cases, that leaves a cell of Les Mystères alone, without a means of getting in contact with other cells. Either they strike out alone — a foolhardy proposition, but one that allows members to retain their pride — or they mend their differences and look to set up links with other cells as soon as they are able.

Though it might seem a contradiction of terms, a rare few atheists are also Mystères. Some may have had life-changing experiences that left them able to channel the underlying forces of the world — or even put them in contact with the spirit world — without any religious underpinnings. Though they deal with the same spirits, other cells often watch these splinter-factions closely. Without the proper respect for the beings who Ride them, it looks like only a matter of time before something terrible happens.

Dangerous Liaisons

For all that Les Mystères believe about the spirit realm and its relationship with the strange beasts that prowl the world, one thing remains constant: by being Ridden, a Mystère allows a spirit to merge with her flesh for a time. She actually voluntarily allows an alien entity — something that has no real concept of how humans think or feel — to enter her body. It doesn't matter what precautions she takes to retain control, she's still doing something that's more than a little dangerous. To a normal person, repeatedly inviting in different spirits to face down werewolves and possessed nightmares is more than a little crazy.

There's no one answer, just as there's no one religion underpinning Les Mystères. Every sect and cult and study group in the confederation has its own ideas about why being Ridden is a good thing.

An unnamed group of *bokor* operating around New Orleans explain that they don't have a choice. The Loa have Ridden their chosen servants since before anyone can remember. That said, only a few can command the Loa in the way that they can. Normally, the Loa take the "horse" (i.e. the possessed) as their vessel. Those few with the willpower to control themselves when Ridden have a special gift — sharing a body with a spirit rather than falling to its control brings a sorcerer closer to Bondye, the creator.

The Starlight Children are a loose confederation of people who have felt the touch of creatures from beyond our world. They treat their ability to invite

language, so each must accommodate the others that he meets. It's hard, but it's the best way forwards.

Rather than choosing one faith over the others, most Mystères instead break it down to the simplest blocks — the entities that possess them are spirits. One Mystère might take that to mean they're aspects of the Holy Spirit, another knows they're the animistic spirits of everything, and a third knows them as the Loa and their helpers. It's an emergent custom alien beings into themselves as little more than a New Age science project. Merging their flesh with the strange energies of the extraterrestrials often has bizarre results. The Star Children trust their patrons, believing that one day they will achieve full union with the extraterrestrials and lead humanity on to the next stage of evolution — once they've dealt with the holdovers from an age of "monsters."

The Bible study group at the Apostolic Pentecostal Church in upstate New York doesn't believe it's drawing on the power of spirits. Theirs is the work of the Lord. The holy fire that burns through them is a sign that God requires them to take up arms against the creatures of Satan. He gives them boons, but they must prove they are worthy of the Lord's love — and his power. To the group, inviting the Lord into their bodies isn't even an act of faith; it's a duty that has been thrust upon them by their closeness to God.

A band of shamans in Siberia enter ecstatic trances to commune with the spirit realm, and drag spirits who can help them back into their bodies. They force the spirits to help them, for they are wiser and stronger, and thus more deserving. While they hold to the Vigil alongside other Mystères — it's hard not to when almost every spirit condemns the very existence of werewolves — the shamans actively seek out spiritual power. To share a body with a spirit, to fight it for control and win, that is the mark of a true shaman. Every time they take a spirit's power, they relish the brief struggle for control as it affirms their own strength.

Every Mystère has an answer to the question of why they allow a spirit into their body. Some do it to get closer to God. Some honestly believe they're doing the spirits a favor by giving them a chance to experience the physical. Others are glad of the rush that comes from retaining control. And some know it's the only way they can make the spirits leave them alone. Whatever her reason, a Mystère will likely defend her decision to the death. She walks with spirits now, and it's not something she could ever give up.

The Crossroads

The metaphor of the crossroads has spread between the divided sects of Les Mystères as a means of defining the areas that a Mystère focuses on as part of his work. Some Mystères try to strike a balance between the four paths, while others focus on one path over the others — or even denigrate the other paths. Rather than some metaphor for spiritual development, the crossroads is more a tool to understand where other hunters are coming from, and thus both their biases and their areas of expertise.

The path leading forward from the crossroads is the **Path of Fellowship**. A Mystère who cultivates the forward path uses his hold over the spirit world to make life a little better for the people around him. Some work from a position gained in a religion, as a minister, confessor, or medicine man. Other Mystères can cultivate the Path of Fellowship as a detective, a police officer, or a lawyer — someone who puts people at the forefront of everything he does. If he focuses on this path, he gains respect and can call on the people he has helped for aid.

Walking the forwards path to the exclusion of the others draws the Mystère away from the spirit realm. The more he settles into his role as a public figure, the more people turn to him for assistance. Ignoring the spiritual draws the Mystère from the spirits who grant him power, making it harder for him to resist the strange creatures that use his body when he invites them in.

- At the third dot of Status, a Mystère gains two dots of Allies, drawn from the people he's helped.

Turning to the left at the crossroads leads to the **Path of Spirit**. Cultivating this path involves more than being Ridden — the Mystère offers himself to the spirits. Whether she listens to the commandments of the Holy Ghost or does as her alien contacts tell her to in dreams, she does whatever the spirits demand. A few allow spirits to possess them without being Ridden, offering the sensations of the physical world to appease the spirit. Others undertake strange rituals, or try to change the "feel" of an area to make it more pleasing to its ephemeral denizens.

Humans shun a Mystère who walks too far along the Path of Spirit, as she lives her life according to the insane rules of the spirit-realm. Even her

STATUS

The paths from the crossroads are more than a metaphor. They define a Mystère's area of focus, the main reason he's driven to the Vigil and to contacting the spirit world.

As noted later on, members of Les Mystères don't get one fixed bonus for their third dot of Status. Instead, they get the bonus indicated in the description of their path. Even Mystères who attempt to maintain spend more time focused on one path than others, and that shapes their development.

cellmates can question her sanity — a killer who tortures his victims isn't something that a pain-spirit would worry about, and so the Mystère may direct her cellmates away from their investigation. A few take their dedication to the Path of Spirit to its ultimate conclusion and voluntarily merge themselves with a spirit. These loose cannons, heretics even to Les Mystères, are the Spirit Emissaries' secret shame.

• At the third dot of Status, a Mystère gains a +1 modifier on all Occult rolls regarding spirits. This bonus is in addition to any appropriate Specialties she may already have.

The right-hand path from the crossroads is the **Path of Beasts**. This path represents Les Mystères' duty to stop werewolves severing the link between the spirit and the flesh. This often leads to werewolves who claim domain over places or groups of humans, believing themselves to be at the top of the food chain, but also leads to vampires, demons, and stranger creatures besides. Focusing on the right-hand path exclusively puts a Mystère in contact with experts in tracking, hunting and killing all kinds of monsters. Whether she faces a strange cult's human sacrifices or an artificial man, she knows someone who can help.

Spending too long dealing with the monsters that lurk in the shadows drags a Mystère from his other duties. While hunting beasts benefits the spirits, they often resent being used as little more than tools. A Mystère who goes too far must always remember where he gets his power from, and pay his respects, just as he must remember the people around him. Some days it's too easy to classify the world into different kinds of monster, becoming overly judgmental and driving away people and spirits who could help.

• At the third dot of Status, the Mystère gains two dots of contacts, each of whom is an expert in one kind of supernatural creatures.

At the crossroads, one path leads behind the Mystère. That's the **Path of the Soul**. If she walks the backward path, she must turn her gaze inwards. She focuses on how the things that she now knows to be true reflect on

what she has been taught. A *bokor* must serve the Loa and the people both, and walking the Path of the Soul leads her to question if she has in fact been doing that. A Catholic boy allows the saints to strengthen him, but focuses on his duties before God. A Parsi outcaste must still take the dead to a Tower of Silence, even when terrible creatures are abroad in the world.

Spending too long on the Path of the Soul leads to inaction. While living up to his religious obligations is undoubtedly a good thing, his duties as a Mystère demand that he takes action to further the ties between spirit and flesh. Working on his soul without interference from the spirits can help re-center a Mystère, but he must be careful not to drive off the very beings who aid him, losing their respect and blessing.

• At the third dot of Status, the Mystère adds one to his Resolve when resisting supernatural powers that attempt to control his mind.

The decentralized nature of Les Mystères makes them very easy for spirits to manipulate. The majority of Mystère cells follow the Path of the Beast, focusing on monster-hunting to the detriment of their other activities. Most of the other sects follow the Path of the Spirit, and it's easy for spirits to redirect Mystères from there back to killing werewolves. Indeed, even Mystères who walk the Path of Fellowship do so more to maintain a cover-story than to actually help people. Only the Path of the Soul remains free of spiritual manipulation, requiring as it does the Mystère to close herself off, and focusing on the backward path makes it much harder for her to gain status.

Traditionally, Mystères refer to the crossroads as if they stood at it — one path to the front, one each to the left and the right, and one to the back. Some sects prefer to associate paths to compass points: to

WHO LEADS?

The spirits do their best to influence Les Mystères, but they're not in total control. It's important to remember that spirits don't act with one mind or one voice. Beyond each spirit's obsession with its aspect spirits don't share a common motivation.

Les Mystères are aware that the spirit world would manipulate them into doing nothing but its bidding. That's why they devised the crossroads to begin with — to recognize the influence of the spirits in a Mystère's life. It's not a perfect system, but it works often enough — though tales of Mystères who fall completely under a spirit's spell never seem to spread far through the network.

Protestant and Pentecostal Christians, the backward path leads east, for example, though that doesn't affect the associations of each direction.

The Hunt

Les Mystères don't go out looking for monsters to hunt. Outside of specific circumstances, they see no benefit in targeting creatures that don't harm anyone. In the end, each encounter with the supernatural is something the Mystère judges worthy of his involvement. Several factors can skew his judgment — if a spirit he trusts warns him of something bad, or he hears of werewolves stepping up their activities, he's going to check it out. Other times, he can afford to be lenient — a vampire who keeps a spirit of pain or hunger happy, or who employs a lot of people above minimum wage is a force for good, until the spirit falters or his workers turn up dead. Indeed, many Mystères don't see a problem in working with monsters temporarily — as long as the Mystère gets something out of the deal. When the monster turns, at least the Mystère has plenty of inside information he can use in his hunt.

Some alliances of convenience pan out over the longer term. A monster may need the services of a mystic or medicine man, or may see nothing wrong in helping hunters if it nets the creature an ally in an otherwise unlikely place. The pressure on the Mystère doesn't come from the monster's existence, or from other hunters, but from its effect on the local people and spirits. Witches, vampires, and strange cultists all gravitate towards the upper echelons of human society, while most Mystères remain steadily working-class by virtue of their place in society. Working closely across the divide of privilege can be hard, forcing her to choose between her newfound ally and the strange beings that grant her power.

Many Mystères work with other monster-hunters, especially groups drawn from the people they meet and help every day. Many such cells support no ties to other compacts or conspiracies, being little more than individuals "sponsored" by the Mystère. A close-knit cell can be a blessing, but it can also really hurt — if the rest of her cell can only turn to her for support, it's a lot easier for threats to overwhelm them by targeting the Mystère. It doesn't help that these disparate people put their trust in someone who knowingly invites strange and terrible creatures into her body. Other cells contain hunters who also have ties to larger organizations. Though they bring valuable expertise, these cells bring their own ideas on how to deal with monsters — with the Mystère

relegated to advisor rather than mentor, it's harder for her to argue the position of the spirits and have her cell listen At worst, her cell may strike at a spirit that they believe is poisoning the area — a spirit that the Mystère has had contact with before.

The Enemy

Despite the range of beasts that walk the world, Les Mystères focus most of their attention on werewolves. That doesn't mean they don't encounter other creatures — a feral creature could be a werewolf, a bestial vampire, or something stranger. All kinds of monsters can rouse the ire of spirits, some by their very presence. Reanimated monsters seem to unite mobs people against them — something that Les Mystères finds very useful — while victims of alien abduction or spiritual visitation may find a monstrous doppelganger on their doorstep.

Werewolves

Every Mystère knows something about werewolves. They disrupt the spirit world with their very presence, and whether a Mystère talks with the saints or receives a download from mysterious aliens, she hears the same story. Some Mystères encounter werewolves who run in packs and change form with ease. Others see desperate men and women sheltering in sacred animal skins and roaming in the shape of a beast. A few share stories of stranger creatures: men and women who change into crows, rats, and even cockroaches. In all cases, what really matters is not how a creature changes shape or what beast gives it power, but how it uses that power. A frenzied beast pays no regard to its surroundings, and werewolves are no different — they destroy people and spirits both with little regard for the world. They're berserk killers who disrupt the world by their presence. At least, that's what the spirits tell Les Mystères.

All too often, that information is borne out by experience. A pack of werewolves marks out territory they use as a base of operations. Anyone moving in on their territory is a threat — even a Mystère who has served the spirits there all her life. Many werewolves can sense those spirits that flock around her, and thus consider her a threat. There's no use talking — nothing the Mystère can say would change their minds. The hatred between werewolves and spirits seems mutual, and sooner or later the two will fight. Some wretched creatures have no connection with the spirit world, but that doesn't mean they have no effect. A werewolf of any kind has a tight core of rage within, and that rage is strong enough to warp the resonance around him. That makes him very dangerous.

TRUTH AND LIES

Storytellers and players familiar with **Werewolf: The Forsaken** or **Skinchangers** are probably wondering just how much Les Mystères know and where they're just plain wrong. Note that individual sects and cults may know more or less than this at the Storyteller's discretion.

- Les Mystères recognize the difference between Skinchangers and other shapeshifters, though not between therianthropes (detailed in **Changing Breeds** and **The War Against The Pure**) and Uratha.

- Les Mystères know there's no love lost between the spirit world and werewolves, though they don't know the real reason why — the spirits prefer an easily-digested lie to the truth about Father Wolf.

- While Les Mystères knows there exists a difference between Pure and Forsaken, they think the Forsaken are the ones in charge and the Pure are dangerous rebels — the underdogs who deserve a Mystère's help.

- Though Mystères know werewolves gather in packs, they don't know that these packs need a totem spirit to function — indeed, they don't realize that some spirits *aren't* antagonistic toward werewolves.

- A few Mystères know that the Forsaken are tied to the moon. They don't know how the moon-phases tie to Auspice roles, and conflate Tribe and Auspice in their ideas of hunting roles.

- Again, Mystères know of Gifts but not the rationale behind them — they believe werewolves steal the powers of spirits to enhance their own power.

- Mystères know about Lunacy, but add their dots in the Ridden Endowment to their Willpower to resist it.

- Mystères know little of the differing Ranks and Byzantine rules of the spirit world. They know enough to tell the difference between a "greater" and "lesser" spirit, but that's about the limit of their knowledge.

- Conversely, all Mystères are aware that spirits have Bans — though spirits guard their weaknesses, they aren't perfect, and Les Mystères are quick to capitalize on anything that gives them a tiny edge over a spirit.

- Most Mystères know spirits can possess people temporarily, but think that it's the same as being Ridden, with the host retaining control. They don't know that the Merged are anything to do with spirits, only that they draw a lot of spiritual attention.

- Many Mystères have an idea of some areas that are important to spirits, but haven't made the jump from that to realizing the importance of Loci.

For their part, it's hard for most werewolves to work out that a Mystère being Ridden by a spirit isn't either Urged or Claimed, and most packs who encounter one will likely react accordingly. Les Mystères is, at its base, a loose confederation of spirit cults. Members open themselves to possession, making them excellent foils for werewolves of any stripe.

Les Mystères understand some of the social structures that werewolves hold to, simply because that makes them easier to attack. Werewolves unaware of the spirit world act a lot like inexperienced groups of hunters — they may band together for protection, but they're ultimately isolated. While some maintain ties to the human world, those are relatively easy for the Mystère to break. Once she's cut off their support, the pack turns inwards. Sometimes, that's all it takes. She doesn't even have to make her presence known if she can alter the resonance around the pack's hideout — spirits of distrust, trickery, and deception can turn the werewolves against each other in a bloody frenzy. At worst, she has to mop up the few survivors.

Many werewolves acknowledge their tie to the spirit world, though their understanding doesn't bear much resemblance to the practices of any Mystère sect. Most beasts revel in their power, striking against spirits whenever the urge takes them. Les Mystères know that more than raw power shields them from spiritual retaliation. For some reason, the spirit of the moon itself shields them from the worst repercussions of their actions, permitting werewolves to act as their instincts take them. It's up to Les Mystères in their role as agents of the spirit world to teach them responsibility. Packs of moon-touched werewolves aren't as susceptible to manipulation as their spirit-blind cousins, so a Mystère has to attend to the matter personally. Physical confrontation is dangerous, but she's got the might of the spirit world on her side. Though she could recruit people to help — especially if she can arm them with silver weapons — her companions would lose it as soon as the werewolf changed. Enough Mystères have tried that every group knows the tactic to be useless. Many Mystères have the same problem early on, though as their connection to the spirit realm strengthens, they gain a slow immunity to the strange fear that werewolves exude.

Les Mystères know three different roles that werewolves can take. Many are nothing more than raging beasts, channeling their power into raw strength. Though they are the majority, most lose themselves in the thrill of battle, using their physical ability in place of useful tactics, and that gives a thinking hunter a chance to strike. Almost as populous are werewolves who stalk their prey, able to track anything over vast distances and strike from the shadows with incredible power. A few embody dominance, channeling their inner rage to control aspects of the world around them much as they command other werewolves.

Fighting werewolves head on is suicidal, even for a Mystère who invites the Gods to share his body. Instead, he must apply the werewolves' own tactics against them. He must become a predator, laying traps in their hideout while they're responding to a spiritual decoy elsewhere, and striking from the shadows when the werewolves let their guard down.

A small number of werewolves seem to understand the effect they have on the mysterious patrons of Les Mystères. These shapeshifters deliberately turn their backs on their fellows, striking against them in the same way as Les Mystères. Some of them make their presence known to the hunters. Though rare, these "Pure" werewolves can be powerful allies to a Mystère dedicated to salving the spirit world's wounds — provided he can deal with the werewolf's odd spiritual compulsions.

Other Monsters

Though Les Mystères react with hostility whenever werewolves are involved, the Spirit Emissaries don't focus exclusively on beasts who walk as men. Depending on her beliefs, a Mystère may prefer to ignore specific monsters it they help maintain the balance of the spirit world — whether they know that's

what they're doing or not. She may even protect it from other hunters, all in the name of balance. It's up to each sect, cult, and coven to decide what atrocities they're willing to allow in the name of the bigger picture. Of course, those hunters then have to deal with a creature they once defended when it turns on them, or pollutes the spiritual landscape.

Les Mystères' understanding of the spirit world colors what each sect knows of the creatures they hunt. A few engage in deep study, looking to scripture or legend for ideas of how to fight a threat. They then share their ideas with other cells through the network, and learn from other groups in return. All but the most remote hunters see some benefit. Most Mystères don't write their ideas down, meaning that every generation has to discover some facets of a monster's capabilities for themselves.

What the Western world calls "vampires," Les Mystères believe to be a blend of flesh and spirit. A weak-willed person (often dying) leaves himself open to possession by a spirit of hate, pain, blood, or even addiction. By the time anyone notices a change, it's already too late — the spirit merges with the host's body, transforming him into a living addiction with physical form and an unquenchable thirst for human blood. Though Les Mystères focus on helping spirits, some remain beyond redemption — especially those who steal human bodies in a perverse reflection of Les Mystères' own Ridden rituals. A Mystère has a duty to destroy the vampire, freeing the human host and banishing the spirit. On occasion, vampires can prove valuable allies. Their merged state no longer ages, and the spirit retains the host's memories and knowledge. With judicious use of Influence, he can gather temporal power beyond the dreams of most; and some offer their assistance in exchange for the Mystère leaving them be — or hunting their foes. At best, any alliance would be temporary. By leaving a vampire alive, Les Mystères give out the message to other spirits that it's fine to steal human lives for their own.

Many witches remain a mystery to the Spirit Emissaries. They're human, rather than the unholy fusion of vampires, yet every witch wields incredible powers. As far as any Mystère can tell, witches breach the barrier between the physical and spiritual world, and spend so long in the otherworld that a small part of them resonates with powerful spirits. Back in the physical world, they must use warped rituals to channel that spirit's Influences. Some instead traffic with spirits directly, summoning and binding the ephemeral to their will. While the rituals that allow a spirit to Ride a Mystère have spiritual sanction, the rituals of a witch have no such protection. Even if the spirit begs for the witch to help it, the witch still wields power that he has no right to in order to "help" it. When dealing with witches, most Mystères prefer to watch and wait. If the witch appears genuine, and doesn't force his will on the ethereal, they might even strike a deal — hoping to draw the attention of his spiritual master.

A few Mystères encounter strange doppelgangers, creatures of spirit that mimic people. One looks like the clerk at the corner store but a heart made of brass cogs, while another brings to mind a missing child, but with a body of twigs and leaves. Most spirits would merge with a host, stealing a body and memories, but for some reason the doppelganger comes to take the place of its double in a created body. Though they're very dangerous, without the fundamental understanding of a creature born to the physical world a doppelganger is easy prey for a clever hunter.

Demons intrigue those Mystères who encounter them, and nobody quite knows what to make of them. One Mystère may command demons into her own flesh, and views those who tempt normal people as creatures that she must educate on their proper place. Another Mystère believes demons to be spirits who break through into the physical world without going through the proper channels. Whatever the case, demons aren't dangerous because they're a threat to be fought; they're more a symptom of spiritual corruption in an area — and a sign that the Mystère isn't doing her duty.

Perhaps the greatest foe Les Mystères face is also their most powerful ally — the spirit world. For all that they aid a Mystère, spirits aren't human. More importantly they don't *think* like humans. Each spirit is totally dedicated to what it is. It knows nothing of humanity, and expecting it to have the best interests of anything beyond itself at heart is foolish in the extreme. While most Mystères will turn a blind eye to spirits that cross into the physical world, those who take human bodies or merge their ephemera with flesh must be stopped. Other spirits can't resist condensing their ephemeral forms into a strange kind of flesh and blood. A Mystère has a duty to the human as well as the spiritual world, so when she encounters such a spirit she must strike against it.

Only Human

Les Mystères don't stop at supernatural threats. Many human threats have terrible repercussions in the spirit realm. A serial killer stalking the backstreets isn't any more supernatural than anyone else. He's very human — but he doesn't think like most humans. To the killer, there's nothing wrong with

slaughtering people. Spirits of pain, hate, and death flock to him, while loss and desperation crowd his victims' families. Their presence unbalances the spirits, throwing the fabric of the world out of line. When a killer hits closer to home, a Mystère may give him a taste of the fear that he inflicts in his victims — or just remove him from the world without a thought.

Cultists present another problem, but a more insidious one. The real evil of a cult isn't in sacrifices or worshipping dark gods. A cultist turns his back on his friends and family, at least those who don't join the cult themselves. Everything he does, he does to further the cult's agenda. Some reward members with money or success in the real world. Others give nothing back but a sense of belonging. A dangerous few give otherworldly power and the patronage of disturbing and powerful spirits. The effect of a cult on the people around them is like a parasite feeding off an animal — the cultists take what they want and give nothing back. Their actions impact the spirit world, but often slowly enough that it looks like a natural change. Often, the first sign of a cult that a Mystère notices comes long after the sickness has taken root. And like any sickness, he's got a tricky job removing the cult without harming the innocent people around it.

Hunters

You've felt the touch of the Loa since an early age. Rather than accepting it, you rebelled — the inner-city doesn't need a *bokor*. You didn't want to become one of those crusty old bastards who stand in silent judgment over everyone. Even when your gang started cutting you out, only coming to you when they needed something, you figured it was just time to move on. Someone else told your gramps, and he took you to see some friends of his. Told you that you had a duty. That was six months ago. You're starting to accept your fate, but some days you just want to see your old friends again.

You saw the Beast up close on a church camping trip. A man with the soul of an animal tore through your camp, and you're the only one who remembered. Soon after, the saints and angels began whispering to you. You daren't tell anyone what you heard, but your gardener heard you shouting at them one day. He didn't tell your parents. Instead, he told you that you'd been chosen by the Lord. He brought you to a gathering downtown, and you learned the truth. The Reverend still scares you, but he's the only friend you have right now.

You woke up atop the Mesa three months ago. You hadn't any ID, just a hundred bucks in used bills. You went down to Grand Junction, hoping to find work, but with no name and no apartment you couldn't get anything for long. Other people stood apart from you when you tried to save them from strange creatures, but it wasn't until you met the medicine man that you realized why: they couldn't see the spirits around them. He could, and he showed you how to use them to great effect. Werewolves took him less than a week later. You've only caught glimpses of them since, but one of them looks awfully familiar.

You were driving home one night when a shaft of light pinned your car in place. Strange creatures probed you and filled your head with a wonderful vision of how the world would be when they shared their bounty with humanity. Nobody believed you. Co-workers joked about the "little grey men," even when you told them that the creatures were sentient energy. One night you went along to see the Starlight Children, a group of people who'd had the same experiences. They understood your story, and gave you the tool to contact the aliens once again. Now you just have to make people ready for their coming.

You read all the stories in the tabloids, like werewolves living plain as day in the modern city. Of course, you knew better than that — until you saw a whole bunch of them tear your apartment super into four pieces. A couple of old friends of his came by, and asked what happened. For some reason, you told them the truth. They didn't call you crazy, but they did ask if you wanted to do something about it. You said yes, and they showed you what he really did down in the basement. You don't really care about the people in your block, but you do care about killing those beasts. Fortunately, that's what the spirit you deal with want as well.

STEREOTYPES

The Bear Lodge: We can't be everywhere at once, but these people sometimes do our work for us, striking down a werewolf who has angered the local spirits. Though members of the Lodge remain ignorant of the real impact of their hunt, that doesn't diminish their usefulness. I know some Mystères join their hunts, acting as a guiding hand, while others prefer to leave them to their flawed understanding.

The Cheiron Group: I saw a group of men take away the body of a werewolf in an ambulance. I didn't realize at the time, but they took it for study. I've seen them since, watching me and my hunt, waiting for me to find something else for their research. Their field agents can handle themselves, but I don't like being used.

The Lucifuge: Though the angels and demons in the world ride me, I remain in control. These children of the Devil do as well, though I can only imagine how they keep their mind from the sway of the demon within. I've made myself known to them in case they need any help. So far we've only talked, but I'm sure we'll be able to help each other when the time comes.

Null Mysteriis: Occasionally, someone who has trouble with a spirit doesn't know to contact a Mystère. Instead, they get in touch with scientists and thinking-men, people without a shred of spirit in their soul. They go on about energy readings and strange concepts, but they've no idea what they're really dealing with. If you're lucky, you can make one listen long enough for him to be useful, but the others never seem to listen to him.

Factions

Without any real organization between the disparate member groups, it's hard for Les Mystères to have any kind of factions. Over time, different cells have organized themselves into rough collectives based around their personal views of the spirit world and how they tie in to their religious views.

The **Children of the Loa** have members from every stripe — from the Catholic girl who talks with the saints to the inner-city *bokor*, and from the Dao Mau to Pentecostal glossolalia. Their main belief is that the spirits are either servants or aspects of a greater force — whether that's the Christian God, a benevolent creator, or some stranger force. Their beliefs can cloud their understanding of the spirit realm: angels have limitations on their behavior that most spirits do not. This makes it easy for spirits to manipulate Children of the Loa. Many of them walk the Path of Beasts, striking out in the names of a hundred gods. Only a few seek to divine their place in the world through the Path of the Soul. Their faith gives these Mystères a direction that some others lack, and some strike at mundane concerns including drug dealers and organized crime just as they attack werewolves.

Servants of the spirits first and foremost, the **Spirit-Chained** incorporate Siberian ecstatic shamans, African animists, many Native American medicine-men, and some — but by no means all — of the African Diaspora religions. Their defining trait is the belief that the spirits, by whatever name, are a fundamental part of the world. There are no Gods above or forces beyond, just the world of flesh and the world of spirit. Many members walk the Path of Spirit willingly, at the behest of their patrons, while others prefer to use the spirits' power to help people on the Path of Fellowship. These Mystères are by far the most insular. Some of them refuse to induct new members who haven't grown up in the right culture, while others don't even trust Les Mystères without their immaterial allies' say-so. On the other hand, there's nobody better at understanding a spirit's motivations than a member of a Spirit-Chained cell.

Transcendent Mystères form the smallest faction of Les Mystères, containing by default any cell, coven, or cult that rejects both of the other labels. New Age crystal-wavers who draw in personal energies, people who bond with phase-shifted aliens, or modern occultists who use creatures from the subconscious mind to empower themselves. Their outlandish ideas about spirits do make it harder for them to manipulate these Mystères, but their uniqueness is also their failing — they have an even harder time adapting new rituals to invite a spirit to Ride them. Other Transcendents reject the idea just starting to bud among sects of the other factions, the idea that Les Mystères need to organize and start acting as an organization. Rather, they see the Spirit Emissaries' loose connections between cells as their great strength. Individual cults can come up with wildly different solutions to the same problem, and sharing that information allows others to find something that *works*.

Status

Among Les Mystères, Status reflects both spiritual power and a Mystère's reputation in the spirit world. A *bokor* in Baton Rouge may live her whole life without rising in the spirits' esteem, while some Mystères hold the spirits' attention from birth. The lack of even an informal hierarchy makes reputation among the spirits the only signifier of how important a given Mystère is at any time.

- • You've felt the touch of something from beyond this world, and understand that you must spend your life on the outside. Only a few spirits come when you call, but you still have the option of spending Merit dots on Ridden rituals.

- ••• You know well the feeling of a spirit infusing your body, and you've seen first-hand the damage werewolves can do. You've spent time on one path or another that leads from the crossroads, and gain the benefit noted for your path (see "The Crossroads," p. 110).

- ••••• You know well what dangers threaten people who aren't careful. You've also felt the touch of powerful spirits, and you know what it is to have a duty that burns with the force of a spirit's ban. You've helped people, you've hurt people, but you know that everything is part of the great cycle of the world. Other Mystères value your input, and often send promising students to you, giving you the equivalent of a three-dot Retainer.

STORIES UNCLE DON TOLD ME

BY MATT MCFARLAND
A FUN FAMILY VACATION THROUGH THE FOLKLORE AND MYTHOLOGY OF AMERICA

It might be morbid, but I have to admit I'm curious about who's going to show up at Uncle Don's funeral.

Uncle Don's pretty old to have a nephew my age. He's in his 70s and I'm only 24. My grandparents had him and my father almost 15 years apart (interspersed with a bunch of others, but my dad and Uncle Don are the ones that everybody thinks of when they say "the Clannan kids"). When I was born, Don was almost 50. That messes with my mind even now. When I was in grade school, he was retiring. He was an "old person." When you're a kid, it's hard to grasp that adults ever had a life, ever did anything beyond what they do every day that you see them.

And yet, every time I talked to Don, I learned something new. I didn't learn that he'd been married or had been in the Army until I was 12. Once I interviewed him for a history project and I found out that, at one point, he spoke six languages (until the dementia set in, he could still get by in German and French, but had lost the others).

One of the things I learned about Don pretty early on — I was about 11 at the time — was that he loved weird stories. The first one he told me was this one:

> White folks wince when they say "black" or "colored" when they're talking about a person, but the black folks have their own legends and their own weird stories. What kind depends on where you are; but when I was about your father's age and I was living in Mississippi with my wife, I had a colored friend. Now, remember this was about the same time that the schools were first getting integrated and the Civil Rights Movement was in full swing, and I lived in Mississippi. I got some letters for being friendly with Marlon, let me tell you, but those cowards could go hang for all I cared.
>
> Anyway, Marlon and I went walking one night. His wife was pregnant and we had to get her some ice cream or something. Women get funny

when they're with child, you know. We looked across the street and we saw a man we'd never seen before. He was hunched over and wore a big hat and a long shirt, and his skin looked wrong. There was enough light to see he was colored, but his skin was pasty and pale, almost yellow.

Now, I didn't know what that might mean, and I was all set to yell to him or wave, but Marlon grabbed my hand. "Don't, Don," he said. "That's a yorka." Of course, I didn't know what a yorka was, and I raised my hand anyway.

That man in the hat walked across the street to us, and Marlon started cursing under his breath. He said, "Don, don't say a word to it. Keep walking with me, don't say a word. If you ever trust me, trust me now."

Well, I didn't know why, but when a friend asks you something important, you know it. So I didn't say a word, and Marlon and me and the man — the yorka — kept walking along the

sidewalk. And every so often I'd look up and see Marlon, and he'd look over at me, and he was just scared to death. He had his wedding ring in his hand, off his finger, and he was squeezing it tight. And I started to get scared, too, because Marlon wasn't a fearful man.

We kept walking and soon we saw the corner store around the next bend, and saw a few teenagers — white kids — on the corner smoking cigarettes and acting tough. And they saw Marlon and me and one of them asked, "What are you two" — and he called us something I won't repeat — "doing out here?" And we didn't even acknowledge him, because we were too busy looking around for the yorka. But it was long gone, probably going off to find someone else who'd walk with it.

A yorka's like a ghost, you see. It used to be a man — or a woman, I guess — but all that's left now is something pale and dead and lost. Marlon never told me what would have happened if we'd spoken to it, and I never dared ask him, either.

THE REAL GHOSTS OF MISSISSIPPI

What may seem to be an old and abandoned home from years ago may still hold secrets from long ago. This home in particular in Hattiesburgh, Mississippi was the scene of a grisly murder spree.

Local legend has it that a poor sharecropper butchered his own family to death with the very axe he used to chop firewood. Local legend also says that late at night you can see a ghostly canlde light show through the windows and tiny bloody handprints appear .

The story doesn't end there however...the man later was found 20 miles away in the middle of a field...with his head chopped off. The twist being it looked like he had done it to himself with the same axe he butchered his family with.

That was the kind of story he liked to tell. I asked my father about the yorka story the day after Don first told it to me. I guess I thought Don made it up, made up the whole thing, just to scare or entertain me. My father told me he didn't know anything about ghosts, but he did know that Don had lived in Mississippi during the Civil Rights Movement and did have a black friend named Marlon, and that Marlon's daughter Lisa was born not long before Don moved up north. That was the last time I ever doubted one of Don's weird stories.

When I was in middle school, I went on a big-time military kick. I learned all the military jargon, the names and classifications of military weapons, where the US has forces deployed, and so on. I harangued Don to death about it, because my father never served in the Army. He answered my questions honestly and good-naturedly a lot longer than I would have in his situation, but the answers

he gave started getting vague. That winter, the power went out during a family Christmas party. My parents and some other relations lit some candles and played cards. My uncle hates card games, so he and I sat by the fire and talked. Of course, I started asking questions about his Army experiences, and finally I asked why he never gave details. He leaned forward and told me this:

Honestly, Mike, I'm having trouble remembering what I'm allowed to tell you and what I'm not. Some of the things I saw and did, I had to promise I'd never talk about, but it's been too long and I don't remember everything that's supposed to be a secret. I guess I can tell you about this one thing that happened during boot, though.

I did boot camp not far from where your Auntie Leila lives now, and I hated it. You know I don't mind getting up and running and so on, but there wasn't much to do when you weren't training except sleep and read and play cards. Anyway, one night four friends and I — I remember one fellow's name was Pete, but we all called him Pie, and another was Chuck, but darned if I remember the other two — we got a weekend pass and we went into town. We thought we'd see a movie or something, but then Pie got the bright idea to go to a girlie show. Wasn't my idea, but Pie was pretty insistent, so we all went and watched the girls dance.

Well, those girls were nothing special. A girl who gets up and dances for drunk soldiers only does it because she's got no other skills to pay her rent. I'm not saying she's wrong for doing it, just that it takes sort of a boring person to do it and a boring person to watch it. There was one girl that even I had to sit up and watch, though. She had her own bit where she danced by herself, and her name was Sadie. She was thin — not like your sister where you can see her ribs but slender like a snake. She was pale and pretty, and she had these big blue eyes you could see from the back row. And Pie just leaned closer and closer and tried to wave her over, and she just ignored him and sat in fellows' laps and blew in their ears and so on. And all the time, Pie's nudging me and the other guys and saying, "Do you see her? Ain't she beautiful?" We all thought she was, but he was really going nuts.

After a while, Sadie left the stage and the boring girls came back on, and I told Pie it was time we were going. The other boys agreed, but Pie said he wanted to go back and talk to Sadie. We all told him not to be an idiot; probably lots of guys tried that and they were all turned away, but he insisted, so we all waited for him out by the car.

We waited there for almost an hour, and Chuck was all ready to go in and drag him out when the door opened and out steps Pie. It was just after midnight, which wasn't so late for us, but Pie looked like he'd been up for a week. He looked sick, and when we talked to him, he took an extra few seconds to answer anything we asked. I knew he wasn't well, so we RTB'd and turned him over to the infirmary.

Next day, we found out he'd been sent home on a Section 8. He never answered our letters or our calls.

Chuck and I went back to that club to find that Sadie, but when she performed that night, it was different. She wasn't so pretty, her eyes were brown and she'd even put on a little weight. She looked normal and boring, like any of those other girls.

I think something rode on that girl that night, like a ghost or a demon. Maybe she asked it to help her, to make her less boring, or maybe it just landed on her and used her. Anyway, that's not the weirdest thing that happened to me in the Army, but at least I know I can tell you that story and Uncle Sam won't come looking for you.

Don and I didn't talk often when I was in college. I got a scholarship and wound up several hundred miles from home. We talked occasionally, but I was in college: I had a new set of friends, and I didn't have much to do with family during that time. The weekend before my 21st birthday, he called me. I was living in an apartment with two other guys, and I remember I was crashed out on the couch in the middle of the afternoon — nursing an absolutely awful hangover — when my phone rang. When I answered, it was Don. "I'm out in the parking lot," he said. "Come on, let's go have lunch."

It turned out he was just in town visiting a buddy and decided to drop by. That's what he said, anyway. Looking back now, I think he had at least two other reasons for coming into town. One, of course, was to see me and straighten my neglectful ass out. We sat there at lunch and he laid it all down for me — how much my parents missed me, and how little time we all had in the grand scheme of things. He didn't want me to feel guilty, though. Like I said, he had another reason to be in town, but I didn't put the pieces together until much later.

I called my parents that night, I bought a train ticket home, and we all went out for dinner on my birthday. I didn't touch a drop of alcohol that night. Don and I got talking about drinking, and that's when I found out he'd been a recovering alcoholic for 10 years. I asked him what had put him on the wagon, thinking maybe my father had found out and helped him straighten out. Of course it wasn't that simple:

You know why they call booze "spirits?" Yeah, me neither. But about 10 years ago, something happened that got me thinking. I was visiting a friend of mine up near where you go to school. Same guy I was visiting when I came over to see you, actually.

Anyhow, I drove out there and I was already drunk when I left. The thing about real alkies, we start drinking early, and we learn how to function while we're drunk. I've never once been stopped for DUI, and that drive wasn't any different. I pulled into my friend's driveway — Anthony's his name — and when I got out, I near fell over from the heat and from the drink. Anthony came off his porch and helped me to a chair, and all the while he's saying, "Shit, Don, I told you to lay off," like it's easy to quit or something. I sat down in the shade and drank some iced tea with him, and then he showed me around his house. He had just bought it, see, that's why I was visiting.

Well, it was a nice enough place, but pretty much normal, except for the basement. The basement had a dirt floor, and I'd never seen that before, so I asked Anthony. He told me the previous owner had torn up the concrete there and had planned on doing something with the space — laying new concrete, hard wood, he didn't know — but had died of a stroke one night and hadn't left any kin. So now Anthony wasn't sure what to do.

That basement, Mike, was weird. I mean, I was still drunk when I walked downstairs, but the minute my feet touched the floor I sobered up. I'd been drinking all day, but as soon I stepped off that last stair onto that dirt floor, I was cold sober and scared half to death.

There was something in that basement, and I don't mean it was rats or big spiders or anything like that. There was something down there, and I couldn't see or hear it; but I knew it just the same. Now, Anthony, he didn't even blink. He's walking around, saying "maybe hardwood, maybe a pool table," and I'm just nodding my head like an idiot.

We went upstairs, and his wife Jenny was waiting in the kitchen. My eyes met hers, and she knew, just like I did, that there was something down there. We both nodded to each other, I think, but we both knew we couldn't say anything, because what do you say? Bright summer afternoon, sunlight streaming in the kitchen window, yellow doggie sacked on the floor, iced tea in the pitcher? What could you say?

That's why you don't see yorkas or weird stuff like that by day, Mike. They know to keep to their basements and their street corners and their holes and their darkness. But now I knew where they hid.

I tried to talk to Anthony about it that night, but he wasn't hearing it. He thought I was still drunk.

We never talked about that basement again, but his wife sure remembered what happened, because she gave me that house.

That's why I was out there last week, Mike; to see you, sure, but also to attend Anthony's funeral and see to his house. He died of a stroke, just like the previous owner, and just like the previous owner, he didn't have any kids to leave the house to. But Jenny, who's doing fine, all things considered, didn't want to put the house on the market, so she wrote me a letter and asked me if I'd take it.

Don didn't live in that house, and he didn't sublet it. I stayed in the same town after I graduated from college, and Don dropped by every couple of months. I knew he visited that house when he was in town, I just didn't know why. I could always tell if he'd gone there before he came to see me, though, because when he did, he was always tired. Drained, I guess, is a better way to put it. He looked like he'd had the worst day of his life every time he went to that house. I tried to ask him about it once or twice, but I never knew how to bring it up. People don't really have

the words to talk about weird stuff, not in any kind of concrete sense. So for just over three years, Don and I talked about my job, my life, my friends, and the parts of his past that I already knew about. It was strange, talking to him without learning anything new.

And then two months ago, he had a stroke.

He called me from the hospital. He'd been leaving the house to come visit me when it happened. It was fairly minor, as strokes go, and by the time I got to the hospital he was out of danger. He slept the whole time I was there, and then my parents and a couple of my brothers arrived and took over. They took him back to their house two weeks later, to recuperate. I was intending to visit next month, when work slows down a little for me.

And then mom called last night. She told me Don had been asking after me, and she sounded a little exasperated. I asked her what was wrong.

"Oh, it's your uncle," she said. "He's just obsessive. He asks the same damn questions every couple of minutes. The last couple of days it's been about that house he owns up by you. He wants you to check on it. Do you know where the house is?"

I said I did, and that I'd go out that afternoon. I knew I had to do it soon, but I also knew I needed to go while it was still light.

So I drive out to that little house, on the outside of town. I let myself in with Don's key, and immediately I feel 10 years older. Sunlight streams in the front window, but the house still seems dark. The light's here, but it doesn't seem to matter somehow.

I just start walking. It's like water running downhill. I'm not surprised when I stop by the basement door. The light above the basement stairs doesn't work, but there's a flashlight hanging on the doorknob. The stairs creak as though they're trying to splinter but can't quite shake themselves free of their nails. When I get to the bottom of the stairs, I smell something powdery and choking — mortar, or concrete.

The basement has multiple rooms. I can see several doors, at least two of them padlocked. Each room has a cross hung on it, and each door has a small glass pane.

I walk to the first door and shine my flashlight in the window, and stumble back with a yell. I see eyes, red, bloodshot eyes. I look more carefully and I see a whole face. It looks pale, yellowed, like a black man's might if he lost his blood.

What strikes me most about the yorka is his teeth. They're four times as long as they should be. It grins at

me through the pane, glad to have someone to acknowledge it. I move on to the next door.

I shine my light in, and across the room I see a woman sitting on a chair. She looks up, and her blond hair seems to shine in the faint light. She has blue eyes, and they brim with tears as she rises and holds out her hands, pleading with me to open the door. I reach down for the padlock, and I find that the door is not only locked, but welded shut around the edges.

I tear my eyes away, and I walk to the door at the end of the hall. I put my hand on the doorknob, and stop.

My right hand starts tingling. I try to take a step back and stumble a bit.

I take my hand away, but the tingling doesn't change. I feel my lips go slack on the right side of my face.

I back up. I can't run, but I can limp pretty fast. I stumble up the stairs and out of the house. By the time I get to my car, the tingling has stopped. By the time I get to the hospital, my lips feel normal again. The doctors tell me that my symptoms are, in fact, indicative of a stroke, but they can't find any evidence of one. Probably I just overexerted myself or something.

I call Don and tell him everything's in place at the house. He tells me I need to come see him so he can transfer the deed to my name. He says I have to finish covering the dirt floor. I nod.

I didn't look in all of the doors, and I know at least a few of them were empty.

He's got other chores for me, I'm sure.

In the den of a damp and dingy cabin, a hunter drips cooked silver into the tops of the 10mm rounds — the fluid metal oozing into X's carved with a sharp penknife.

In a sealed, climate-controlled vault, a hunter of the Aegis Kai Doru stares at a display case of feathered spears, bone knives, and fist-sized Zuni fetishes; all the weapons of the werewolf. Which one would work best against its own?

In a forest clearing, a lone hunter stands surrounded by seven cackling shadows, each with human bodies but each with the heads of different animals. The hunter does not know how to kill these things; silver seems to do little. So he takes the pin out of the grenade in his pocket just as they rush to feed.

Hunters and werewolves: the clash of predators, man versus beast, a blasted bullet versus the swipe of a claw. The shapeshifters have a wealth of weapons at their disposal: gnashing teeth, hulking flesh, and a knack for commanding invisible spirits to do their will. But the hunters have their own weapons, too: strange technology, rituals both divine and demonic, and ceremonies that allow them to invite spirits into their bodies for a time.

This chapter is about the tools available to both hunter and werewolf — useful for players looking to enhance their characters, or for Storytellers aiming to create memorable and challenging antagonists in a **Hunter: The Vigil** (or **Werewolf: The Forsaken**) game.

New Tactics

It takes more than nerve and a steady hand to defeat a werewolf. More so than against almost any other type of monster, a battle with a werewolf leaves little room for error: the fact that werewolves tend to travel and hunt in packs makes them even more dangerous than even the most vicious of solitary horrors. Even more than their prodigious "natural" weaponry, the pack dynamic makes werewolves very dangerous prey.

Spirits form ephemeral opponents for hunter cells. They attack from the spirit world or from the body of a possessed human, slipping out of a hunter's grasp even when defeated. The inability of most hunters to battle spirits in a physical manner forces hunter cells to cast about for any possible solution to defeat their foe.

Bait and Switch

Prerequisites: *All:* Composure 3, Manipulation 2, Subterfuge 2. *Primary:* Stealth 2

Requires: 4; 5 or 6 grants a +1 bonus to primary actor, 7 or more imposes a -3 penalty on the primary actor.

Dice Pool: *Primary:* Dexterity + Stealth. *Secondary:* Manipulation + Expression.

Action: Instant and contested; target rolls Resolve + Composure reflexively.

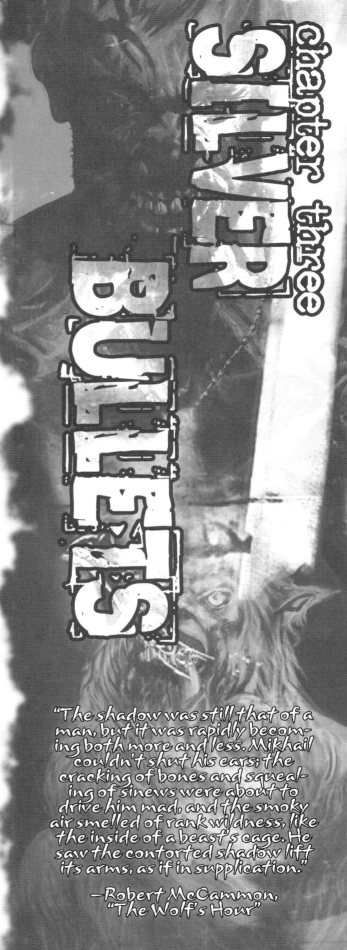

"The shadow was still that of a man, but it was rapidly becoming both more and less. Mikhail couldn't shut his ears; the cracking of bones and squealing of sinews were about to drive him mad, and the smoky air smelled of rank wildness, like the inside of a beast's cage. He saw the contorted shadow lift its arms, as if in supplication."

—Robert McCammon, "The Wolf's Hour"

Description: Werewolves are creatures of feral emotions that teeter on the brink of berserker frenzy every minute of every day. Intentionally provoking the rage of such a monster is nigh on suicidal in most circumstances. Fury erases even the smallest hint of conscience or self-control and turns a werewolf into a merciless killing machine. For hunters with the balls to attempt it, the frenzy of a werewolf can be turned against his pack.

This Tactic works by goading a werewolf into a frenzy, then misdirecting him so the only target he has for his rage is his own pack. First the hunters poke, jab and needle the target, both physically and verbally, working the monster up to a fury — the equivalent of poking a dog with a stick. Physical attacks are intended to belittle rather than damage. Intentionally frustrating a werewolf into a murderous rage requires serious composure from every hunter involved; inciting a werewolf to violence is no place for cowards. Once the werewolf is frothing at the mouth, the primary actor attracts the creature's attention with a particularly humiliating attack (a slap to the face, spitting on the werewolf, knee to the groin) and sidesteps to hide behind another member of the werewolf's pack. It should go without saying that this Tactic can go horribly wrong. Primarily designed for combating werewolves, this Tactic can also be useful in pushing vampires into a frenzy and turning them on each other.

Organizations: The Union likes the idea of turning enemies against each other, especially since it means fewer hunters are likely to be injured in the fracas. Similarly, Task Force: VALKYRIE prefers to battle an enemy that isn't thinking clearly and causes problems for their own side.

Potential Modifiers: Target is currently in bestial hybrid form (+2 to secondary actors); target is currently in wolf or near-wolf form (-2 to primary actor); target suffers from three or more points of lethal damage (+1 to secondary actors).

Roll Results

Dramatic Failure: The werewolf flies into a frenzy fixated on the primary actor.

Failure: The werewolf refuses to give in to his rage and may respond normally.

Success: The werewolf becomes enraged and attacks his own pack. As long as hunters stay out of his line of sight the infuriated werewolf will not attack them for the duration of his frenzy (unless he's out of targets and all that remain are hunters). Additionally, by forcing the pack to deal with one of their own, the hunters steal the Initiative in the fight. During the next turn, all members of the cell may choose to act at any time (though they retain their Initiative score for the remainder of the combat), even interrupting enemy actions.

Exceptional Success: The werewolf becomes enraged and will *only* attack his own pack for the duration of the frenzy, regardless of whether a hunter comes into his line of sight or not.

To Purchase: 17 Practical Experience, 14 for the Union, 12 for Task Force: VALKYRIE.

Confuse the Scent

Prerequisites: *All:* Wits 2, Stamina 2, Survival 2. *Partial (1):* Survival (Tracking) 3 (primary actor).

Requires: 2; up to 4 imposes no penalty, 5 or more levies a -1 penalty to the primary actor for each extra hunter.

Dice Pool: *Primary:* Wits + Survival. *Secondary:* Stamina + Survival.

Action: Extended and contested

Description: Sometimes running away is a valid strategy. Not every hunt goes exactly to plan and it is easy for hunters to become the hunted. The problem with running from werewolves is that they have the tracking capabilities of wolves combined with the problem-solving capacity of humans. Simply running upstream or through a crowded area isn't usually enough to baffle pursuit. Feigned flight can also be a useful device for drawing werewolves away from innocent bystanders or as a precursor to another Tactic, like Divide and Conquer (see below).

This Tactic assumes that the hunters are already well outside of visual tracking range and have forced the werewolves to fall back on tracking by scent and animal instinct. The secondary actors move in ways intended to disrupt their scent, making them more difficult to track. They cross moving water, travel along rocky areas, and even double back every now and then to disguise their true course. This requires at least a basic idea of how to disguise signs of passage and the wherewithal to keep at it for an extended length of time. The primary actor follows along behind his companions and utilizes his greater knowledge of tracking to further confuse the trail by eliminating errant signs of the cell's movements (sweeping the path with branches, gathering bits of torn clothing or eliminating any blood trail as much as possible) and attempting to muddle their scents by introducing stronger smells (such as bleach, perfume or setting small, smoky fires) to cover the back trail. This is a valid ploy against any type of monster that tracks by scent and sense.

Each roll for this Tactic is equal to five minutes. Pursuing werewolves must succeed on Wits + Survival + any bonuses for heightened senses. The target number for the hunters is 15. The pursuing werewolves aren't assigned a target number. Instead, if the pack's number of successes exceeds the cell's number of successes at any time it has caught the scent and, given the speed of a four-legged creature versus a two-legged one, it is unlikely to let its prey's scent go a second time. If the hunters reach 15 successes without being caught, they have managed to shake off the pursuit.

Organizations: Members of Aegis Kai Doru that venture into the wilds in pursuit of mystical knowledge or artifacts use this Tactic to make a clean getaway from infuriated guardians. Their pursuit of knowledge and first causes also frequently takes Null Mysteriis deep into the wilderness; they have developed this Tactic for when they get in over their heads.

Potential Modifiers: Strong winds or rain (+1 to all participants); pursued in an urban or rocky environment (+1 to all participants); extraordinarily potent materials used to confound scent (+1 to primary actor); a hunter is wounded or bleeding (-2 to primary actor); recent rainfall or travel through wet, soggy areas (-1 to all participants).

Roll Results

Dramatic Failure: The secondary actors got lost or separated, someone scraped off enough flesh in a fall to spatter the area with blood or the primary actor spilled some of the stuff he was using to cover the cell's scent on himself. All successes gained thus far are lost and the tracking pursuers gain +3 to their next roll.

Failure: The cell's efforts to disguise their trail prove futile or are temporarily stymied by terrain or circumstance. No progress is made towards eluding pursuit.

Success: The cell continues to progress towards eluding their pursuers and each hunter gains a +2 bonus on their next roll in the extended action. Achieving the full 15 successes means that not only have the hunters escaped, but if the foiled werewolves attempt to track these hunters again, attempts will suffer a -3 penalty.

Exceptional Success: No additional benefit beyond the number of successes gained.

To Purchase: 16 Practical Experience, 13 for Null Mysteriis, 11 for Aegis Kai Doru.

Defile

Prerequisites: *All:* Intelligence 2, Wits 2, Science 2 *or* Occult 2. *Partial (2):* Investigation 2. *Partial (1):* Crafts 2.

Requires: At least 4.

Dice Pool: *Primary:* Intelligence + Science *or* Intelligence + Occult. *Secondary:* Wits + Investigation.

Action: Extended

Description: For the most part, the material realm is separate from the strange and terrifying world of spirits. Though little is known by hunters about the spirit world, some scholars realize spirits are kept out of the material realm (and humans kept from the spirit world) by an invisible barrier of unknown power. Places do exist where the barrier between the worlds is thin, allowing spirits to slip into the material realm more easily. These places, called Loci by the enlightened, also seem to draw the attention of werewolves. Werewolves seem to gather at a Locus to replenish their energies, as though the Locus were a kind of watering hole. Hunters that seek to diminish the capacity of werewolves to make war or have an interest in keeping the spirits out of the material realm attempt to locate and shut down such places.

To Defile a Locus, the cell must first have identified the nature of the Locus they are dealing with. This could have been accomplished in advance of the mission by gathering information about the Locus, or on the scene by searching for clues. Once the cell believes it has properly identified the nature of the Locus, it can attempt to close it by altering the phenomena that contributed to its creation. A Locus that formed around despair might draw its power from paraphernalia left by suicides (razor blades, guns, empty drug bottles), the cell might disrupt a Locus with the nature of silence just by its very presence, or a Locus empowered by death might be fed from a number of unmarked graves and a general blight in the area. The secondary actors go around and identify the best places to "defile" the area — the primary actor follows-up on their identifications and advice, acting as the one to truly disrupt the nature of the "hot spot."

The target number of successes per roll for this extended action varies on the strength of the Locus in question. A weak Locus might only require a five or six successes to close, while a particularly strong locus might require 20-30 successes to close. Each roll is equivalent to 10 minutes' worth of time. Although intended to close doorways to the spirit world, this Tactic might be useful for closing gateways that lead to other, more perilous, supernatural realms.

Note that plenty of danger exists in trying to defile a Locus. First, werewolves may sense the disruption and will come with furious vengeance to stop the marauding hunters. Second, spirits *feed* from these places, and will do whatever they must to block the hunters' success.

Organizations: The Lucifuge views such places as if they're basically open doorways to Hell itself. Not only does a so-called "Hellmouth" help to strengthen

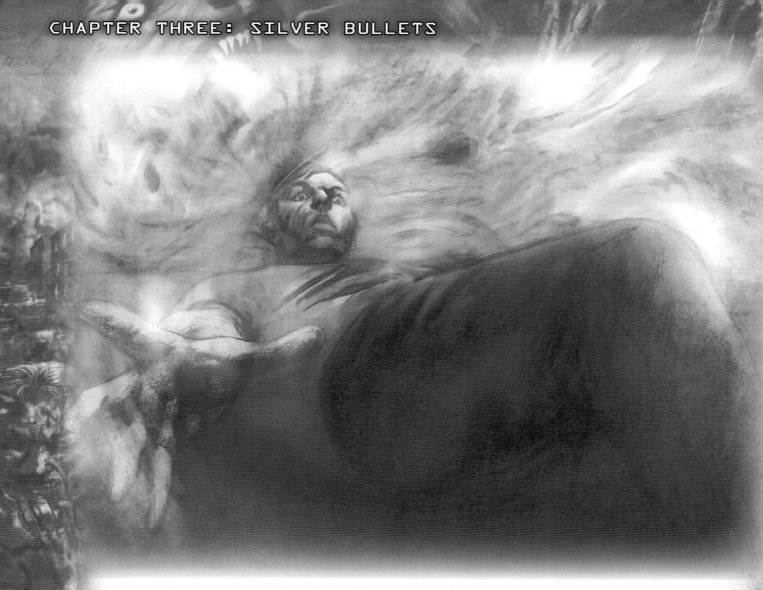

their werewolf enemies, it also allows demon-like spirits to slip through the thin membrane that separates the worlds. The Long Night believes the existence of such places is proof that the seven seals are starting to crack and that the demons have been given doorways into the world of men; the Long Night aims to close those doors with prayer and the power of God.

Potential Modifiers: The Locus is watched over by a guardian that attempts to indirectly thwart the cell (-3 to all participants); the phenomena responsible for the Locus are particularly obvious or fragile (+2 to all participants); the phenomena responsible for the Locus are hidden or exceptionally sturdy (-2 to all participants); the Locus is the result of a spirit's influence (-2 to all participants); the cell is attacked (-2 to all participants), the Locus has previously been investigated with the "Resonance" Tactic (+3 to all participants).

Roll Results

Dramatic Failure: All progress towards defiling the Locus is lost; a spirit guardian materializes to defend the Locus, or werewolves descend upon the area.

Failure: No progress is made towards defiling the Locus.

Success: Progress continues towards defiling the Locus. When the target number of success set by the Storyteller to reflect the strength of the Locus has been met or exceeded, the cell has managed to sever the link between the material realm and the spirit world, and the Locus closes. The cell gains a +2 bonus to Intimidation rolls made against spirits with a nature similar to that of the Locus for the next week. (Note that Loci do not necessarily stay closed; hunters must be vigilant custodians carefully watching for a resurgence of spiritual energy around that place.)

Exceptional Success: No additional benefit is gained beyond the number of successes rolled.

To Purchase: 16 Practical Experience, 13 for the Long Night, 11 for the Lucifuge.

Disarm

Prerequisites: *All:* Intelligence 2, Wits 2, Occult 2. *Partial (1):* Varies (see below) (primary actor).

Requires: 3 or more.

SPIRITUAL RETUNING

The "Defile" Tactic could also be adapted to target the influence a spirit holds over a place to help drive it off. Spirits with the power to do so exert their influence into the material realm to feed off the energies created or to bolster their dominance of the area, even in the spirit world. Used in this way, the Tactic would identify ways in which the cell might go about recalibrating the spiritual energy of the place. This might include mediating between rival gangs to reduce instances of violent crime, instigating a neighborhood cleanup project to drive off a spirit of litter, or even figure out ways to foment anger in an area where a happiness spirit has gone a little too far.

Dice Pool: *Primary:* Varies (see below). *Secondary:* Intelligence + Occult.

Action: Instant

Description: Werewolves are formidable opponents even when employing only their "natural" weaponry against a cell (claws, teeth, strength). Like most of the creatures that haunt the World of Darkness, werewolves can also call upon mystic powers to increase their lethality. Werewolves use their powers to increase their hunting and killing abilities, but they also employ those same powers in the creation of magical tools and devices: an axe that a werewolf has enchanted seems to hunger for blood; a carved piece of bone can jinx opponents with misfortune; or round clay balls that contain bomb fragments can be used like grenades. Depending on the fight or the potency of the magical object, the first course of action taken by a cell might require it to relieve the enemy of their magical devices.

Disarm can be performed in a variety of ways depending on the specialties of the cell involved. One method of negating the impact of a magical device is to steal the device from its owner. This isn't necessarily the most permanent solution to the problem considering most werewolves are more than capable of reclaiming their property. The more permanent method of dealing with a magical device is to destroy it outright. Some magical devices can also be neutralized by exposure to an opposing force. The aforementioned clay balls that explode like grenades might work as the result of binding a fire spirit into the clay. Dunking the balls in water might act to neutralize the power of the fire spirit contained within.

The secondary actors attempt to identify a magical implement used by a werewolf and quickly devise a method of neutralizing the item. They then assist the primary actor in putting the plan into action, even if only by distracting the target. The primary actor can attempt to steal a magical tool through brute force (Strength + Brawl) or through misdirection (Dexterity + Larceny), depending on the talents of the hunter in question. Similarly, the primary actor can attempt to destroy the magical object by either whacking it with a melee weapon (Strength + Weaponry) or attempting to shoot it (Dexterity + Firearms). See the **World of Darkness Rulebook**, p. 135 for rules on destroying objects.

Neutralizing magical tools through other means will require different types of rolls from the primary actor. Dousing the clay grenades with water might call for a Dexterity + Athletics check to determine if that bucket of water thrown by the primary actor manages to soak all the grenades or just irritate the werewolf. This Tactic can be useful against other opponents as well; werewolves are hardly the only creatures that use magical tools to gain an edge.

Organizations: Unsurprisingly the scholars of both Aegis Kai Doru and Null Mysteriis both attempt to steal, rather than destroy, magical objects from their werewolf owners. Aegis Kai Doru hopes it might discover a way to use the magical device and even if they can't immediately figure it out, they have just the place to store it. Null Mysteriis attempts to capture the objects to figure out what makes them tick, always seeking a rational explanation.

Potential Modifiers: The object is currently in use or is a weapon (+1 to secondary actors, -2 to primary actor); the object looks completely normal (-2 to secondary actors); the object is Size 1 or smaller (-2 to all participants); the object is Size 3 or larger (+2 to all participants); the object is currently stowed in a pocket, bag or backpack (-4 to all participants); the cell has previously witnessed the object or a similar object at work (+3 to secondary actors); the cell has never seen the object or a similar object (-3 to secondary actors); attacking an object is always considered a specified target (-1 to -3 to secondary actor, depending on Size of the object); normal ranged and close combat modifiers also apply.

Roll Results

Dramatic Failure: The cell both identifies the wrong object as a magical device and the attempt to neutralize the item is detected. As a result of their bumbling, for the remainder of the scene each hunter involved in the Tactic has their Initiative score reduced by five.

Failure: The attempt to neutralize the magical item fails.

Success: The attempt to steal or neutralize the magical item succeeds. The target is temporarily stymied by the loss of the magical device and may take no actions the following turn.

Exceptional Success: As above except that the primary actor moves to the top of the Initiative order for the remainder of the scene.

To Purchase: 16 Practical Experience, 13 for Null Mysteriis, 11 for Aegis Kai Doru.

Divide and Conquer

Prerequisites: *All:* Wits 2, Manipulation 2. *Partial (3):* Stealth 2. *Partial (1):* Expression 3 (primary actor).

Requires: 4; 5 or 6 participants grants the primary actor a +1 bonus, more than 7 imposes a -1 penalty to all participants.

Dice Pool: *Primary:* Manipulation + Expression. *Secondary:* Dexterity + Stealth

Action: Instant

Description: While a hunter cell is a match (or so they hope) for a single werewolf, the shape-changing beasts rarely operate as individuals. More often than not werewolves run in packs, which tips the balance of power in the numbers game back towards the monsters. For most cells, facing off in a battle of even numbers with werewolves is a tall order. The trick is to pick them off one by one in fights where the superior numbers of the cell can even the odds. From a practical standpoint, the best way to accomplish this task is by keeping an eye on the creatures and seizing opportunities for attack as they present themselves. Once the beasts know they are under siege or during a battle that is already underway, separating a single werewolf from her pack becomes much more difficult. This Tactic aims to solve that particular dilemma.

The secondary actors hoot and holler at the pack, then scamper out of sight and hide allowing the beasts to charge past them. The primary actor, meanwhile, taunts and belittles a single member of the pack with the intention of focusing all of the creature's attention on him. In essence, the secondary actors distract the werewolves, save for the one targeted by the primary actor, by way of a feigned flight, moving them away from the primary actor. Secondary actors that fail their Stealth check may find their feigned flight becomes a real race for survival. This has no effect on the overall success of the Tactic as the werewolves are still moving away from their packmates. Once the secondary actors have managed to ditch their pursuers, they double-back and rejoin the primary actor.

A hunter cell suffers a cumulative -2 penalty each time this Tactic is used against the same pack, whether it be in the same battle or several weeks later. Werewolves are too clever to fall for the same trick over and over again. Other creatures that practice their depredations in groups can also fall victim to this Tactic.

Organizations: The Ashwood Abbey calls this Tactic "Wolfbait" and has members that practice insults and slurs to draw the ire of the werewolf to be singled out. The fact that the "bait" often suffers the same fate as a worm attached to a fishing hook simply adds to the excitement. With their inside appreciation for the application and leveraging of vice, the members of the Lucifuge also employ this Tactic to good effect.

Potential Modifiers: All secondary actors involved know the "Confuse the Scent" Tactic (+2 to secondary actors); Tactic is performed after dark (+1 to secondary actors); in a pre-prepared location (+2 to secondary actors); personal knowledge of the target (+2 to primary actor); performed in an unfamiliar location or in a wide open space (-3 to secondary actors).

Roll Results

Dramatic Failure: The werewolves decide they are more interested in the puny human insulting their packmate than the fleeing hunters, and they turn on him instead of chasing the other members of the cell.

Failure: The intended target ignores the insults and stays with her pack.

Success: The target werewolf is separated from her pack and the hunters that succeeded on their Stealth roll temporarily shake off pursuit. For each success gained past the first (the first success compensates for travel time), the cell has two turns to fight the werewolf that was separated from her pack. After the turns are up, the rest of the pack figures out they've been conned and enter the combat.

Exceptional Success: Even hunters that failed their Stealth roll go unnoticed by the werewolves as they rumble past hiding spots and all participants gain a +2 bonus to their attack rolls for the first turn of combat.

To Purchase: 14 Practical Experience, 11 Ashwood Abbey, 9 for the Lucifuge.

Domesticate

Prerequisites: *All:* Intelligence 2, Intimidation 1 *or* a Specialty in Psychology (in either Medicine or Academics). *Partial (1):* Manipulation 2, Persuasion 2, Animal Ken 2 (primary actor).

Requires: 2, maximum of 3 hunters at any one time; see below.

Dice Pool: *Primary:* Presence + Animal Ken (beast), Manipulation + Persuasion (man). *Secondary:* Wits + Expression (beast), Presence + Empathy (man).

Action: Extended and contested.

Description: Some hunter cells believe they have a moral compunction to at least attempt to rehabilitate the monsters they fight. Other cells look at the creatures as potential allies or subjects for experimentation. Regardless of the reasoning behind the use of this Tactic, every cell that employs it is after the same thing: a compliant, willing werewolf that is sympathetic to their goals. Kinder, gentler souls might refer to the process of turning a werewolf as brainwashing or even torture (Storytellers are left to determine if the methods used constitute a Morality sin), but most hunters are more interested in results than philosophical debate. Every convert to the cause is one less moldering body left to rot in a shallow, unmarked grave.

Werewolves are much more difficult to convert than most humans. Not only do werewolves recover from abuse much faster than humans, they can also attempt to cut deals with spirits for assistance. The location chosen to detain a werewolf is just as important as the methods used. A newly constructed building, set in an area that has recently undergone extensive development, is the best choice. For reasons unknown to most hunters, werewolves have a more difficult time attracting the attention of spirits in these kinds of locations. Detaining a werewolf is also a greater challenge than detaining a human. Because of their shapechanging ability and natural strength, werewolves can't simply be bound with rope or shackles (unless the cell also has a way of keeping the werewolf from shifting). Although it seems slightly cruel, the best method of detaining a werewolf is to lock them in a solidly-constructed, steel cage. A cage will hold the creature regardless of the form the werewolf takes and sturdy bars have a better chance of containing it. Hunters must also take the animalistic side of the werewolf into account. Werewolves aren't human (or are so ravaged by the lycanthropy disease they don't respond in the same way as humans) and the cell must overcome both the rational and instinctual halves of a werewolf's thought processes for total success.

Domesticating a werewolf begins by going to work on their bestial nature. The creature is taught obedience in the same way humans train animals. One

hunter (the primary actor) assumes the role of the alpha male. The rest of the cell defers to the wishes of the "alpha" whenever they are in the presence of the werewolf; reinforcing the alpha image. The werewolf is rewarded for good behavior with praise from the alpha and "treats" in the form of better quality food, creature comforts or entertainment in the form of access to a television and remote control. Similarly, the alpha punishes the werewolf for misbehaving with physical punishment (the werewolf might be zapped with a Taser or beaten), a reduction in food or creature comforts, while the alpha vocally rebukes the creature for its lack of discipline. Frenzies are dealt with by subjecting the werewolf to days of solitary confinement in a darkened cage with minimal and low quality food and water.

After the beast has been quelled, the cell goes to work on the man. At least two hunters can assist the alpha at this stage. The alpha talks with the werewolf, breaking down his self-esteem, then building it back up, acting friendly one moment and then growing violent the next. The werewolf is conditioned to accept the hunter's creed. The alpha asks questions about the beliefs of the werewolf and wrong answers are punished with mild physical punishment (no sense in provoking the creature's rage at this point) and humiliation mixed with a feigned concern for the well-being of the werewolf. The secondary actors stay in the background and lend support to whatever the primary actor is saying or doing. These question-and-answer sessions are bolstered by inducing fatigue, hunger and anxiety in the werewolf by disruptions to their sleeping schedule, cutting their allotment of food, and confusing their internal clock.

A roll for domestication is made once each day. The werewolf rolls Resolve + Stamina + Subterfuge and must meet or exceed the primary actor's total number of successes to resist domestication. The primary actor must achieve a number of successes equal to the subject's Resolve + Composure + Stamina.

Organizations: The Long Night uses this Tactic to bring converts to the fold. A werewolf that can be made to give up its brutal past can aid the compact in the future and is a beacon of hope in these troubled times. The Ascending Ones use their potions and Elixirs to expedite the process and sometimes use "domesticated" werewolves as trackers in their hunts.

Potential Modifiers: The werewolf has been subjected to the same kind of reprogramming in the past (+1 to the primary actor); the werewolf has been trained in techniques designed to resist mental coercion (-3 to all participants); the werewolf has been able to make contact with a spirit of at least middling

power (-2 to all participants); the werewolf isn't part of a pack (+2 to primary actor); the werewolf suffers from one or more derangements (+1 to all participants).

Roll Results

Dramatic Failure: If the werewolf suffers a dramatic failure at any point in the proceedings, he frenzies then reverts to his bestial nature for a number of hours equal to 10 – [Resolve + Composure]. When he recovers, he develops a mild derangement. If the primary actor suffers a dramatic failure, the cell believes the subject to be completely converted, when in fact no progress at all has been made.

Failure: No successes are accumulated toward the total. Additionally, the werewolf gains a +2 bonus to resist domestication the following day.

Success: Successes are accumulated toward the total. If the werewolf rolls more successes than the primary actor, the primary actor's successes are *not* counted toward the target number. That is, the primary actor only counts successes toward his total when his roll turns up as many or more successes than the werewolf does. If the primary actor achieves the total described above, the werewolf is brainwashed or domesticated. The werewolf must immediately roll Resolve + Composure. If this roll fails, the creature develops a mild derangement. Any member of the cell that participated in the domestication process gains a +3 bonus to any Social rolls made in future dealings with the converted werewolf. (Conversion doesn't necessarily mean slavish devotion, but it does indicate that the creature has been tricked into a kind of Stockholm Syndrome, acting favorably toward its new "pack" and "alpha.")

Exceptional Success: Considerable successes are accumulated. If the werewolf beats the primary actors's successes *and* achieves an exceptional success, successes equal to the subject's Resolve are *subtracted* from the primary actor's total. If the primary actor's successes equal or exceed the werewolf's *and* the primary actor achieves an exceptional success, the werewolf suffers a –3 penalty on his next resistance roll.

To Purchase: 13 Practical Experience, 10 for the Long Night, 8 for the Ascending Ones.

Effigy

Prerequisites: *All:* Intelligence 2, Presence 2, Occult 2 *or* Science 2. *Partial (1):* Crafts 1. *Partial (1):* Expression 2 (primary actor).

Requires: At least 3; additional hunters will be required to gain the attention of more powerful spirits.

Dice Pool: *Primary:* Presence + Expression. *Secondary:* Intelligence + Occult *or* Intelligence + Science.

Action: Instant

Description: The majority of the creatures that stalk humanity and are, in turn, stalked by hunters are corporeal in nature. Even an eight-foot tall mass of fur, muscle and rending talons can eventually be put down through purely physical means. Spirits, though, are harder to combat. Hunters can combat the influence of a spirit and hope to drive it off, but this is a time-consuming prospect without any real guarantee of success. Lacking the ability to reach into the spirit world, most hunters have no way of directly combating a spirit unless that spirit happens to be at a Locus and happens to materialize. This Tactic attempts to trick spirits into materializing at a time and place dictated by hunters, allowing them to bargain with or combat a spirit in the material realm.

To begin with, the cell must have at least a vague idea about the nature of the spirit they are targeting. This information can be most reliably gained through use of the "Resonance" Tactic, though painstaking research can also produce enough basic information to use. Once the cell has determined the basic nature of the spirit, they begin construction of an effigy that represents the nature of that spirit in physical form. Creation of the effigy is an extended Dexterity + Crafts action, with 10 successes minimum (note that this extended action is *not* part of the Tactic roll) and each roll equal to an hour. The more time and effort put into the creation of the effigy, the more effective it will be when used in the Tactic. The shape and materials used to create the effigy should reflect the nature of the spirit the cell is dealing with. An effigy created in the image of a murder spirit might contain bullets, knives, blood, and human flesh along with whatever materials are used to shape the effigy as a whole (clay, wood, etc.). Different hunter organizations will also put their own spin on the creation process: the Lucifuge might bake the base materials with Hellfire; the Ashwood Abbey might bathe the effigy in the not-so-fresh blood of a vampire; and the Cheiron Group might include medical waste and implant scraps to give their creation the semblance of life. Note that at least one member of the cell must be personally involved with the creation of the effigy to attune the thing to the cell.

When the cell has finished creation of the effigy, they transport it to the center of the spirit's influence and the Tactic begins. The secondary actors focus their attention on the effigy and speak aloud (almost like a chant) the qualities of the spirit. They concentrate on imagery in tune with the nature of the spirit while they speak and scatter sympathetic materials in the area directly around the effigy. Continuing with the murder spirit example, the secondary actors might

THE GOLDEN COW

A spirit that manifests in an effigy as the result of a successful use of the "Effigy" Tactic uses that effigy as an anchor to the material realm. The spirit is bound to the effigy for five minutes per successes gained on the Tactic roll. While bound, the spirit may not return to the spirit world and its power is slightly diminished. For as long as it remains bound to the effigy, the spirit's Attributes are reduced by three (to a minimum of one) and its Defense is halved (round up). Though the capacities of the spirit may be reduced while it is bound, its form is not. Bound spirits may manipulate the materials of the effigy to create a Size 6 body.

Even while bound, spirits are under no compulsion to obey the wishes of the cell and may decide to attack them or attempt to flee. Less aggressive spirits with the ability to communicate with humans may decide to discuss their situation with the cell before launching into an attack (or attempting to flee), opening the way for the cell to bargain with the spirit. If combat is initiated by either the spirit or the cell, the material body of the spirit may be wounded by ordinary weapons and those wounds will carry over to the actual Health (Corpus) of the spirit. Regardless of the materials used in the construction of the effigy, a bound spirit deals lethal damage in combat. If the bound spirit is killed it will discorporate in the usual manner, but will require twice the normal amount of time to pull itself back together.

every 10 successes gained in the construction of the effigy (+1 to all participants); the spirit has previously been bound (-5 to all participants).

Roll Results

Dramatic Failure: A different, more aggressive spirit takes this opportunity to materialize in the body of the effigy. Unlike the spirit for which it was intended, the effigy holds no power to bind the spirit (see sidebar) and it may manifest at full strength. This also has ruins the effigy.

Failure: The spirit doesn't respond to the Tactic and a new effigy must be constructed before repeating the attempt.

Success: The spirit hears the call of the cell and manifests in the effigy. See sidebar ("The Golden Cow") for rules governing a spirit in this form.

Exceptional Success: As above and the spirit is utterly bound to the effigy until it is either released by the cell or the effigy is destroyed (see "The Golden Cow" sidebar).

To Purchase: 16 Practical Experience, 13 for Null Mysteriis, 11 for Aegis Kai Doru.

My Brother's Keeper

Prerequisites: *All:* Resolve 2, Brawl 2 *or* Weaponry 2. *Partial (2):* Athletics 2. *Partial (1):* Expression 2 (primary actor)

Requires: 4; a maximum of 6 hunters may participate.

Dice Pool: *Primary:* Wits + Expression. *Secondary:* Strength + Brawl *or* Strength + Weaponry.

Action: Instant

Description: A large part of the success of a werewolf pack in battle results from the entirety of the pack acting as a group rather than individuals. The werewolves watch each other's backs in a fight and coordinate their movements so that if one of them is attacked the entire pack can respond. When a battle moves to close combat range, a hunter with a gun can be just as dangerous to his cell as he is to the monsters they fight. Reluctantly, hunters turn to melee weapons to reduce the chances of friendly fire. Taking a page from the monsters they fight, some hunter cells have begun to adopt forms of the pack tactics they've witnessed or, lacking such experience,

lay out press clippings of particularly brutal killings or clothing from murder victims. Meanwhile, the primary actor calls out directly to the spirit, asking it to manifest itself in the body of the effigy so that they might witness its glory in the flesh.

A modified version of this Tactic could also be used to combat ghosts or other *things* that lurk in Twilight.

Organizations: Aegis Kai Doru turns this Tactic into a full blown ritual, complete with chanting, incense and sacrificial offerings. The scientists of Null Mysteriis perform this Tactic like they would any other experiment; with practical efficiency. In place of the candles and other magical fripperies used by more mystically-inclined compacts, the scientists record the event with a battery of equipment designed to measure quantifiable evidence for future analysis.

Possible Modifiers: The cell knows the name of the spirit (+3 to all participants); the nature of the spirit has been identified with the "Resonance" Tactic (+2 to secondary actors); performed at a Locus (+2 to all participants); the cell has only very basic information about the nature of the spirit (-2 to secondary actors); the cell has successfully used this Tactic in the past (+1 to all participants); the cell has previously witnessed the materialized form of the spirit (+2 to secondary actors); for have simply learned to rely on each other for physical and moral support.

When the call to use this Tactic is made, the cell closes ranks into a loose combat formation with the primary actor in the center, behind the lines. They stand near enough to each other to provide support and far enough apart to reduce the chance of accidents. The primary actor doesn't engage directly in battle, but relies on his cell (the secondary actors) to defend him from harm and allow him to direct the fight. He calls out changes in formation to adapt to enemy movements and shouts encouragement to his cell to boost their spirits. Performed correctly, My Brother's Keeper allows the cell to defend each other from attacks, respond to threats with alacrity, and reinforce the morale of the cell as a whole. (If the primary actor is attacked directly, this Tactic ends and must be reattempted.)

Organizations: Union members understand well the advantages of working as a team. Whether the job is fixing an engine, assembly parts on a factory line, or fighting the nasties that threaten their families, these hunters function as part of a whole. The Malleus Maleficarum relies on the discipline and resolve of their members to carry them through a fight just as much as they do the Benedictions they've been gifted with. Many members of the Shadow Congregation are powerful orators and inspire their comrades in the heat of battle with fiery condemnations of their foes, Bible quotations, and reminders that they serve the will of God.

Potential Modifiers: The cell has successfully performed this Tactic in the past against the same or similar opponents (+1 to all participants); the primary actor has military training (+2 to primary actor); poor visibility or footing makes holding the formation more difficult (-2 to all participants); the cell holds a prepared defensive position (+3 to all participants); the cell holds a position naturally inclined towards defense, i.e. top of a hill, narrow alley (+2 to all participants); the primary actor is wounded during the battle (-1 to the primary actor for each point of lethal damage taken).

Roll Results

Dramatic Failure: The formation crumbles under an unexpected attack and may not be reformed this scene. The Initiative modifier of each participant is reduced by three as they scramble to recover.

Failure: The formation fails to hold up under attack, though the cell may attempt to reform at a -4 penalty (this includes the -3 penalty for repeating a Tactic) next turn.

Success: The cell forms up and responds efficiently to the calls of the leader. Each participant gains a bonus to their Initiative equal to successes gained on the primary actor's roll, and a bonus to Defense equal to *half* of the primary actor's successes (round down). They also gain +4 to any attempt to resist mental compulsions of any type (including Lunacy caused by a werewolf's Predatory Aura) for the remainder of the scene or until they consciously break formation.

Exceptional Success: As above, except that all participants gain a +1 bonus to any attack roll for the rest of the scene and are wholly immune to the fear caused by mental compulsions.

To Purchase: 16 Practical Experience, 13 for the Union, 10 for Malleus Maleficarum.

Resonance

Prerequisites: *All:* Resolve 2, Science 2. *Partial (1):* Academics 2 *or* Computer 2. *Partial (1):* Science 3.

Requires: 2 or more

Dice Pool: *Primary:* Intelligence + Science. *Secondary:* Resolve + Composure.

Action: Extended (each roll represents one turn of scrutiny)

Description: Though similar to the "Measurements" Tactic (see **Hunter: The Vigil**, p. 225), Resonance attempts to gather useful information about spiritual rather than physical entities. Data is collected in many of the same ways as for the "Measurements" Tactic, but also includes more pseudo-scientific equipment such as ghost-lenses, Kirlian photography, and live electronic voice phenomenon playback. The cell also monitors changes in ambient temperature, erratic behavior in participants and notes anything that seems out of place, unusual or downright bizarre for the location. Resonance is also useful for identifying the type of spirit possessing a human, determining the qualities of a Locus, or recognizing the influence a spirit has over a specific area.

In essence, the hunters are attempting to identify trace elements of the influence a spirit has over a place or; if dealing with a manifested spirit, hunters are looking for clues about the nature of the spirit gathered from observations about its appearance, activities and behavior. Storytellers will have to decide how to describe the information gathered. A spirit of mourning that haunts a cemetery incorporeally might register as a quiet sobbing on the EVP playback, arouse feelings of soul-crushing loss in the hunters, and cause even freshly picked flowers laid on gravestones to wither. A manifested anger spirit might appear agitated, kicking trash or barging through whatever is in its path, and people it passes might suddenly begin to fight for no apparent reason.

The secondary actors skulk in the background, taking readings, running cameras, and noting significant phenomena. The primary actor interprets this data as it comes in, making adjustments to the machinery, if any, or giving instructions to the secondary actors. Measurements can be sustained over a number of turns, for as long as the secondary actors keep their cool under the pressure. Simply standing in the influence of an aroused spirit can be unnerving, especially if that spirit focuses its influence on one of the cell. In the case of a manifested spirit, the Storyteller may call for Wits + Stealth rolls to avoid the attention of the spirit in addition to Resolve + Composure rolls. Data can continue to be collected as long as at least one secondary actor and the primary actor remain on the scene and are able to focus on their work. This Tactic not only relies on the composure and perceptive capabilities of a cell but also on their equipment. To successfully conduct this Tactic, the cell must have the proper gear for the job.

Organizations: Null Mysteriis takes credit for the creation of this Tactic and it's hard to argue with its claim. Task Force: VALKYRIE uses the Tactic in its intelligence-gathering activities.

Potential Modifiers: The cell has previously dealt with spirits on two or more separate occasions (+2 to all participants); extreme temperature, cold or hot (-2 to all participants); at least an hour of prep time in the area (+3 to primary actor); state-of-the-art equipment (+1 to +3 to primary actor); sub-par or outdated equipment (-1 to −3 to primary actor); spirit has actively engaged the hunters (-2 to primary actor).

Roll Results

Dramatic Failure: The data collected is dangerously misleading. Assumptions based on the data collected lead to the cell entirely misinterpreting the nature of the spirit. Any future attempts to communicate, bargain with or combat the spirit based on the data collected suffers a -5 penalty.

Failure: No relevant data is collected. The data might be redundant, or maybe a power hiccup prevented the data from being stored.

Success: Data on the creature or phenomenon is collected. The hunters can later analyze the data (this requires at least three hours of study); after which each of the participants may make either an Intelligence + Science *or* an Intelligence + Occult roll to make conclusions about the nature of the spirit. Any future attempts to communicate, bargain with, or combat the spirit based on the data collected gains a +2 bonus.

Exceptional Success: No additional benefit is gained beyond the number of successes rolled. If an exceptional success is rolled to interpret the data collected, the cell may be able to make accurate guesses about the ban of the spirit.

To Purchase: 14 Practical Experience, 11 for Null Mysteriis, 9 for Task Force: VALKYRIE.

Roadkill

Prerequisites: *All:* Composure 2, Dexterity 2. *Partial (1):* Drive 2 (primary actor), *Partial (1):* Athletics 2.

Requires: 2; 3 or 4 hunters grant a +1 bonus to secondary actors, more than 5 imposes a -3 penalty on all participants.

Dice Pool: *Primary:* Dexterity + Drive. *Secondary:* Manipulation + Dexterity

Action: Instant

Description: Fully transformed, a werewolf in bestial hybrid form stands seven or eight feet tall and weighs upwards of 400 lbs: any creature that massive gains serious momentum as it charges towards its next victim, momentum that isn't easy to redirect on short notice. Some hunter cells have attempted to take advantage of this momentum by stringing wire or other impediments in the path of a charging werewolf and waiting for the creature to clothesline itself. Although the idea has merit, it is rarely as effective as the hunters had hoped it would be. Werewolves have keen enough senses that they always have an outside chance of noticing and dodging the trap. Even if the monster doesn't notice the line, it is very difficult to securely anchor a thin enough wire that might avoid detection yet will hold up under the strain of a charging werewolf. The solution to the problem is to hit a werewolf with an object both solid enough to damage the creature and to provide protection for the operator. After some debate, the hunter cell that first devised this Tactic decided to use a truck.

The secondary actors gain the attention of a werewolf through whatever means are at hand, positioning themselves in such a way as to screen the vehicle driven by the primary actor. This can be accomplished by standing at the end of an alley, near a side road that is screened by foliage or even on a street corner where the sight of an oncoming vehicle wouldn't seem unusual. Attracting the attention of a werewolf can usually be easily enough accomplished by shooting at the creature, though such attacks aren't really intended to seriously wound their foe. The secondary actors then stand their ground as the werewolf charges them, waiting until the very last second before they leap out of harm's way. While the hunters that are acting as bait draw their target towards them, the primary actor puts pedal to metal and drives his truck as fast as he can directly towards his friends. If everything goes exactly right (the timing must be almost perfect) the truck will plow into the werewolf just as the other hunters dodge out of the way. Having an additional hunter

VEHICULAR ASSAULT

The rules on p. 144 in the **World of Darkness Rulebook** state that hitting someone with a vehicle results in points of bashing damage: this was incorrect. As stated in the **World of Darkness Rulebook** errata (which you can find at the White Wolf website, www.white-wolf.com), hitting someone with a vehicle results in *lethal* damage. Ouch.

act as a spotter increases the chances of timing the Tactic correctly. Though not technically part of the Tactic, the spotter can give the driver a heads up when he should start the truck moving.

Even though the original cell decided to use a truck, other solid vehicles can easily be substituted. It should also go without saying that this Tactic works just as well against vampires and slashers as it does werewolves; few creatures can easily shrug off vehicular assault.

Rules for damage caused to both vehicle and target can be found in the **World of Darkness Rulebook**, p. 144.

Organizations: The Long Night is always eager to find new tools to use in its crusade. The last thing more than one werewolf has seen has been lights in the shape of the cross on the grill of a truck. The time-honored tradition of running the enemy over with a heavy object is gleefully practiced by Task Force: VALKYRIE.

Potential Modifiers: Treacherous driving surface (-2 to primary actor); spotter for the driver (+2 to primary actor); unstable or slippery footing (-1 to secondary actors); poor or partial concealment of vehicle (-2 to all participants); full concealment of vehicle and/or background noises to cover the sound of the vehicle (+2 to all participants).

Roll Results

Dramatic Failure: The werewolf manages to halt before being stuck by the vehicle and the secondary actors may be distracted by the creature's sudden stop. Each secondary actor must succeed at a Resolve + Composure roll or find themselves on the receiving end of the vehicle. The driver of the truck is also likely to be distracted and must succeed at a vehicle control roll (see the **World of Darkness Rulebook**, p. 39) with a -3 penalty or crash.

Failure: The werewolf manages to halt before being struck by the vehicle. The secondary actors manage to get out of the path of the vehicle, but the driver must succeed at a vehicle control roll or crash.

Success: The werewolf looks up just in time to get a face full of truck. The secondary actors succeed at throwing themselves clear and the driver maintains control of the vehicle. Assuming the werewolf is still in a condition to fight after being struck by the vehicle, it is placed dead last in the Initiative order for the rest of the scene.

Exceptional Success: In addition to the above effects from a success, the werewolf is automatically knocked out by the collision (see the **World of Darkness Rulebook**, p. 168).

To Purchase: 14 Practical Experience, 11 for the Long Night, 9 for Task Force: VALKYRIE.

Silver Bullet

Prerequisites: *All:* Dexterity 2 *or* Strength 2, Firearms 1 *or* Weaponry 1. *Partial (1):* Crafts 2.

Requires: 4; up to 6 grants a +1 bonus per extra hunter to the primary actor, 7 or more impose a -3 penalty on all participants.

Dice Pool: *Primary:* Dexterity + Firearms *or* Strength + Weaponry. *Secondary:* Dexterity + Firearms *or* Strength + Weaponry.

Action: Instant

Description: Nearly anyone with even the slightest amount of occult knowledge can tell you that silver is the bane of werewolves. Theories abound as to the reason why this is so. Null Mysteriis theorizes that the dominant gene responsible for lycanthropy also carries with it an extreme allergy to silver. The Malleus Maleficarum believes that the type of demon that possesses humans to create a werewolf is unable to stand the holy purity of the metal. Regardless of the reason why, the fact is that nothing pains a werewolf like silver. The monsters are fully cognizant of this weakness and will flee from those who wield silver weapons or attempt to deprive a hunter the use of that weapon. Of course, hunters can't just stroll down to the local gun shop and buy silver bullets, and finding pure silver melee weaponry is even more difficult. Each cell must have at least one member that can work the metal into ammunition or other weapons (thus the Crafts 2 requirement).

Unlike the stories, a single silver bullet or wound from a silver dagger is unlikely to kill a werewolf. Given the creature's tendency to flee or react violently to the presence of silver, use of such special weaponry results in fewer confirmed kills than might be expected. Certainly a werewolf will suffer a serious wound or two during a battle with a silver-wielding hunter, but most of the monsters are too clever to stand and fight when faced with silver weaponry. The Silver Bullet Tactic coordinates the attacks of the entire cell into a flashing ring of silver death. No matter which direction the werewolf turns he is confronted by silver.

The secondary actors spread out and surround the target, attempting to cut off possible avenues of escape. They cut, slice and menace the werewolf with their silver weaponry, slowly herding the creature into position. As the creature's desperation to escape reaches a climax, the ring parts slightly, offering the illusion of withdrawal. When the werewolf moves into the gap, the primary actor steps forward and delivers a single, brutal attack.

Organizations: The Malleus Maleficarum uses weapons of silver to drive the demons possessing werewolves from their host body. It is lamentable that the human host rarely survives such treatment and the Shadow Congregation hopes the tainted souls of the possessed might be cleansed by use of the pure metal. The Loyalists of Thule have often found that the easiest way to part werewolves from their treasures is to take said treasures by force. The Silver Bullet is the ultimate expression of that philosophy.

Potential Modifiers: Apply the usual modifiers for ranged combat to all participants where appropriate.

Roll Results

Dramatic Failure: Unlike normal attacks, this Tactic can result in a dramatic failure. If firearms are used, the hunters manage to catch themselves in their own crossfire. Roll five dice of lethal damage against every participant. If melee weapons are used the hunters manage to get in each other's way and chaos ensues. Roll three dice of lethal damage against every participant and roll five dice of damage directly against the Structure of the weapons they carry. The werewolf remains unharmed.

Failure: The werewolf manages to dodge every attack or evade every shot.

Success: Damage dealt by the primary actor causes an automatic number of wounds (beyond those rolled by him) equal to the number of secondary actors that succeeded on their own roll.

Exceptional Success: No additional benefit is gained beyond the number of successes rolled.

To Purchase: 13 Practical Experience, 10 for the Loyalists of Thule, 8 for Malleus Maleficarum.

Thin the Herd

Prerequisites: *All:* Strength 2, Subterfuge 2, Weaponry 1. *Partial (1):* Expression 2 (secondary actor).

Requires: 3; more than 6 hunters imposes a -3 penalty to the secondary actor's roll.

Dice Pool: *Primary:* Strength + Weaponry (or another appropriate attack roll). *Secondary:* Manipulation + Subterfuge

Action: Instant

Description: Wolves instinctively seek out weak and lame members of a herd to attack and werewolves, for all their greater intellect, have the same basic instinct. When a hunter trips and falls down or seems to be favoring one leg, the predator instinct of a werewolf is to bring down that hunter and thin the herd.

This Tactic works a little differently than others in that it has one secondary actor and several primary actors. Thin the Herd begins when the secondary actor pretends to trip and fall or feigns some other weakness intended to trick a werewolf into committing himself to what he believes will be a killing blow, while her companions sham concern over her plight. If the werewolf takes the bait, the primary actors (the rest of the cell) take advantage of the distraction to attack the werewolf while he is vulnerable.

Vampires can be tricked into becoming overeager for a taste of blood through use of this Tactic. A weak or disabled opponent is nearly as attractive to them as it is to werewolves.

Organizations: It's safe to assume that an average member of Network 0 has probably watched more than his share of horror movies. With all the examples of heroines tripping over roots or stumbling up stairs, their use of this Tactic isn't a big surprise. The Cheiron Group, on the other hand, finds it easier to harvest bits and pieces of their victims once said victim is off balance.

Potential Modifiers: The werewolf has previously witnessed use of this Tactic (-3 to all participants); the hunter is naturally weak or sickly looking (+2 to secondary actor); narrow confines (-2 all participants); werewolf is alone (+1 to all participants).

Roll Results

Dramatic Failure: The werewolf isn't fooled by the feint and the secondary actor *really* does fall down, losing her Defense for the turn and is considered prone (see the **World of Darkness Rulebook**, p. 165).

Failure: The werewolf isn't fooled by the feint and may act normally.

Success: The werewolf is completely fooled by the feint and loses his Defense in his eagerness to attack. The primary actors gain a bonus to their attack rolls equal to the number of successes gained by the secondary actor, but each primary actor suffers a penalty to their Defense rating equal to the bonus gained (similar to the overextension suffered from an all-out attack).

Exceptional Success: The werewolf is not only fooled by the feint but trips himself and is considered prone for the following turn as well as losing his Defense.

To Purchase: 15 Practical Experience, 12 for Network Zero, 10 for the Cheiron Group

New Traits

Below you'll find new traits available to hunter characters. These traits are, for the most part, geared toward combating werewolves or spirits.

Merits

What follows are a number of new Merits available to hunter characters.

Kin (•••)

Effect: Werewolves start out life as ordinary people. Whether they later become werewolves through magic ritual, a pact with Satan or because of an inherited genetic abnormality is open to debate, and different hunters have different opinions. It certainly seems likely that some people are predisposed towards lycanthropy, perhaps as the result of a curse that strikes every seventh child. A character with the Kin Merit was born carrying the legacy of lycanthropy in his blood, even though that legacy never came to fruition. Because of this legacy, werewolves respond slightly more favorably to the character than they do to regular humans and the character shares some of this empathy. The character gains a +2 bonus to all Social rolls in his dealings with werewolves, gains the benefit of the Unseen Sense Merit applying specifically to werewolves (see the **World of Darkness Rulebook**, p. 109) and receives a +3 bonus to resist the effects of Lunacy.

Drawback: Mortals with this Merit are typically viewed as potential breeding stock by werewolves and will have to deal with potential suitors at some point. Depending on the werewolf involved, the suit may be presented to the character as a practical arrangement, take the shape of a brief love affair or – and this happens with an alarming regularity – the character may simply be dragged off in the middle of the night to fulfill his "duties." Even if the werewolves aren't interested in propagating the species, they still might hang around just to see if the curse ever fully kicks in. This possibility could haunt the hunter. Might he become what he hunts? If other hunters become aware of the character's background they might be leery of him as well. In addition, the hunter suffers a -1 Social penalty when dealing with normal humans (including most other hunters).

Natural Medium (•••)

Prerequisite: Presence •••

Effect: You've heard the voices ever since you were a kid. You remember the first time you *really* tuned in on them was during a long, boring car trip.

The whispers told you horrible secrets and later that night came the nightmares. Crying and terrified, you told your parents about the things you heard and they took you to see a doctor. Years of pills and psychological treatment didn't make the voices go away, but you learned to pretend they did, just like you learned to stifle your screams and hide your tears after another nightmare.

Spirits are kept locked away from the material realm in the spirit world. From that strange and unruly place they exert their will, influencing mortals to act in ways similar to the nature of the spirit. Every now and then a human is born that shines out through the thin membrane that separates the worlds, drawing the attention of the spirits. People born with this gift (or curse) are sometimes called shamans or witch doctors. Many modern spiritualists prefer the term medium. Eager to more directly influence the realms of flesh, the spirits congregate around these people and speak to them through the barrier. The more attention the medium pays to the spirits, the more excited the spirits become and the more they communicate and work to exert their influence over her.

A character with this Merit instinctively understands the language used by spirits and, by concentrating and spending a point of Willpower, can project her thoughts into the spirit world to commune with its denizens. The character also receives the Unseen Sense Merit applying specifically to spirits (see the **World of Darkness Rulebook**, p. 109) and is immune to possession by spirits (though the medium may voluntarily allow herself to be possessed). Exactly how one becomes a medium is something of a mystery. Each medium has a different theory or story that could possibly explain their gift. Some mediums were born with a caul over their face, some developed their ability after serious head trauma, and a few mediums have cancerous growths in their brains. Whatever the cause, the end result is the same.

Drawback: Each time the medium uses her ability to speak with spirits, she excites the spirits that respond. Until the next sunrise, the spirits direct their influence at the medium, attempting to overload her senses and possess her. The character can attempt to resist these influences by rolling Resolve + Composure – the Resistance of the most potent spirit with whom she has recently communicated. If the roll succeeds, the character experiences uncomfortable lurch-

MENTAL FLAW: NIGHTMARES

Some people are naturally predisposed towards nightmares, perhaps as a result of events they have witnessed or just as the result of a weak psyche. People with this Flaw dread the hours they must give over to sleep and do so as little as possible. Each time the character beds down for the night she must roll Resolve + Composure. With success, the character manages not to dream at all and regains the normal point of Willpower. If the roll fails, the character is plagued by nightmares and doesn't gain the benefits of a peaceful night's rest. Storytellers should feel free to modify the roll based on elements such as the Morality rating of the character, derangements, recent events, or use of sleeping aids.

es of sensation and emotion until the next sunrise, but otherwise suffers no ill effects. If the roll is failed, the character is subjected to the Mental Flaw: Nightmares (see sidebar) the next time she sleeps and is considered to have automatically failed the roll to resist.

Null (••••)

Effect: Because of an accident of birth, ancient family curse, or blessing from a higher power, your character is surrounded by an aura that is antithetical to spirits and spiritual energy. Spirits don't like being near you and will go out of their way to avoid contact with the character. Simply visiting a Locus is enough to temporarily shut off the flow of Essence from that place while you remain present. Werewolves can sense the unnatural disruption of spiritual energy caused by proximity to your character and they have a harder time using their magical rites and abilities with you around.

The character is completely immune to possession or influence by spirits. The aura of spiritual null extends for 10 yards in every direction around the character. Spirits prefer not to deal with the character if they can possibly avoid it, which gives the character a +1 to Intimidation rolls made against spirits. Spirits also suffer a -5 penalty on any attempt to materialize within the aura (this includes attempts to summon or force spirits to manifest), except at a Locus, where the penalty is reduced to -3. Werewolves within the aura must spend twice the amount of Essence normally required to perform a ritual or activate a Dominance that requires expenditure.

Characters with the Null Merit are something of an aberration. Every attempt made to quantify or reproduce the phenomenon has, thus far, met with failure. One possible explanation is that Null characters represent a sort of balancing force to the spirit world. It is possible that these characters exist to help maintain the separation between worlds, their mere presence acting to reinforce the barrier. Organizations like the Cheiron Group and the Loyalists of Thule are very interested in finding a way to intentionally create Null humans. *Available at character creation only or with Storyteller approval.*

Drawback: The character suffers a -2 penalty to all Social rolls (excluding Intimidation) when dealing with werewolves or spirits. This penalty is extended to any other hunter that attempts to peaceably contact or negotiate with werewolves or spirits while standing in the aura of the character.

Equipment

No serious hunter ever leaves the house without his gear. It might be packed in a duffle bag or stowed in the trunk, but everything will be primed and ready to go. The Vigil is a way of life and hunters that aren't prepared don't last long.

Bear Mace

Durability 1, Size 1, Structure 2, Cost •

Standard Mace is an effective, non-lethal deterrent against human predators, but less so against a snarling seven-foot tall mass of muscle. Marketed mainly in Alaska or other areas where bears are commonly found, Bear Pepper Mace features a higher concentration of the active ingredients found in standard Mace. Packaged in slightly larger bottles than the regular stuff, Bear Pepper Mace can still be sprayed with one hand. Developed for use against animals that are dangerous up close, Bear Pepper Mace has a maximum range of 20 feet. Each bottle contains enough Mace for five uses before running dry. A Dexterity + Athletics roll is made at a -2 penalty to hit the target at 10-20 feet or a -1 penalty at less than 10 feet.

Used against werewolves or other creatures Size 7 or greater, Bear Pepper Mace imposes the same penalties as standard Mace (see the **World of Darkness Rulebook**, p. 140). In addition to the standard penalties, if employed against human sized targets (Size 5) or smaller, Bear

Pepper Mace has a chance of inducing anaphylactic shock unless the target succeeds on a Stamina + Composure roll. Victims of anaphylactic shock can be stabilized enough for transport to emergency facilities with an Intelligence + Medicine roll. If the victim isn't stabilized within 10 minutes of going into shock or doesn't receive emergency care within an hour of being stabilized, the victim is likely to die or (at the very least) suffer serious brain damage from lack of oxygen.

Caltrops

Durability 3, Size 1, Structure 4, Cost •

A werewolf in any form other than human is a great, slavering beast filled with rage and the urge to kill. They are tireless hunters with fearsome natural weaponry and can literally tear a man limb from limb. Thing is, in non-human forms, a werewolf can't really wear shoes, can he? Hence, caltrops.

"Caltrop" is a broad label that can be applied to any object with four points that is constructed so that no matter how it lands, one point always faces up. Originally used to deter cavalry or poorly-equipped infantry, caltrops still see use today for puncturing the

tires of wheeled enemy vehicles. Employed against werewolves, hunters scatter caltrops behind them to discourage pursuit or spread them around an area to assist in defense. Anyone that steps on a caltrop suffers one point of lethal damage and has their Speed reduced by half until the caltrop is removed. Stepping on multiple caltrops incurs multiple wounds, but Speed remains halved until all caltrops are removed.

If caltrops damage a car's tires, the tires may rupture (see "Tire Statistics" on p. 142 of the **World of Darkness Rulebook**). Against vehicle tires, a horse's hooves or anything with a Size of 8 or greater, the Damage trait of caltrops is 2(L); they do two automatic points of lethal damage, and two dice are rolled for additional damage. Caltrop damage automatically bypasses one point of an item's Durability. If done to a person or animal, caltrops are considered to have Armor Piercing 1.

Caltrops are easily constructed given a supply of pointy objects and a soldering gun. Though attempts have been made, silver is just too soft a metal out of which to make structurally sound caltrops, though coating iron or steel caltrops with silver plating does give them a bit of an extra sting against werewolves (add an additional lethal wound, cost increases by •). Assuming they notice an area is strewn with caltrops, characters can attempt to pick their way through safely with a Dexterity + Athletics roll. This roll suffers a cumulative -1 penalty for every three caltrops in a 3'x 3' area.

Man Catcher

Durability 1, Size 4, Structure 5, Cost • •

A man catcher is a type of polearm that is topped with a metal ring or a rope noose. The metal ring variant features a simple device constructed from a section cut out of the ring (large enough to fit a neck) then reattached with a hinge and a spring. The man catcher is pushed against a victim's neck and the section that was cut out gives way under the weight of the pressure before snapping back into place and trapping the head of the victim. The rope noose variant is looped over the head, arm or leg of the victim and the rope (which is loosely attached to the pole with rings) pulled taut. Occasionally, the metal variant will also be fitted with spikes on the inside of the ring to dissuade a captive from struggling. Both variants are used to capture a target through non-lethal force. The military use of man catchers mainly faded away by the end of the 18th century, but modern hunters have rediscovered the effectiveness of the weapon when they seek to capture, rather than kill.

Using a man catcher against a live opponent requires a grapple roll, except the attacker must use Strength + Weaponry. The usual modifiers for attacking a specific target apply, as well as the Defense of the victim, but any

Armor is ignored. With success on the roll, the hunter has managed to capture the head, leg or arm of his target and the victim is considered grappled. Victims at the receiving end of a grapple from a man catcher may not attempt to reverse the grapple, though they can try to break free (see the **World of Darkness Rulebook**, p. 157) at an additional -2 penalty. Alternately, the subject may try to break or damage the pole. Assume the man catcher to have Durability 2 and Structure 5 for the purposes of taking damage. If a cell manages to loop a man catcher around all four limbs and the head of a target, that target is considered immobilized and helpless.

Pit Trap

Cost: • •

When werewolves shift to the forms most suited for battle, they gain muscle mass to go along with razor-sharp teeth and claws. Most of the time the extra mass gained by a werewolf after a transformation works in their favor, but clever hunters have found ways to turn it against them. A floor that will easily bear the weight of an adult human can sometimes give way under the increased weight of the werewolf, especially if it has been rigged that way.

Construction of a pit trap requires advance preparation. Under the direction of the primary actor, who plays the part of foreman, the hunters work to carefully weaken select floorboards and support beams. Prepared properly, the floor will still handle the weight of a single person, but will buckle and fold under the weight of a werewolf in bestial hybrid or near-wolf form. Depending on the aims of the cell, the area the werewolf falls into might simply be a cellar they have sealed off from the rest of the house or it could be lined with sharpened stakes (two points of lethal damage for every two yard fallen). Especially ambitious hunters might even go so far as to tip stakes with silver points (improves damage to aggravated against werewolves). If the aim of the hunter cell is containment, it must ensure the "pit" a werewolf falls into is deep enough so the creature can't simply jump out and constructed of materials that keep the werewolf from climbing the sides.

Alternately, a pit trap may be bought as security for a Safehouse at two dots for a basic pit, three dots for a stake-lined pit or four dots for a silver-tipped stake-lined pit.

Dice Pool: *Primary:* Intelligence + Crafts. *Secondary:* Dexterity + Crafts.

Action: Extended teamwork roll. The target number for the extended action is 10 successes and each roll is equal to half an hour.

Possible Modifiers: House is old or poorly maintained (-1 to all participants); house is new or properly maintained (+1 to all participants); the cell has blueprints of

WOLFSBANE

Wolfsbane, properly named *Aconitum*, has for centuries been associated with werewolves. Depending on which story you hear, Wolfsbane is alternately the cause or the cure for lycanthropy. Separating truth from myth is always difficult when dealing with unnatural forces and a fair number of hunter cells have experimented with the herb in an attempt to ascertain a use for it in their Vigil. Dried Wolfsbane is easily acquired by visiting any craft store that keeps a variety of dried plants in stock. Identifying the herb in the wild requires an Intelligence + Science roll. Different cells have used the herb in different, sometimes seemingly contradictory, ways which leads scientific observers (like Null Mysteriis) to speculate that there must be extenuating circumstances involved with either the collection, preparation, or uses of Wolfsbane that account for the disparity. Presented below are some of the rumors floating about hunter society about Wolfsbane:

- When left to dry, crushed, detoxified, and steeped into a tea, Wolfsbane helps to fight the feelings of terror associated with witnessing a werewolf in bestial hybrid form.

- If ingested during a full moon, even unknowingly, *Aconitum* causes lycanthropy.

- Werewolves are attracted to the smell of Wolfsbane, even though it acts like a deadly poison to them just like humans. Some cells claim to have used the scent of Wolfsbane to lure packs into ambushes. Other cells claim to have been ambushed while harvesting the herb, almost like the werewolves were protecting it.

- Hiding the flowers of the plant about your person tricks a werewolf into believing a human is one of them. The creatures' sense of smell seems to be tricked by the scent given off by the plant.

- Wolfsbane is considered a sacred flower of the moon-spirit that blesses werewolves with their powers. Any werewolf that intentionally destroys an *Aconitum* plant is cursed by the moon-spirit for their arrogance and becomes like the ravening beasts of legend that can only transform at the full moon and hunger for flesh.

the house (+1 to primary actor); any hunter involved has the Giant Merit (-1 to all participants); majority of the house features hardwood floors (+1 to all participants).

Roll Results

Dramatic Failure: All progress on the project is lost and part of the floor gives in prematurely. Alternately, the Storyteller might rule that one of the characters accidentally falls through the floor while testing it.

Failure: The hunters fail to make progress on the project. If three or more failures are rolled during the extended action, the Storyteller might allow potential victims of the trap a reflexive Wits + Composure roll to notice the shoddy workmanship and avoid that area of the floor.

Success: The hunters make progress on their project. If the total number of successes exceeds the target number, any person (or creature) in excess of 300 lbs that steps on the weakened section of floor falls directly through it.

Exceptional Success: No additional benefits are gained beyond the number of successes rolled.

Silver Weaponry (per item)

Cost +• per Size category (or Cost +• per 10 bullets)

Proof that not every legend is useless, silver weaponry effectively closes the gap between the combat capabilities of hunters and those of werewolves. The touch of silver is deathly cold to werewolves, leaving welts and burns on exposed skin. Wounds caused by silver burn the creatures, resulting in wounds that they find more difficult to heal. Werewolves suffer an aggravated wound any time they take damage from a silver weapon that would normally cause lethal damage.

Other than non-functional, ornamental pieces, finding a weapon made of pure silver isn't easy. Instead of ordering one or picking up silver ammo at a store, hunter cells generally have to make the items themselves. Creation of silver weapons or ammunition is an extended Dexterity + Crafts roll that follows the rules found in the **World of Darkness Rulebook**, p. 58.

Silver is a soft metal. Blades made of silver are less effective than those made of steel. Because of this, silver weapons inflict a -1 modifier to attacks and only have a Durability 2, as opposed to steel, which has a Durability of 3 or more. When used to make bullets, silver incurs a -1 penalty to the weapon's Damage.

NEW PROFESSION: OUTDOORSMAN

AIN'T A CRITTER ALIVE THAT GOES ON TWO LEGS OR FOUR I CAN'T TRACK.

Outdoorsmen live their lives and make their livings in the great outdoors. Their hearts are captivated by the wilderness and the animals that bring the wilds to life. They disdain people who live their lives in cages of wood and brick, oblivious to the wonders that surround them. Outdoorsmen that hunt animals with rifles rather than cameras are affirming their place as the deadliest of natural predators, even if that knowledge is subconscious.

Outdoorsman can take up the Vigil for any number of reasons. The big game hunter might seek out deadlier prey while a park ranger might find mutilated corpses with wounds that don't match those caused by a bear, no matter what the ranger puts in his report. While searching for new sights to show the tourists, a trail guide might stumble across one of the sacred places of the werewolves and barely escape with his life. No matter how they are drawn into the hunt, an outdoorsman keeps the Vigil because they are affronted by the very existence of the creatures they battle. Werewolves have no place in nature and, in the weather-beaten eyes of an Outdoorsman, shouldn't be allowed to sully the wilderness they so love.

Background: Most Outdoorsman fell in love with nature at an early age, perhaps because their parents were also the outdoor types or simply because something in the wilderness called to them. A few people join this Profession later in life, usually after a life-changing event like a near-terminal illness or some other brush with death. Outdoorsman can come from any walk of life and, depending on their background, approach their treks through nature in different ways. The child of neo-hippies that journeys through the forest with a cell phone and digital camera doesn't love that woodland scene any less fervently than the child of mountain folk that took his first steps among the pines and learned to shoot to feed his family.

In game terms, Outdoorsman often have high Stamina as a result of trudging through underbrush and up and down hilly terrain. Depending on their motivations, outdoorsman can also have high Intelligence (those who study nature), Wits (explorers) or Dexterity (hunters) scores. Physical Attributes are usually the primary focus for Outdoorsmen with the least emphasis put on Social Attributes. Common Skills include Crafts, Science, Athletics, Firearms, Survival and Animal Ken. Other popular skills include Academics, Stealth, Weaponry and Expression. Danger Sense, Direction Sense, Iron Stamina and Strong Back are all reasonable Merits for this Profession.

Concepts: Eco-terrorist, eager big game hunter, earnest environmentalist, grizzled mountain man, manic biologist, mountain climber, park ranger, search and rescue, shifty poacher, Sherpa, survivalist nut, wildlife photographer.

Asset Skills: Survival and Animal Ken
- Enthusiast
- • Trail Guide
- • • Park Ranger
- • • • Big Game Hunter
- • • • • Jacques Cousteau

NEW ENDOWMENTS

By dint of birth, surgery or training, the conspiracies are better equipped to challenge the predators of mankind than other hunters. Such power always comes with a price.

Advanced Armory

The hunters of VALKYRIE have lost too many soldiers and agents to the juggernauts that are werewolves. As such, they've upped their game when it comes to bringing the fight against the Lupines.

Frequency Pulse Emitter (••; Renewable)

Durability 2, Size 1, Structure 3

Canines can hear noises pitched in ultra-high frequencies that humans cannot. The scientists who designed the devices for TF:V created Frequency Pulse Emitters working with the same general principles applied to werewolves. A Frequency Pulse Emitter (sometimes called Dog Whistles by TF:V soldiers) is a modified flashbang grenade that emits an eardrum rupturing pulse of sound that can only be heard by canines and werewolves.

Function: A Frequency Pulse Emitter is used like any other grenade. The operator primes the grenade and tosses it towards the enemy with a Dexterity + Athletics roll (see the **World of Darkness Rulebook**, p. 67 for throwing rules). Frequency Pulse Emitter grenades have what is called a short fuse, meaning the grenade will go off within a few seconds of being primed. This gives an enemy little chance to pick up the grenade and throw it back at its former owner. Any werewolf within 10 yards of the Dog Whistle when it "explodes" must succeed at a Stamina + Composure roll at a -3 penalty or be stunned (see the **World of Darkness Rulebook**, p. 167). The penalty to resist being stunned is increased to -5 if the werewolf is in either wolf or near-wolf form. A Frequency Pulse Emitter has no effect on humans unless the character has increased their normal range of hearing in some manner. It may work on any creature (vampire, witch, etc.) assuming an animal-form or using heightened senses.

Urban Response Vehicle (•••••; Special)

Durability 8, Size 16, Structure 24, Acceleration 15, Safe Speed 110 (75 mph), Maximum Speed 176 (120 mph), Handling 1.

Though it's difficult to drive an armored car through town and not draw attention, the fact is that some jobs and locations require a more forceful and timely response than others. Recently put into limited production, the Urban Response Vehicle (URV) provides Task Force: VALKYRIE members with light armored vehicle capability disguised as a standard full-sized van. As the name implies, the URV was designed for covert urban operations and would require some serious overhauling for use off-road.

Function: Every TF:V member of a cell may contribute towards the Merit cost of the URV in the

same way a cell would cooperate to construct a Safe House (see **Hunter: The Vigil**, p. 70).

Standard features of the URV include onboard computer and GPS, bullet-proof glass, RFID locks (the normal locks are dummies), military winch, run-flat tires (each blown tire only imposes a -1 penalty to Drive rolls and a 10% speed penalty), and police cruiser type search lights. It is equipped with air conditioning and internal oxygen supply (the URV can quickly be rigged to operate as air-tight), an overcharged engine, and enough juice from a mini-generator to power all of the features and any add-ons. The vehicle sports concealed armor plating that makes the URV nearly invulnerable to small arms fire and was designed to transport one driver, three passengers and one gunner.

The standard package also comes with a "pop-up" .50 caliber machine gun. To operate, the gunner seats himself in the gunner chair, pushes a button, the roof of the vehicle slides open and the .50 cal is elevated via hydraulic lift to a height even with the top of the URV. The machine gun uses both a swivel mount and pedals to achieve an 180 degree field of fire, which requires additional training (any gunner that fires the .50 cal, or replacement weapons, without a Heavy Weapons specialty for Firearms suffers the untrained penalty). The .50 cal comes with a casing catcher as standard. If purchased as an option, the pintle-mounted Bleeder (see below) unfolds from the front passenger side roof and unlocks a hatch that allows a standing passenger to operate the weapon. The .50 cal has the following statistics.

Type	Damage	Ranges	Capacity	Size	Special
HMG	5 (8 again)	300/600/1200	50	5	Autofire

In addition to the onboard features, an URV can be further enhanced for field work by investing in up to a maximum of 10 Merit dots worth of options. The following items from the Advanced Armory Endowment are available as options for the URV: Etheric Rounds (replaces standard .50 cal ammunition), Etheric Windows (functions exactly like Etheric Goggles, may be toggled on and off by voice command), pintle-mounted Bleeder (operated by passenger), Equalizer Grenade Launcher (co-axial mount on the .50 cal), Gungnir System (may be added to any weapon), vehicle-mounted Mjolnir Cannon (replaces standard .50 cal machine gun).

Example: A cell wishes to add a Mjolnir Cannon and Etheric Windows to the URV. The total Merit cost would be 12 (five for the URV, five for the Mjolnir Cannon and two for the Etheric Windows.

Drawback: Even with a casing catcher to gather up spent shells, firing a .50 cal machine gun downtown is apt to attract some attention. The machine gun is included as an "oh shit" weapon to help cover retreats and take down serious opposition when unwanted attention is preferable to the continued existence of a large and scary monster.

Benediction

It is, perhaps, not their fault that they are werewolves. Perhaps they were cursed by God or seduced by the Devil. It matters little; heresy, whether intentional, must be handled. These Benedictions offer hunters of the Witches' Hammer aid in that regard.

The Miracle of Gadarene

Even many non-Christians know the story of Jesus and the Gadarene demon. While traveling through the region of Gadarene, Jesus came across a man that was possessed by demons. Christ compelled the demons to speak their names and the demons replied that their name was Legion. Jesus then forced the demons out of the man and into a herd of swine, which then threw themselves off a cliff.

Cost: None

Effect: Mechanically, Cast into Swine works in the same way as "*Vade Retro Santana*" (see **Hunter: The Vigil**, p. 162) except that the focus of this Benediction is on the exorcism and consequent binding of spirits. To perform Cast into Swine, the hunter must have a general idea of the nature of the spirit he is working against. The hunter then procures an animal that is either metaphorically or literally the opposite of that nature. In the case of violent spirits, the hunter could choose a dove, which is traditionally a symbol of peace. The exorcism is performed as usual with the animal close at hand. When the spirit is driven from the body of the possessed, it is forced into the body of the animal and bound there. The opposing nature of the animal keeps the bound spirit in check and denies the spirit the ability to direct the actions of the animal. Members of the Malleus Maleficarum place the animal in seclusion until they can decide on a more permanent solution. If the animal dies, as a result of natural causes or violence, the spirit is freed.

The Binding of St. Amabilis

Amabilis of Riom served as a cantor at the church of St. Mary at Clermont. Revered as the patron saint against (among other things) demonic possession and wild beasts, his image is that of a bishop listening to an angel playing music. The brethren of the Malleus Maleficarum have found the invocation of the saint's name works to weaken the demonic possession purportedly responsible for werewolves.

Cost: 1 Willpower

Action: Instant

Dice Pool: Presence + Benediction

Effect: By spending a point of Willpower and invoking the name of St. Amabilis, the hunter seeks to limit the superior regenerative properties of werewolves by binding the demons that possess them through the power of holy song. When working this Benediction, the hunter sings a wordless song of celestial praise that affects any werewolf that can hear it. The song is beautiful regardless of the normal capabilities of the singer and fills the hearts of his friends with peace. The hunter only needs to succeed on the instant roll once, but *must* keep up the singing. While he is concentrating on singing, the hunter may not attack, may only move at half his normal Speed, and his Defense is halved (round down). Any distractions that might cause a lapse in concentration (a werewolf biting him, for example) require the hunter to succeed at a Resolve + Composure roll to maintain concentration.

Potential Modifiers: Performed in a noisy area -3; performed on All Saint's Day (November 1) +5, performed on holy ground +2.

Roll Results

Dramatic Failure: The invocation is uttered without sufficient belief and the Benediction fails. This leads to a minor lapse in faith and all Benediction rolls suffer a -2 penalty until the hunter is able to receive the balm of confession.

Failure: The binding fails.

Success: For as long as the hunter concentrates, any werewolves that can hear the song lose their unnatural regenerative abilities and heal no faster than regular humans. While the music continues, werewolves may not heal themselves or each other by any means.

Exceptional Success: The above effects continue for 24 hours even after the hunter stops concentrating.

Castigation

Are werewolves demons, or are they simply goaded and cursed by demons? Are spirits infernal — a choir of diabolical elementals existing behind the sighted veil? It matters philosophically, perhaps, but for its part, Castigation doesn't care. The ceremonies of the Lucifuge can be used against a werewolf just as they can be against any other.

Familiar Betrayal

Many werewolf packs follow a tradition of binding a spirit to the pack as a whole. This familiar spirit can aid the creatures by lending them some of its strength, as a liaison to other spirits and as a spy or guardian. The Children of the Seventh Generation are well versed in the aspects of familiar relationships and use that knowledge to force pack familiars to turn against their masters.

Cost: 1 Willpower each day in addition to other costs (see below)

Effect: Mechanically, Familiar Betrayal works in the exact same way as the summoning aspect of "Calling Forth the Pit" (see **Hunter: The Vigil**, p. 164), with the exception that the hunter *must* know the name of the pack familiar he is attempting to summon. Hunters could learn the true name of the familiar by questioning other spirits in the area, by overhearing the pack talk about the spirit, or by tricking the familiar into revealing it to them. If the hunter succeeds in summoning the spirit she may immediately bind that spirit to serve her as a temporary familiar (characters may only have one familiar at a time) as per the "Familiar" Castigation. For the next six days the spirit is bound to follow the wishes of the hunter to the letter, even if it means turning against the spirit's former masters. To maintain her hold over the spirit, the hunter must reinforce the binding each evening at sunset by spending one Willpower. Unless the familiar does something to betray its new allegiance, the werewolf pack remains ignorant of the betrayal.

Mark of the Beast

Though formidable, the strength of a werewolf is nothing when compared with that of true demons of the pit. As their lord and ruler, the strength of Lucifer eclipses that of even the mightiest of his legion and his children can call upon that unholy strength. The process isn't pleasant. To call up the strength of hell requires the Children of the Seventh Generation to take on the guise of their demonic ancestor in a painful transformation.

Cost: 2 Willpower; 1 point of lethal damage
Action: Instant
Dice Pool: Resolve + Intimidation
Effect: The child of Lucifer calls upon her demonic heritage and takes the form of a demon. The transformation takes one turn and the hunter twists and writhes in agony as her body changes, resulting in one point of lethal damage. No two members of the Lucifuge share the exact same features after the transformation. One member might take the form of a fallen angel with ripped and tattered wings, weeping tears of blood that mar otherwise perfect features, while the form of another member might echo the bestial nature of her sire complete with burning red eyes, claws, and fangs. The demonic visage remains consistent each time the hunter activates the Castigation, leading some of the Lucifuge to wonder if the demonic version isn't their soul's "true" form.

While transformed, the hunter gains a pool of points equal to her Castigation score that she may use to increase any Physical Attribute in any combination she desires. A hunter with four dots in Castigation could, for example, raise her Strength by two and her Stamina by two, or instead raise her Dexterity by two, her Strength by one and her Stamina by one. This effect ignores the usual Attribute maximum for mortal characters. The character's Size is also increased by one (remember to recalculate secondary Attributes such as Speed and Health based on the new form). The hunter may heal wounds of any type by spending one Willpower (one Willpower spent heals one wound) and she gains an Armor rating of two. The presence of the demonic form can inspire fear and terror in those who witness it (even other hunters) similar to the effects of Lunacy. The flesh of a mortal can only maintain the form of a demon for a limited time and is physically, mentally, and spiritually exhausting. The hunter can only remain in her demonic form for a number of turns equal to her Stamina + Castigation each day, though she may voluntarily end the transformation at any time (turns may be divided over multiple uses).

Any wounds suffered by the character that exceed her normal Health after she returns to mortal form are not carried over to her human body. Instead, the twisted nature of the demonic form inflicts the wounds on the very next person (or thing) the hunter sees before lapsing into unconsciousness (the presence of extra wounds indicates that the normal Health track of the hunter has already been filled). Any damage caused by the hunter while in demonic form is considered lethal damage, regardless of source, unless the hunter does something to change his damage to aggravated (using silver against werewolves, for example).

After the hunter reverts to her normal form she suffers from a wave of exhaustion that hinders her ability to act or even think clearly. Until the hunter sleeps for a full eight hours, any action taken by the character is penalized -3 dice. Potentially more dangerous is the spiritual exhaustion. Calling on her demon form is recognition of the dark side of her nature and her pool to resist degeneration is reduced by one for the next 24 hours.

Potential Modifiers: Mark of the Beast is used within six minutes of 3 A.M. (+3).

Roll Results

Dramatic Failure: The hunter fails to transform but still suffers the aftereffects of a transformation.

Failure: The transformation fails.

Success: The hunter successfully transforms.

Exceptional Success: As above and the turns spent in demonic form don't count against the maximum number of turns for the day (the character is still limited to the number of turns she can maintain the transformation for that scene, however).

Elixir

The Elixirs of the Ascending Ones work as a great balancer, helping to make human equal to beast in some regards.

Vapors of Mercury (••)

The element mercury is also known as quicksilver. Extremely toxic, quicksilver poisoning can result from simple skin contact with the element or by inhaling the fumes. The alchemists of the Ascending Ones combine quicksilver with other esoteric ingredients to brew the Vapors of Mercury. The Elixir is inhaled by breathing in the vapors from a censor or, more commonly, from a modified asthma inhaler.

Action: Instant

Roll Results

Dramatic Failure: The hunter fails to process the toxins carried by the vapor and is afflicted with a Toxicity 4 lethal poison. This poison may be resisted with a contested Stamina + Resolve roll against the poison's Toxicity.

Failure: The hunter is affected as though she had taken a moderate (-2 to all dice pools and traits) dose of hallucinogen.

Success: The hunter manages to process the Vapors of Mercury and benefits from its effects for the rest of

the scene. The Elixir transmutes the blood of the hunter into a watery silver substance that burns like acid if touched by a werewolf. Each time the hunter suffers a wound that causes at least one point of lethal damage, any werewolf within one yard of the hunter takes an equal amount of lethal damage from the silvery blood spatter. Wounds caused by the spatter are considered aggravated for the purposes of healing for werewolves.

Exceptional Success: As above, but the werewolf suffers an additional one point of lethal damage per instance of toxic blood spatter.

Balm of Chronos (••••)

The empire of ancient Egypt traded and warred with other Mediterranean powers and the Egyptians' exposure to other cultures led to exchanges of religious and philosophical ideas. From the Greeks, the Egyptians learned about the god Chronos, who was revered by the Greeks as the personification of time. The Egyptians noticed similarities between the stories of Chronos and that of their own god P'tah (both gods featured in creation myths) and discussed the possibility that both gods were aspects of each other.

When the Ascending Ones began their alchemical studies, they sought out the power of Chronos to use time in their favor. The Balm of Chronos looks like a thick paste, white in color, and smells slightly of oleander. The Balm is activated by rubbing it into the skin like a lotion.

Action: Instant

Roll Results

Dramatic Failure: The Ascending One is affected by a Toxicity 4 lethal poison, which may be resisted by a contested roll of Resolve + Stamina versus the poison's Toxicity.

Failure: The hunter receives no benefit and is affected as though he had taken a moderate (-2 to all dice pools and traits) dose of heroin.

Success: The Ascending One enters a trance-like state in which his perception of passing time is slowed. For the rest of the scene, the hunter doubles his Initiative modifier and Defense score. If used in a non-combat situation, the hunter gains a +3 bonus to extended rolls as a result of his enhanced concentration.

Exceptional Success: As above and the hunter has the option of acting at any point in the Initiative order he chooses or, in non-combat situations, gains a +1 equipment bonus to all actions.

Drawback: If the Balm of Chronos is used a number of times in one day greater than the hunter's Stamina, the hunter suffers the effects of a Dramatic Failure regardless of roll.

Relic

The hunters of the Shield and Spear have little love for werewolves. They've sworn an oath to destroy them, and whatever Relics they pick up along the way that help them achieve that effect, well, all the better.

Idol of Gévaudan (•••••)

Between 1764 and 1767, a large wolf that was named the Beast of Gévaudan terrorized the small cities and hamlets of south-central France. Supposedly responsible for over 300 attacks that resulted in estimated casualties of around 50 wounded and 120 dead, the wolf eluded capture or death by hunters dispatched by King Louis XV and was finally put down by a local with silver bullets. The beast was said to measure four feet tall at the shoulder and witnesses claimed it could leap 30 feet. Aegis Kai Doru hunters tell a slightly different version of the story. They claim the Beast of Gévaudan was the last remaining member of a werewolf pack that hunted in the area. The Guardians of the Labyrinth say they helped a French local hunt the Beast to its lair and provided him with the silver bullets used to slay it. After the Beast was dead, the hunters searched its lair and found a crude stone idol of a great wolf, which had been placed in a niche and surrounded with the heads of the Beast's victims, like grotesque offerings. Aegis Kai Doru took possession of the idol and paid the local to never discuss either the idol or their involvement in the incident.

Cost: The user must splash werewolf blood on the Idol of Gévaudan to activate the Relic

Benefit: Figuring out exactly how to use the Idol of Gévaudan proved something of a quandary for Aegis Kai Doru. Testing proved that simply showing the Idol to a werewolf provoked no response and it wasn't until one of their "test subjects" was wounded in a struggle and accidentally spattered some blood on the Icon did the hunters figure out how to activate it. When active, the Idol becomes warm to the touch and calls to any werewolf that views it to take ownership of the Relic. This call stirs the animal instincts of a werewolf and the monsters will literally fight to the death to claim the Idol. Whenever a werewolf sees the Idol while it is active they must roll Resolve + Composure with a -4 penalty. With success, the werewolf manages to fight the call and can behave normally. If the roll fails, the werewolf will stop at nothing to take possession of the Idol for itself and *only* for itself, even fighting other pack members for control of the Relic. The Idol remains active until the next full moon after it tastes the blood of a werewolf. If a werewolf manages to take possession of the thing, the Idol remains active an additional month for each head offered to it as tribute by the werewolf.

In addition to the other effects, a werewolf that succumbs to the call of the Idol is locked into near-wolf form for as long as the Idol remains active. Aegis Kai Doru hunters that have used the Relic say the best way to employ the thing is to activate it then toss it into the middle of a werewolf pack. The monsters will kill each other to claim ownership of the Idol and the remaining survivor can then be dispatched. Not the type to take chances, the Guardians of the Labyrinth have tagged this one-of-a-kind Relic with a tiny GPS locator that will allow them to find it even if a werewolf manages to escape with the Idol.

Phylactery of Commius (•••••)

The Gaulish Atrebates (a tribe that lived in what is today northern France) were beaten into submission somewhere around the year 57 BC just as the Legions under the command of Julius Caesar expanded the reach of Rome to the north. Julius Caesar appointed a man named Commius (a Gaul) to act as the new king of the tribe. Commius acted the part of loyal ally to Julius Caesar until 53 BC when, after hearing rumors that Commius was conspiring against Rome, Titus Labienus (Caesar's second in command) set an ambush to assassinate Commius. Though sorely wounded, Commius escaped the ambush and fled to Britain where he took up arms against the Romans. By dint of personal bravery and political acumen, he managed to set himself up as king of the Atrebates in Britain in 30 BC and coins were minted bearing his image until 20 BC.

The commonly accepted theory is that there were two kings named Commius, father and son, one who ruled in Gaul and the other in Britain. Commius was thought to have been elderly when he first assumed the throne in 53 BC and for him to have survived both his wounds and the passing of the years would have been extraordinary for the time period. The Aegis Kai Doru has a different theory. It claims both kings were one and the same and that Commius managed to survive as long as he did directly as a result of his ownership of a magical phylactery.

Cost: 1 *dot* of Willpower when first acquired to attune the Relic to its new owner.

Benefit: In the time of Julius Caesar, a phylactery was a small box that contained magical texts and sacred herbs that was supposed to protect its owner from harm. The Phylactery of Commius is just small enough to fit into a coat pocket and has no obvious mechanism for opening. The Aegis Kai Doru members go out of their way to make sure no one tam-

pers with whatever contents the box might hold and they are instructed to deal firmly with anyone that attempts to open it.

By itself, the phylactery is just an old stone box with some interesting carvings. To gain the full benefits of ownership, the user must bind a spirit to the Relic. Binding a spirit to the phylactery can be tricky. No spirit will willingly allow itself to be bound to the thing (spirits instinctively understand the effects of such a binding) so the owner must summon a spirit into the material realm to bind it. This task can be accomplished though use of the "Effigy" Tactic (see p. 132), or whatever other means are available to the owner. Once a spirit has been drawn into the material realm, the owner must thrice name the spirit (its true name) and touch the phylactery to the spirit's materialized form. The owner then completes the ritual by daubing a bit of his blood on the box.

Once the binding is complete, the spirit is drawn into and contained inside the phylactery. From that point forward, as long as the phylactery is within two yards of the owner, he gains the following benefits.

- The owner ages at half the normal rate and is immune to disease or poison.

- Any wounds suffered by the owner are first subtracted from the Health of the bound spirit. If the spirit is slain as a result of this damage, a new spirit must be bound to the box..

- The owner gains the ability to speak the language of spirits.

Drawback: If the spirit is ever freed from the phylactery or the phylactery is destroyed, the owner of the Relic suffers a spiritual backlash and takes three points of aggravated damage. Unless the bound spirit was destroyed along with the phylactery, it will likely seek some kind of retribution against the person who imprisoned it.

Thaumatechnology

Harvesting Lupine parts ain't easy; but Cheiron's managed it — and, when that doesn't work, they simply use parts of other mad creatures to help their agents take down the rampaging *homo lupines*.

Ectocrine Gland (••)

When a materialized spirit is forced back into the spirit world or killed, it sometimes leaves behind a gooey, semi-material fluid that is referred to as ectoplasm (the same substance sometimes left behind by ghosts). Even though ectoplasm dissipates quickly in the material realm and is near impossible to gather samples of, the Cheiron Group has managed to conduct some experiments with the stuff. The experiment that eventually led to the creation of the Ectocrine Gland featured a quick-thinking field agent and a syringe. After defeating a materialized spirit that had somehow escaped containment and was wreaking havoc in a graveyard, the agent scooped up some of the ectoplasm left by the spirit. Noticing that the ectoplasm was dissipating and not wanting to miss an opportunity to experiment with the substance, the agent poked some of it into a syringe and injected himself. Subsequent to his release from the mental ward, the agent reported that after the injection he had been able to see non-corporeal ghosts and spirits (those existing in the state of Twilight).

Not long after the results of that experiment had been filed, a different team of scientists sent a report to the Cheiron head office that claimed they had detected trace amounts of ectoplasm in the blood stream of a girl who had been the victim of possession. Seeking a way to verify these new claims, Cheiron ran a battery of tests on a kidnapped spiritualist. They discovered that the spiritualist also had trace amounts of ectoplasm in his blood and, more exciting than that, his body seemed to manufacture the stuff. Following further months of experimentation along with trial and error, Cheiron discovered a way to manufacture a gland that would release ectoplasm into the bodies of their agents. The result? The Ectocrine Gland.

Benefit: By concentrating, the hunter can activate the Ectocrine Gland. This allows him to see into Twilight and communicate (though not physically interact) with non-manifested entities. This effect lasts for one scene and the gland can produce enough ectoplasm to be used a number of times each day equal to the Stamina of the hunter. The things that dwell in Twilight aren't *forced* to communicate with the hunter and the gland doesn't bestow the ability to understand any languages beyond those already spoken by the hunter.

Drawback: While the hunter gazes into Twilight it can be difficult to concentrate on events going on around him. The concentration required to separate what is "real" from what is Twilight results in a -2 penalty to all Perception rolls. Additionally, the presence of ectoplasm in his bloodstream also makes the hunter an easier target for possession. For an hour after the Ectocrine Gland is activated, the hunter is penalized -2 dice to resist possession.

Berserker Splice (•••)

No one that has had a close encounter with a werewolf can help but remember the primal fury exhibited by the creatures. Wounds that would be fatal to a human simply serve to enrage a werewolf and that anger gives them strength. The scientists of the Cheiron Group have studied both the human-looking remains of werewolves and have performed dissections on still-living specimens (a trickier proposition) searching for, among other things, a physiological reason for a werewolf's rage. When their data was compiled, the scientists noticed that every one of the werewolves studied had an enlarged *medulla oblongata*. Believing they had found the answer to the riddle, the scientists performed a transplant on a willing (hey, no one made him sign the waiver) Cheiron field agent, replacing his human *medulla oblongata* with one taken from a werewolf. The results were spectacular, if messy. Upon awakening after the surgery, the agent attacked anyone he could get his hands on, killing 11 Cheiron employees with his bare fists and teeth before he was subdued. Tapes of the incident suggested that the subject exhibited increased strength and fortitude. Later examinations of the body revealed the subject had been shot nine times before he collapsed.

Despite the mishap, the scientists in charge of the program were eager to continue with their project and with comparatively minor losses to the company (only around 50 employees were killed all told) eventually perfected a stable transplant procedure. Instead of a direct transplant, the scientists carved off small sections of a werewolf's *medulla oblongata* and spliced them directly into the sensory and motor areas of a subject's cerebral cortex. When stimulated by adrenaline produced during the fight-or-flight instinct, the splices became active and pumped additional chemicals into the body that increased natural strength and physical resiliency. The program was declared a success by the head office and instructions on the procedure were disseminated throughout the company and its subsidiaries.

Benefit: Whenever the hunter is in a dangerous situation, the adrenaline produced by the stress activates the Berserker Splice. For the remainder of the scene, a hunter with the implant gains two Strength plus an additional +1 Strength for every point of lethal damage taken (this ignores normal human Attribute limits) and gains the Iron Stamina ••• Merit whether he meets the prerequisites or not. (The advantages during a fight are obvious, but in flight situations remember that the Speed of the character is also increased by the boost in Strength.)

Drawback: Other than suffering from a ravenous hunger after the implant is activated, agents with a Berserker Splice also have a tendency to, well, go *berserk*. While the Splice is active, each time the agent takes two or more points of lethal damage from a single attack he must succeed at a Resolve + Composure roll or fly into a killing rage or cowardly retreat (player's choice). The hunter is unable to tell friend from foe while in the rage and will attack the closest target if the player chooses a "fight" response. The berserker rage lasts for a number of turns equal the Stamina rating of the hunter, after which the splice shuts down and the hunter collapses from exhaustion (count the hunter as stunned for a number of turns equal to those spent in the rage). Cells that have prior warning about this possible "side effect" can plan accordingly for this eventuality by attempting to stay out of the line of sight of a hunter with the implant during combat.

NEW ENDOWMENT:
RITES DU CHEVAL

The hunters of Les Mystères invite spirits into their bodies to combat the common enemy of both hunter and spirit: werewolves. Unlike other forms of possession, the hunter retains control of his own body and senses while the spirit rides his form. It is for this reason that Les Mystères refer to the blessings of the spirits as being "ridden" rather than being possessed. Learning to control the *Rites du Cheval* requires training and discipline. The hunter must learn how to summon and appease the spirits that ride him so the merging of body and spirit is a partnership, rather than a full-blown possession. Each spirit demands a different type of offering or gift to appease them and part of the training of Les Mystères involves memorizing which kind of appeasement works best for different spirits.

Even though Les Mystères is a fairly open confederation, the members don't share their knowledge with just anyone. After a hunter has been accepted he must still prove himself worthy and capable of the training he hopes to receive. Because the conspiracy is so spread out, a member that wishes to learn all of what Les Mystères has to offer must be willing to travel to train with different mentors and it is in this manner that the conspiracy as a whole comes to know the hunter. Rites with a dot rating of four or better are likely to require a hunter to travel well outside his territory to learn. A Les Mystères hunter can only learn rites with a dot rating equal or less than his Status in the conspiracy. So, for example, a hunter with Status •• only has access to one or two dot rites. Members of Les Mystères may purchase rites within their range of access at the cost of two experience points per rite.

Because of their intimate relationship with the spirits, the members of Les Mystères bear an ephemeral mark that discourages uninvited spirits from attempting to possess them. Only spirits with a Rank higher than the Status rating of a member can attempt an unwilling possession, and even then the spirit suffers a -3 penalty to do so. While a hunter is ridden he shares some of the perceptions of the spirit sharing his body. Sensory feedback from sight, smell, touch, taste and hearing is altered by the nature of the spirit. When possessed by a spirit of death, the hunter might see signs of decay all around him, smell the sickly-sweet aroma of rot, hear the wails of mourners, and anything he eats or drinks tastes of ashes. The sensation of touch is affected in a different way. Spirits are eager to experience the tactile sensations of the material realm and when they ride a hunter they hijack the sense of touch. The hunter retains enough feeling to operate normally, but the sensations seem far away and ghost-like. A ridden hunter suffers no wound penalties, giving rise to the stories about Les Mystères members that can eat glass or burning embers with no apparent discomfort. This lack of sensation does have a negative aspect. While a hunter is ridden all Perception rolls not obviously related to the nature of the possessing spirit (sensing fire or heat while being ridden by a fire spirit, for example) suffer a -1 penalty.

Appeasements

Very few spirits are altruistic in nature. Even when they provide hunters with assistance to battle

WHO DO VOODOO?

Although many of the rites listed have obvious voodoo ties, the membership of Les Mystères is worldwide. A hunter from Thailand and a hunter from Haiti might have different names for a rite that produces the same effect. Similarly, though *Rites du Cheval* is the most commonly used title to describe the collective occult knowledge of the conspiracy, members from other parts of the world may refer to it by a different name.

the shared enemy of both spirits and Les Mystères (i.e. werewolves), they expect to receive more than just heartfelt thanks and a pat on the back. While some might argue that possessing a fleshy body is a reward in and of itself, the spirits don't see it that way. They want more and so the hunters of Les Mystères offer up appeasements. An appeasement can take a variety of shapes, depending on the nature and power of the spirit being invoked. Minor spirits are usually happy with simple recognition and a minor material token of thanks. More powerful spirits demand greater sacrifices and greater displays of recognition. Included in each rite are a number of possible appeasements tailored to fit the power of the spirits invoked for that rite. Players and Storytellers are encouraged to devise new appeasements based on the examples given.

Calling Down the Thunder

The dice pool to perform a rite is always Presence + Expression. Each *Rite du Cheval* targets a different spirit or general type of spirit. The more powerful the spirit to be summoned, the longer and more complicated the rite becomes. More powerful spirits can also ride their host for longer periods of time before having to return to the spirit world. Hunters may only play host to one spirit at a time. The specific requirements of each rite vary, but all of them share the following common modifiers:

Suggested Modifiers:

Modifier	Situation
+3	The rite is performed using especially valuable or rare appeasements
+2	The hunter knows the true name of the spirit
+2	The rite is performed in a place sympathetic to the nature of the spirit

-2	The hunter demands cooperation rather than asking for it or treats the spirit with disdain or arrogance
-2	The rite is performed with inappropriate appeasements
-3	The rite is performed lacking any appeasement

Skin of the Loa (•)

One of the first lessons Les Mystères teaches its initiates is how to protect their bodies from harm. The hunter invites a minor spirit to share her body and encourages it to partially manifest in their flesh. The spirit hardens the skin of its host to better withstand the biting teeth and slashing claws of werewolves. The skin color of the ridden changes as a side effect of this merging of body and spirit, turning her flesh a shade associated with the spirit. Spirits of earth turn the skin dark brown, spirits of water tint the skin greenish-blue, a minor spirit of pain might color flesh the pale white of clenched knuckles and so on.

A Korean *mudang* might perform a slightly altered version of a *Gangneung Danogut* (a ritual to protect against attack from wild animals) to ward off attacks from werewolves or other enemies by calling on the spirit of a mountain god with an appeasement of song and dance.

Possible Appeasements: A snatch of song that compliments the spirit, the hunter slaps or pinches her own skin, drumming.

Cost: None

Action: Instant

Roll Results

Dramatic Failure: The spirit is angered by the feeble attempts of the hunter to impress it. The rite fails and the spirit curses the hunter with clumsiness. The hunter has her Defense reduced by two for the remainder of the scene.

Failure: The spirits fail to respond.

Success: The spirit hears the call of the hunter and works to protect her from harm. The hunter gains an Armor rating of 2 that protects her from close combat attacks *only* for the remainder of the scene.

Exceptional Success: The spirit is truly impressed and puts forth a greater than normal effort. The spiritual Armor protects against both melee and ranged attacks for the remainder of the scene.

Ephemeral Disguise (•)

Even when manifested, many spirits can easily hide from the eyes of men or can take on a familiar form to lull suspicion. The hunter asks the spirits to share this power with him to hide him from his enemies sight or allow him to walk undetected in their midst. While ridden with this intention, the hunter feels an odd loss of identity as though he were just another face in the crowd.

Possible Appeasements: A bite of food that is particularly pungent or sour, dousing a flame in water, an offering of a faceless doll.

Cost: None

Action: Instant

Roll Results

Dramatic Failure: The hunter somehow insults the spirit and rather than helping them to hide or pass unnoticed, the spirit causes the hunter to emit a soft red glow. The glow imposes a -5 penalty to all Stealth rolls for the remainder of the scene.

Failure: The spirits fail to respond.

Success: The spirit responds favorably and guides the steps of the hunter or gives the hunter an unremarkable visage. The ridden gains a +3 bonus to all Stealth rolls for the remainder of the scene.

Exceptional Success: In addition to the above effects, the spirit reaches out and muddles the senses of cameras and other security devices. Security systems refuse to register the presence of the hunter and cameras record their image as a blur.

Elemental Rebuke (••)

This rite specifically targets spirits of elemental forces such as wind, lightning and fire. The spirit enters the body of the hunter and channels its energy to influence and damage the bodies of his enemies. The physical effects of damage caused vary with the nature of the elemental spirit: spirits of wind suck the breath from the lungs of a target, causing a sort of rapid internal depressurization; and spirits of lightning overload the electronic impulses of the brain causing strokes and seizures.

Minor spirits quickly expend their energy with such overt displays of power and the flesh of a mortal has difficulty containing more powerful elemental spirits. As a result, rather than a continual ride, spirits either burn out helping the hunter or they bob in and out of the hunter's body to avoid causing him permanent harm. The sensation of spirits moving in and out of his body in quick secession is somewhat distracting to the hunter and he suffers a -1 penalty to Perception checks for the turn immediately following use of the rite.

A hunter need only pay the Willpower and appeasement costs of this rite once per scene.

Possible Appeasements: Doing a shot of 100-proof liquor, eating a bit of the spirit's element, enumerating the magnificent qualities of the element in a loud voice.

Cost: 1 Willpower

Action: Instant

Roll Results

Dramatic Failure: The spirits are disdainful of the hunter's cries for aid and give him an unpleasant taste of their element that causes one point of bashing damage.

Failure: The spirits fail to respond.

Success: The spirits give of their element willingly to the hunter. The ridden can target any single enemy within 10 yards with the power of elemental force. This is a contested action that pits the hunter's Resolve + Occult + Les Mystères Status (greater Status brings with it the knowledge required to summon more powerful spirits) versus the target's Resolve + Stamina. The target suffers one point of lethal damage for every success gained beyond the victim's roll.

Exceptional Success: In addition to the above, the pain caused by elemental forces ravaging the body of the target cause him to be stunned for one turn.

Light as a Feather (••)

The hunter calls on the spirits of air, wind, birds and other flying creatures to join with him. Although true flight is beyond the power of the spirits to grant, the body of the hunter becomes nearly weightless allowing him to jump further and fall from great heights without serious injury. Enemies of the hunter also find it hard to land a solid blow, their attacks simply pushing the hunter back rather than tearing into his flesh. While he is ridden by these spirits, the hunter feels incredibly happy, giddy even, and can't restrain the booming laughter that wells up inside him. Onlookers will probably find the sight of a man cackling as he drops 30 floors before running away uninjured more than a little disturbing.

Possible Appeasements: Wild dancing, offering the blood of a bird or other creature capable of flight, a (literal) leap of faith off a building at least two stories high.

Cost: None

Action: Instant

Roll Results

Dramatic Failure: The spirits decide man wasn't meant to fly and impose vertigo on the hunter. For the rest of the scene, the hunter suffers a -1 penalty to his Defense and to any action involving a Physical Skill.

Failure: The spirits fail to respond.

Success: The spirit grants the hunter its buoyancy and revels in the sensation of physical weightlessness with him. The hunter gains the following effects for the remainder of the scene:

- A +5 bonus to any jumping roll.

- The hunter only suffers one point of bashing damage from falling, no matter how far he fell.

Exceptional Success: In addition to the above effects, the hunter can move his full Speed as a reflexive action once per turn.

The Hands of Raphael (•••)

According to the beliefs of Vodoun practitioners, the *houngan* and *mambo* pray to the Loa to intercede on their behalf rather than the one true God because they believe God has more important things to do. In a similar fashion, this rite calls on the *spirit* of Raphael rather than the angel himself to heal the wounded and cure the sick. When a member of Les Mystères is ridden by the spirit of Raphael, their face takes on an angelic countenance that makes even the ugliest hunter seem beautiful. After the spirit leaves them, hunters that served as host for the spirit claim to remember a feeling of warmth that flowed through them as they performed the miracle of healing. Werewolves and demons can't abide the sight of a hunter being ridden by Raphael and target that hunter first in a fight.

The Inuit believe that humans have multiple souls and sickness is caused by soul theft, either by evil spirits or rival tribes. By communing with their tribal totems, the shaman can retrieve the portion of the soul that was stolen and restore health to their patient. Appeasement might require chanting in the shamanic tongue and certain bans on their behavior during the healing, such as not speaking certain words or referring to specific items by name.

Possible Appeasements: Continual recitation of the Lord's Prayer throughout the healing, consuming the gallbladder of a fish, facing east and tossing an offering of gold or an emerald into a natural body of water.

Cost: 1 Willpower

Action: Extended

Roll Results

Dramatic Failure: Raphael decides a further test of faith is in order. The rite works, but any wounds healed or diseases cured are transmitted to the healer.

Failure: The spirits fail to respond. No progress is made towards the target number.

Success: The hunter makes progress towards his goal. The target number of the extended roll is 10, with each roll equal to five minutes. In addition to the required appeasement, the hunter must remain sequestered and in prayer during the time spent calling to Raphael. Once the spirit of Raphael takes up residence in the body of the hunter, it remains for seven hours. While the hunter is ridden by Raphael, she can perform the following miracles:

• **Cure the Sick:** The hunter can cure his patient of any sickness. Curing the sick is an extended Wits + Medicine roll with each roll equal to 15 minutes. Minor maladies such as colds or flu's have a target number of 5, while more serious and life threatening illnesses such as cancer or Ebola have a target number of 15. Regardless of symptoms, any disease that is supernatural in origin has a target number of 20 to cure.

• **Heal the Wounded:** The hunter can mend the wounds of his patient. Mending wounds is an extended Wits + Medicine roll with each roll equal to 10 minutes. Bashing damage is healed at a 1:1 ratio of wounds to successes, lethal damage is healed at a 1:2 ratio, and aggravated damage is healed at a 1:4 ratio.

Exceptional Success: No additional benefit is gained beyond the number of successes accumulated towards the target number.

Drawback: The shaman of the Native American tribes were frequently described as "wounded healers" because they accepted the burdens of pain and suffering as the cost of working their magic. Wounded healer is an apt description in the case of this Rite. Wounds spontaneously appear on the body of the hunter when healing the sick. Each roll of the extended action inflicts a point of damage to the hunter, the type of which is based on the severity of the illness being cured. Minor maladies cause bashing damage (colds, flu's), more serious and life-threatening illnesses (cancer, HIV) inflict lethal damage and illnesses with a supernatural origin inflict aggravated damage. Wounds taken from curing the sick are immune to extraordinary forms of healing and may only be healed by the normal passing of time.

Note that it is quite possible for a hunter to die from accumulated wounds while trying to cure the sickness of another. A hunter can voluntarily end the extended action of curing the sick at any time rather than kill himself. If the extended action is voluntarily ended before the target number of success is reached, all successes accumulated towards curing the illness are lost and the spirit of Raphael departs from the hunter.

Spiritual Guidance (•••)

It might be an exaggeration to say that the spirit world is populated by enough spirits to mirror everything humans know, feel, think, see, or do. It might be an exaggeration, but not much of one. The spirit world is a busy place. The hunters of Les Mystères

certainly believe this and they call on specific spirits to assist them with the job at hand. A spirit of war can guide their weapons, a spirit of information can assist research, or a spirit of automobiles can help with difficult or dangerous driving. To invoke a spirit in this way is to become an instant expert in one field. While a hunter is ridden for this rite, she becomes a bit obsessive about her new field of expertise, mirroring the nature of the spirit within her. As a result of this obsession, the hunter suffers a -1 penalty to any roll not directly related to the nature of the spirit within her.

Possible Appeasements: Painting representations of the activity on her body in white, offering up a symbolic representation of the activity, singing or making music of some kind about the activity.

Cost: 1 Willpower

Action: Extended (10 successes necessary; each roll is equal to one minute.)

Roll Results

Dramatic Failure: The spirits find the nature of the task unworthy of them and curse the hunter with incompetence. Any accumulated successes are lost and the hunter suffers the unskilled penalty for whatever Skill they had hoped to enhance for 24 hours.

Failure: The spirits fail to respond. No progress is made towards the target number.

Success: The hunter makes progress towards his goal. Once the spirit joins the host it remains in the hunter's body for 24 hours. (The hunter can forcibly expel the spirit before then by spending another Willpower point and succeeding on a Wits + Intimidation roll.) One Skill of the hunter's choice gains the rote action quality (see the **World of Darkness Rulebook**, p. 134).

Example: Mary calls upon a hound spirit before the cell goes out and attempts to physically track a werewolf pack back to their lair. She gains the rote action quality for Survival and the spirit remains with her until 24 hours has passed or her cell finds the werewolves' lair.

Exceptional Success: As above and the hunter manages to maintain her composure and doesn't suffer the obsessive -1 penalty to other actions.

Clinging Leech (••••)

Leech spirits are just one example of the type of spirits that hunger for the blood or life energies of the living. Most humans might consider that kind of hunger evil, but Les Mystères knows it is just the nature of the spirit. The hunger is no more evil than the desire of a pain spirit to cause agony or the need of a spirit of joy to inspire happiness. While the type of spirit targeted by this rite rides the hunter he has a ravenous appetite and suffers acute hunger pangs that can't be silenced no matter how much food he devours.

Possible Appeasement: Eating a large amount of anything, spilling his own blood on the ground (causing one point of lethal damage), the sacrifice of a chicken or other small animal.

Cost: 1 Willpower

Action: Instant

Roll Results

Dramatic Failure: The spirits decide the hunter isn't hungry enough to join, so they inflict hunger on her. The hunger is strong enough to be distracting and she suffers a -1 penalty to all actions until she is able to sate her hunger.

Failure: The spirits fail to respond.

Success: The spirit agrees to ride the hunter. For the remainder of the scene whenever she succeeds in grappling an opponent, she can steal Health from that opponent once each turn as a reflexive action. The hunter rolls Wits + Larceny versus the target's Resolve + Stamina. For each success on the roll, the theft inflicts one point of lethal damage which the hunter can use to heal her own wounds (lethal or bashing damage only, bashing damage heals first). Additionally, the hunter clings like a leech to the body of her target. For the purposes of maintaining the grapple *only*, count the Strength of the hunter as twice its normal value.

Exceptional Success: As above, except the Strength of the hunter is considered three times its normal value for the purposes of maintaining the grapple.

Drawback: After the initial scene, the spirit inside the hunter refuses to exit her body or assist her further until she has gorged herself to near sickness on food and drink.

Voodoo Doll (••••)

A staple of horror tales and B-movies for years, the voodoo doll is easily the most recognizable piece of paraphernalia associated with the practice of Vodou. Voodoo dolls can be constructed from almost any material and are commonly made from wax or corn husks. Actual sewn voodoo dolls (also known as poppets) aren't as common as is widely believed. Creating a voodoo doll requires an extended Dexterity + Crafts roll with a target number of 10. Each roll is equal to five minutes.

Rather than construct a voodoo doll, the *sangomas* of West Africa might use a monkey's paw to inflict good or bad juju on their targets after offering up the specially prepared and bleached bones of an animal as an appeasement.

Possible Appeasements: Burning an effigy of the target, the hunter drives pins into his own body matching the pin locations of the doll (one point of bashing damage), wearing clothes owned by the target.

Cost: 1 Willpower

Action: Instant

Roll Results

Dramatic Failure: The spirits are displeased with the voodoo doll and shatter it causing five dice of bashing damage to anyone within one yard. This destroys the doll.

Success: Voodoo dolls work though a sympathetic connection to the intended target by adding blood, hair or nail clippings from the target to the doll. If the hunter knows the target personally or knows the target's true name, simply tacking a picture of the targets face over that of the dolls is enough to gain a sympathetic connection. Once the sympathetic connection has been made, the hunter calls on a spirit to inhabit both his body and the voodoo doll. If the voodoo doll is used to reinforce positive aspects of the target's personality, the hunter will call on spirits of love, happiness, or positive energy. If the doll is used to reinforce negative aspects of the target's character or to harm the target, the hunter will call upon spirits of anger, pain, or negative energy.

Once a spirit has entered the doll, the hunter determines the amount of torment or positive reinforcement the target is to be subjected to, based on the number and location of the pins pushed into the doll. A single pin placed in the extremities (hands, feet) causes minor effects. Multiple pins placed in all the extremities as well as the head cause greater effects and the most potent effects result from placing a single pin in the heart of the doll. When the hunter has finished placing pins in the doll, the spirit is freed from the doll and speeds towards the target to administer the blessing or curse (the hunter spends a point of Willpower). Hunters may not choose themselves as the target of a voodoo doll.

• Pin Placement: Single pin in an extremity. *Blessing:* A +1 bonus to all (choose one) Physical, Mental or Social Skills for three hours. *Curse:* A -1 penalty to all (choose one) Physical, Mental or Social Skills for three hours *or* a single point of bashing damage.

• Pin Placement: Multiple pins in extremities plus a pin in the head. *Blessing:* The target gains the 8-again quality (re-roll 8s, 9s and 10s) on any one endeavor chosen by the hunter. *Curse:* The target may only count rolls of 9 or 10 as successes on any one endeavor chosen by the target *or* a single point of lethal damage.

- **Pin Placement:** Single pin in the heart. *Blessing:* The target gains benefits of both the above blessings and regains either a point of Willpower or heals a single wound. *Curse:* The target is subjected to both the above curses and loses a point of Willpower *or* a single point of aggravated damage.

Exceptional Success: In addition to the above effects, the Willpower cost is refunded.

Drawback: The Storyteller should keep track of the number of times a character uses a voodoo doll to cast curses. Once per chapter, the Storyteller can impose a penalty equal to the number of curses on a single roll made by the character. The character *may not* choose not to roll if the penalties reduce this roll to a chance die. Karma is a bitch. Regardless of whether the roll fails or succeeds, this returns the tally of curses cast to zero.

Deny the Moon (•••••)

Werewolves bear marks of favor on their bodies from the great moon-spirit in the form of shimmering silver tattoos. Why the moon would choose to honor werewolves in this way is a mystery to Les Mystères, though other spirits have hinted that the creatures might be her "offspring." The moon-spirit herself wields a great deal of influence and power among other spirits, but there exist a few spirits that are willing to oppose her and can, for a short time, hide werewolves from her sight. Hunters call upon these spirits to join with them to negate the power of the gifts the moon gives werewolves. While ridden by these spirits, a hunter feels strangely dispassionate and may not regain Willpower by fulfilling a Virtue or exploiting a Vice.

Possible Appeasements: Breaking a bow that was used to hunt, sacrificing a dog or wolf, mixing molten silver into mud.

Cost: None

Action: Extended

Roll Results

Dramatic Failure: The moon-spirit overhears the hunter's pleas and decides to interfere with the rite. Any accumulated successes are lost and the moon-spirit whispers the name of the hunter to the leader of the nearest werewolf pack.

Failure: The spirits fail to respond.

Success: The hunter makes progress towards his goal. The target number of the extended roll is five with each roll being equal to 10 minutes. In addition to the appeasement, while the rite is underway the hunter must beat drums covered in black velvet and pour rum on a fire. Once the spirit has joined with the hunter, it remains in his body for two hours. While ridden, whenever a hunter witnesses a werewolf using a Dominance he sees one of the creature's tattoos sparkle with a silvery glow. The

hunter can reach out and temporarily erase the tattoo, negating the effects of that Dominion and denying the werewolf the use of the Dominance for the remainder of the scene. Touching a werewolf requires the hunter succeed at a Dexterity + Brawl roll (the Defense of the target applies, any Armor does not).

Exceptional Success: No additional benefit beyond the number of successes gained.

Wearing the Baron's Hat (•••••)

Baron Samedi is a Loa of death usually depicted wearing a black top hat and suit along with dark glasses. It is said he stands at the crossroads between life and death and points the souls of the departed toward the afterlife. Baron Samedi is generally considered to be a smooth and sophisticated spirit with a wicked sense of humor and an earthy sensuality, but, like all Loa, when his wrath is raised he becomes terrible to behold: the bringer of death rather than spiritual guide. It is this aspect of the Loa that hunters call upon to join them in their hunts when the time comes to battle their werewolf foes. Unlike many of the other rites that require longer to perform, Baron Samedi can be called upon at a moment's notice. Death is never very far away. While a hunter is ridden by Baron Samedi he cannot help but to behave in a rude and darkly cynical manner, which levies a -3 penalty on all Social rolls.

Instead of calling on the Baron, a Nganasan (the indigenous people of Siberia) shaman might draw upon the strength of a polar bear after imitating the sounds the bears make, shuffling around in a bear-like manner, and consuming seal blubber.

Possible Appeasements: Burning a box of expensive cigars, drinking a bottle of rum, disinterring a skull.

Cost: 1 Willpower

Action: Instant

Roll Results

Dramatic Failure: Baron Samedi decides the hunter should make love rather than war. For the next six hours, any roll made to inflict damage suffers a -2 penalty. Conversely, any roll made in an effort to get laid gains a +5 bonus.

Failure: The spirits fail to respond.

Success: Baron Samedi merges with the hunter, enhancing his combat capabilities. For the remainder of the scene the hunter gains +3 to his Defense, +5 to his Initiative and five temporary points of Health (subtract damage taken from temporary Health first). Additionally, the attacks of the hunter bear the touch of death and any attack roll gains the Advanced Action quality (see the **World of Darkness Rulebook**, p. 135).

Exceptional Success: As well as the above effects, all rolls made during combat gain the 9-again quality (re-roll 9s and 10s).

Drawback: Baron Samedi is a busy man and can get irritated by frequent interruptions to his business. Each successive use of this rite in a 12-hour period suffers a cumulative -2 penalty.

CLAWS AND TEETH

The World of Darkness hides a savage truth beneath a thin veneer of civilization. People lie to themselves because they desperately want to believe in something: that good people go to heaven; that they can walk away from the mob; that there aren't monsters hiding in the shadows. They're wrong, of course. Most people even know that they're wrong — deep down, in the blood and the bone, they recognize their lies for what they are. It's just too painful to admit.

This section provides an overview of that savage truth — the spirits that common sense dictates should be comprehensible but that are fundamentally alien, and the werewolves who personify the two sides to the world. Along with the innate abilities of both, this section includes the tools necessary to build a truly memorable antagonist.

Werewolves

Werewolves live their lives as a tiny reflection of the world. A werewolf has to tell herself that she's got standards, that she's not a monster; if she doesn't, the beast within takes her far from human contact, where she can live as the monster she has become. Living amongst humans, she knows she's deluding herself. It's the only way she can hide, the only way the sheep's clothing stands a chance of fitting.

Beyond mere shapeshifting, a werewolf's Primal Urge sets her apart from the human world. Despite growing up human, she's anything but. Primal Urge is a measure of her connection to the beast within: both how much of the world's savage rage burns within her breast, and how well she has learned to harness it. A werewolf's Primal Urge ties in to her shape-changing abilities, and her ability to assert her alpha-predator nature against the spirits of the world.

Merit: Primal Urge (• to •••••)

Effect: The character isn't actually human. The heart of a beast burns within her chest, and manifests primarily by warping her flesh. The Primal Urge rating of the character is a measure of the power of her feral soul, as well as how much dominance she can exert over the spirit world. Primal Urge is also added to any contested dice pool to resist supernatural effects. A character must possess this Merit to shape-shift, and cannot have a Dominion rated higher than her Primal Urge.

Drawback: Most people can unconsciously tell that the character isn't human any more. She suffers a penalty to all Social die pools equal to her dots of Primal Urge. This penalty only applies when the werewolf is dealing with normal human beings (including hunters) — and applies as a bonus if the werewolf is trying to intimidate someone.

Changing Shape

Most werewolves can assume five forms, along a spectrum between human and wolf. Each form has unique abilities and is best-suited for different situations. Changing form is an instant action, requiring a roll of Stamina + Primal Urge. On a dramatic failure, the werewolf takes a point of lethal damage as her bones crack and muscles tear under the strain. An exceptional success allows the werewolf to focus on things other than her change — she can take another instant action immediately after shapeshifting.

The bonuses from alternate forms are each added to the werewolf's traits in Man form.

The five forms that a werewolf can take are:

Man: The werewolf's human guise. The character is biologically human, but retains his ability to regenerate. His abilities are on a par with normal humans, though Social rolls still suffer penalties from Primal Urge.

Near-man: The character gains muscle mass and hair. He naturally hunches over as his body's basic shape starts to adapt for quadripedal movement. His voice deepens, and he growls even when he doesn't mean to. His nails extend and harden, though not enough to cause damage, and his teeth sharpen. His senses become sharper, and he can track by scent.

The Near-man form gains Strength +1, Stamina +1, Manipulation -1, Size +1, Speed +1, Health +1, and two extra dice on Perception rolls.

Bestial Hybrid: Fully halfway between Wolf and Man, the Bestial Hybrid is a towering mass of muscle and fur, teeth and claws. The werewolf grows until he's almost half as tall again as his human form, and bulks out with muscle. His head is made for biting, with powerful jaws and razor-sharp teeth, and his fingers end in wicked claws. The character can manage to bark single words in a human language, but most communication is impossible. The werewolf's bestial rage takes over in this form, and he struggles to do anything other than killing.

The Bestial Hybrid form gains Strength +3, Dexterity +1, Stamina +2, Size +2, Health +4, Initiative +1, Speed +4, bite and claw attacks that deal lethal damage and add two dice to attack rolls, three extra dice on Perception rolls, and Armor 1/1. A Bestial Hybrid ignores wound penalties and never rolls for unconsciousness. The werewolf cannot use complex tools or Fighting Styles, or engage in complex Mental or Social tasks. The werewolf remains in control of her actions for a number of turns equal to her Stamina + Survival + Primal Urge. Every turn after that, she must either attack or move towards a visible enemy. The only way to end this frenzy is to assume one of her other forms.

Near-wolf: The Near-wolf form is a hulking monster from the nightmares of prehistory. This form superficially resembles a wolf: powerful muscles ripple over the werewolf's body, and his claws and teeth remain wickedly sharp. The Near-wolf form dampens the rage of the Bestial Hybrid with the wolf's hunting instinct, allowing the werewolf to remain in control for longer.

The Bestial Hybrid form gains Strength +2, Dexterity +2, Stamina +2, Size +1, Health +3, Initiative +2, Speed +7, bite and claw attacks that deal lethal damage, and three extra dice on Perception rolls. All Manipulation rolls to interact with humans fail automatically, and rolls to interact with wolves suffer a -3 penalty.

Wolf: As with the form of Man, a werewolf wearing a wolf's body is biologically a wolf — though he retains his ability to regenerate. His abilities in this form are mostly on a par with normal wolves.

The Wolf form grants Dexterity +2, Stamina +1, Size -1, Initiative +2, Speed +5, bite attacks that deal lethal damage, and four extra dice on Perception rolls. All Manipulation rolls to interact with humans fail.

Healing: A side-effect of a werewolf's changing body is enhanced healing. In any form, a werewolf heals one point of bashing damage each turn, and one point of lethal damage every 15 minutes.

When in Bestial Hybrid, Near-wolf, and Wolf forms, a werewolf doesn't have to grapple before biting. A human, including a werewolf in Man and Near-man forms, must successfully grapple a victim before sinking their teeth in (see p. 157 of the **World of Darkness Rulebook**).

Silver

For whatever reason, silver remains a bane to werewolves in a way that nothing else does. Attacks made with silver weapons deal aggravated damage. The attack has to deal damage — simply holding a silver object doesn't cause a werewolf to take damage. Further, the weapon has to contain a significant amount of pure silver. Compounds and salts, including silver nitrate, have no special effect on werewolves.

Rage

The primal fury that boils within a werewolf's breast manifests in moments of terrible Rage. When he's confronted with something that might cause him to lose control — taking aggravated damage, or taking a wound in one of the character's last three Health boxes, or being betrayed by a close ally — the beast with-

in takes hold. To avoid this, the werewolf's player can roll Resolve + Composure. If that roll fails, the werewolf immediately enters Bestial Hybrid form, and remains in that form until the Rage passes. Any creature he can see becomes his prey, friend or foe. The Storyteller decides who he attacks, and he fights until his prey stops moving then moves on to his next prey immediately. This frenzy of blood and death lasts until the end of the scene.

If a werewolf takes damage in one of his last three Health boxes when in the grip of Rage, the urge for self-preservation takes over. He flees as fast as he can, attacking anyone who gets in his way — though only to the point that they get out of his way. He stops his flight at the end of the scene.

Essence

Essence is the raw fundament of the spirit world. Werewolves, being intimately connected to the spirit world, can store and channel that Essence. Mostly, a werewolf uses it to fuel his Dominions, burning Essence to

SKINCHANGERS AND THERIANTHROPES

The World of Darkness is home to all manner of strange creatures that change their shape. From a wolf carrying the scalp of a human and able to take its skin to the old woman who sends her mind into a wolf's body to slake her hunger for human flesh, anything is possible. These Skinchangers work slightly different from other werewolves.

Each form apart from Man that the Skinchanger can use requires one dot of Primal Urge. A Skinchanger usually needs a token — a wolf-skin inscribed with blasphemous runes, or a human scalp torn free by a wolf's jaws. The character must hold his token close to shapeshift, and cannot change without it. With an extra dot of Primal Urge, the character can change shape at any time, but suffers a -2 modifier without his token. A Skinchanger can never have more dots of Primal Urge than are required for his specific shapeshifting abilities. A Skinchanger cannot possess more than one Dread Power (see **Hunter: The Vigil**) per point of Primal Urge, and may take Dominions of one or two dots.

Many shapechangers aren't even werewolves. From fish-men with strange cities beneath the waves to the cockroach-men who live among the detritus of the city, these therianthropes have the soul of a beast but wear the bodies of men. Mechanically, therianthropes have the same abilities as werewolves, though many can only access the Bestial Hybrid and Wolf (or Cockroach, or Crow, etc.) forms. The bonuses of those forms will probably need altering to reflect the animal in question. Most therianthropes have a few twisted abilities that work well as Dominions, though rarely more than one per dot of Primal Urge. Whether they have any connection to the spirit world, and thus access to rituals, is up to the Storyteller.

It goes without saying that Skinchangers and therianthropes aren't mutually exclusive. From the girl who weaves owl-feathers in her hair and changes to hunt under the moon's light to the hunter who dons a sacred elk-skull and stands in domain over both animal and man, the world is full of strange beasts. A combination of the systems above represents them well enough.

focus his Rage into a form that no spirit can ignore. He can also draw Essence into his physical form to enhance his control over his own body.

A werewolf's body can hold two points of Essence per dot of Primal Urge. Most werewolves can only spend one point of Essence per turn, though powerful shapechangers with Primal Urge at 4 or 5 dots can spend two points per turn.

By spending a point of Essence, a werewolf can shift to any form as a reflexive action without needing to roll. A werewolf can also reflexively spend a point of Essence to regenerate one point of lethal damage. This regeneration occurs instead of the point of bashing damage that she normally regenerates each turn.

Werewolves regain one point of Essence when they first see the full moon each month. They have to actually see the moon in person, even looking through a closed window doesn't work. The spirit world's a fickle place, and doesn't often reward those with a close tie. Werewolves must hunt for their otherworldly energy, consuming the meat of spirits, humans, or wolves to feel whole once more.

In combat, a werewolf who does lethal damage to her opponent with a bite attack can opt to swallow the flesh she's just torn free. She regains one point of Essence per point of damage dealt. She can only gain this bonus when attacking humans, wolves, or spirits — other creatures, including other werewolves, don't release their Essence in the same way. Therianthropes instead must consume the flesh of their animal-form. If the target creature is particularly small, the character may have to eat a handful of creatures to regain a single point.

Lunacy

There's a defense mechanism hard-wired into the human psyche, a little switch that prevents people from recognizing the true monsters out in the world. It dates from back in the days when humans lived in caves, when fire and pointed sticks hadn't yet conquered nature's domain. It's the source of humanity's primal fear of the dark and the strange, but over the millennia humanity has attempted to ignore it.

Facing a werewolf brings that feeling front and center. An avatar of savage fury, a werewolf has a predatory aura that triggers that defense mechanism. A human facing a hybrid werewolf is right back in the mouth of the cave as monsters howl in the dark and the fire goes out. The urge to run the fuck away, curl up into a weeping ball, or just stop responding to the world overrides everything else, and her short-term memory refuses to record the werewolf's presence.

As noted on p. 319 of **Hunter: The Vigil**, humans witnessing a werewolf in Bestial Hybrid form suffer a penalty to all actions that don't involve running in abject terror. That penalty depends on her Willpower: (10 – her Willpower) divided by 2, rounded against the human. This fear is so powerful that it overrides common reactions learned over centuries — an armed human suffers that same penalty when bringing his weapon to bear, even if he's armed for bear and beyond. The werewolf's triggering a primal flight reaction that the hunter can't fully override. A hunter with the Rites du Cheval Endowment adds his dots in that Endowment to his Willpower for the purposes of resisting Lunacy. More information on how Lunacy affects a hunter's mental state, and tricks that hunters use for mitigating the worst of the fear are dealt with on p. 202.

Example: Andy Wagner faces a werewolf in Bestial Hybrid form. His Willpower is 5, meaning that he suffers a -3 penalty (half of 10 – 5, rounded appropriately) to all actions that don't involve getting away from the werewolf.

A werewolf's other unnatural forms can bring about a similar fear, but at a reduced level. Anyone seeing the Near-wolf form suffers the effects of Lunacy as if her Willpower were two points higher. Those seeing the Near-man form in good light, or another situation where it's obviously not human, suffer the Lunacy as if their Willpower were four points higher. Note that these extra dots can't turn the penalty from Lunacy into a bonus, they can only reduce it to zero.

Worse than impeding his attempts to fight the beast coming to eat him, a human's mind refuses to remember the werewolf. Someone affected by Lunacy won't voluntarily recall the incident. If her Willpower (adjusted for seeing other forms as above) is below five, she won't remember the incident at all. Her short-term memory works fine, but when she gets a chance to rest and reflect, she blanks the event from her mind. She doesn't accurately remember anything apart from the need to get away. Only once she's nowhere near the werewolf does her memory start working. She may come up with crazy stories about what really happened, possibly involving enraged bears, or simply refuse to acknowledge any gap in her recollection of events. A few hunters have confused the witnesses of werewolf attacks with victims of alien abduction who suffer from "missing time."

A human with an adjusted Willpower above five dots will remember her encounter with a werewolf, but normally covers it in a thin layer of metaphor. She may rationalize it to get through her day, claiming she had to get away from a huge wolf, or unload her shotgun into some PCP-crazed nutcase to get him to stay down. She can remember the truth if she concentrates, and someone who mentions a similar encounter will often bring it to the front of her mind. If her adjusted Willpower is 10 or above, she recalls the incident just fine.

If a werewolf's Lunacy affects a group of people, the individual with the highest Willpower can roll Resolve + Composure. Each success adds one to his companions' Willpower with regards to taking actions only, up to a maximum of his own Willpower - 1. His confidence can't bolster their memory, only their ability to override their fear.

Lunacy only affects people who see a werewolf in person. Video and photographic evidence doesn't have the same effect — though a human looking through binoculars or a scope suffers the penalties as normal.

Some therianthropes inflict a lessened form of Lunacy. If their animal-form is obviously predatory — birds of prey, big cats, spiders, and the like — witnesses to their Bestial Hybrid form suffer the full effects of Lunacy. Animal-forms that inspire disgust without being predatory — everything from carrion-crows and rats to cockroaches and locusts — inflict Lunacy as if the witness had an extra dot of Willpower. This bonus doesn't carry through to the Near-man and Near-beast forms, however.

Finally, Lunacy only affects humans and animals. Spirits are entirely immune, as are people possessed by spirits, while the Claimed enjoy temporary immunity after a time as a spirit's host (see "The Claimed," p. 180).

Dominions

Werewolves don't just change their shape. Perhaps they have a naturally closer tie to the spirit world than other supernatural creatures, or perhaps the threat of primal rage within them scares spirits into obedience. Whatever the cause, werewolves can assert their dominance over lesser spirits, and through them, affect the physical world. Even the lowest werewolf might make the lights flicker and die from fear as he changes into a more bestial form. More powerful beasts can make a whole city quake in fear, cutting off their prey's retreat. Some Dominion powers work internally to the werewolf, magnifying his already impressive strength or empowering his claws to rend flesh and bone with ease. Such powers are "gifts" from spirits — bribes, given to save them from the werewolf's wrath. An observer who can perceive spirits can see the burning runes covering a werewolf's body, the obvious representations of her power.

A Dominion is a single, unique power. A werewolf who can turn out lights can do only that; he can't make electronics go haywire or summon darkness in the sun's light — at least, not without another Dominion. Some werewolves delight in finding new uses for their abilities, flexing their muscles — creating a handful of water is a fine way to survive in the desert, and an even better way to wreck a computer system. Others look on their Dominions as just rewards for their station as the apex predator of flesh and spirit, but prefer to use their raw physical power.

Each Dominion has a rating in dots, from one to five. A werewolf cannot have a Dominion rated higher than his dots in Primal Urge. A werewolf must possess at least one Dominion of each level — a werewolf with a four-dot Dominion must have a one-dot, two-dot, and a three-dot Dominion, but can possess any number of Dominions at any dot ratings. The following section breaks down each level, including mechanical guidelines and sample effects.

Most werewolves never develop a Dominion above three dots. A werewolf must constantly remind the spirit world of her position and her power, and few can maintain their position for long in the face of hostile spirits. Those who do are powerful leaders, with many werewolves under their command. The few werewolves who manage to hold on to a five-dot Dominion must struggle every day to reassert their power, at least until they perform a deed of such legendary savagery that the spirit world bows before them. Those few werewolves are like gods amongst other werewolves, able to marshal hordes of beastmen from across a state.

A werewolf's Dominions are perhaps the most obvious indicator of her ties to the spirits' world: any shapeshifter who possesses a Dominion can transform her body into ephemera and cross into the spirit world. The werewolf can only cross over at a Locus. Her player rolls Composure + Primal Urge as an Instant action, and she vanishes into the spirit world on the next turn.

Dominions are a type of Dread Power that demonstrate the command a werewolf has over the world. Other supernatural creatures could have Dominions, especially if they have a similar command over some facet of the world.

One-Dot Dominions

One-dot Dominions are simple, basic effects. The werewolf can make the world obey him in crude, simple ways — he barks and it jumps, but he's not taught it any tricks yet.

Clarity (•)

The werewolf focuses for a moment, instinctively absorbing every facet of the world around her. The battle around her is perfectly clear, and her reflexes heighten to the point that her victims never know what hit them — unless she wants them to.

Dice Pool: Wits + Brawl + Primal Urge
Action: Reflexive

Roll Results

Dramatic Failure: The werewolf is overwhelmed by everything going on, and falters. Her Initiative is reduced by 5 for the remainder of the combat. Her new place in the Initiative order takes effect on the next turn.

Failure: The werewolf acts no faster than normal.

Success: The werewolf acts on pure instinct. Each success adds two to the werewolf's Initiative for the rest of the combat. The werewolf's new place in the Initiative order takes effect on the next turn.

Exceptional Success: The werewolf reacts to external threats as well as enemies. Increase his Defense by one for the remainder of the turn.

City Eyes (•)

The werewolf touches one of the windows of the building, and commands it to share everything it sees. With but a moment, she can see everything that the building can, changing her perspective and looking in on hidden sights without ever entering a room.

Dice Pool: Wits + Composure + Primal Urge
Action: Instant

Roll Results

Dramatic Failure: The window shatters under the werewolf's hand, dealing a point of lethal damage.

Failure: The building doesn't respond.

Success: The werewolf can see through any of the windows of the building, either in or out, though only one at any one time. Her new viewpoint completely replaces her normal sight, and lasts for up to thirty seconds per success.

Exceptional Success: The werewolf gains +1 to Perception rolls involving tracking prey within the building.

Malfunction (•)

The werewolf touches a piece of technology and growls low, focusing his inner rage. The device shuts down out of fear, desperate to avoid the anger of an enraged werewolf. The technological item in question must rely on chemical or electrical energy to function — a werewolf can't stop a knife from cutting, but can make a car engine fail or a computer crash. If some-one else is holding the item, the werewolf must make a successful roll to touch the object (see "Touching an Opponent," **World of Darkness Rulebook**, p. 157).

Dice Pool: Presence + Crafts + Primal Urge

Action: Instant

Roll Results

Dramatic Failure: The item in question isn't affected, but the next technological object that the werewolf touches is disabled for three turns.

Failure: The item isn't cowed by the werewolf's rage.

Success: The item ceases to function for one turn per success rolled. Any attempts to repair the item while it is affected by this Dominion automatically fail.

Exceptional Success: The object's spirit remains frightened of the werewolf. After the normal effects end, reduce the object's equipment bonus by one.

Terrible Strike (•)

The werewolf is such a prominent force of de-struction that he does not need to use claws or fangs to inflict grievous wounds. He can tear flesh and crack bones without ever leaving his human form.

Dice Pool: Strength + Brawl + Primal Urge

Action: Reflexive

Roll Results

Dramatic Failure: The werewolf injures himself rather than his foes, taking one point of lethal damage.

Failure: The werewolf's blows are no more po-tent than normal.

Success: Any bashing damage that the werewolf deals in close combat is converted to lethal damage for one turn per success rolled.

Exceptional Success: In addition to the en-hanced duration, the werewolf's blows stun his target. The first character damaged by the werewolf after us-ing this Dominion subtracts five from his Initiative.

Unnatural Senses (•)

The werewolf emanates an aura of power that scares electronic devices into announcing their pres-ence, betraying their human masters. He can hear the location of any electrical device, though he doesn't know what it does.

Dice Pool: Resolve + Computer + Primal Urge

Action: Instant

Roll Results

Dramatic Failure: The werewolf can't differenti-ate the screams of individual devices. His next roll suffers a -1 modifier from the confusion.

Failure: The werewolf scares the devices into si-lence.

Success: The werewolf can pinpoint the loca-tion of any electronic devices, from toasters to cell phones, within five yards per dot of Primal Urge. The effects last for 30 seconds.

Exceptional Success: The werewolf has a rough idea of the kind of electronic device that's scream-ing — a blender doesn't signify a target, but a Taser or PDA does.

Warning Growl (•)

The werewolf growls, locking his eyes on one person; he channels his nature as an apex predator through that gaze, reminding his target of the world's order and striking sudden fear in her heart.

Dice Pool: Presence + Intimidation + Primal Urge versus Resolve + Composure

Action: Contested; resistance is reflexive

Roll Results

Dramatic Failure: The targets resolve strength-ens. Treat the target as though his Willpower were one point higher for purposes of the werewolf's Lu-nacy (p. 163) for the rest of the scene.

Failure: The target feels no particular dread.

Success: The target feels the cold grip of fear as she looks at a creature that could kill her with a swipe of a clawed finger. The target of this Dominion subtracts two dice from all attacks made against the werewolf for the rest of the scene. This Dominion can be used on multiple targets, but the werewolf must use it separately against each one.

Exceptional Success: As a success, but the pen-alty increases to -3.

Two-Dot Dominions

Two-dot Dominions expand the range of a were-wolf's capabilities. Rather than provoking an instinc-tive response, he can instead force the world to obey a simple command, though anything complex remains out of his reach.

Commandment (••)

The werewolf snarls a single, short command. His words, imbued with his predatory soul, force his tar-get to obey — though the target won't take any act that would (directly or indirectly) harm himself. This Dominion simply removes the target's normal resis-tance to the werewolf's authority.

Dice Pool: Presence + Intimidation + Primal Urge versus Resolve + Composure

Action: Contested; resistance is reflexive

Roll Results

Dramatic Failure: The target's resolve strength-ens. Treat the target as though his Willpower were two points higher for purposes of the werewolf's Lunacy for the rest of the scene.

Failure: The target feels no compulsion to obey.

Success: The target must obey the werewolf's command, as long as it would not harm the target to do so. The command must be short and to the point, the sort of thing that the werewolf could say with a single snarl. The target won't carry out a command that's drastically out of character, nor will he carry out a command if locked in combat. Fortunately, the target believes that her will was her own and that she chose to follow the command.

Exceptional Success: The target rationalizes her experience, coming up with an explanation for why going along with the werewolf was in her best interests.

Nightfall (••)

The werewolf takes away his prey's most powerful weapon: the ability to see clearly. With but a snarl, all electric lights — from battery-powered flashlights to streetlights — hide themselves from the werewolf, afraid that he will notice them and wreak terrible revenge. The lights don't just switch off; they refuse to function at all.

Dice Pool: Wits + Larceny + Primal Urge

Action: Instant

Roll Results

Dramatic Failure: The lights shine defiant, focusing their gaze upon the werewolf. All Stealth attempts suffer a -2 die penalty until the sun next rises.

Failure: Nothing happens.

Success: The werewolf specifies a single area that he can see clearly. The lights within that area — large enough to encompass a family home or an entire floor of a large office building — die instantly. Electric lights refuse to function. The effects last for one scene, or until the werewolf chooses to end this power.

Exceptional Success: The werewolf gains selective control over all the lights in the area, able to switch them on and off at a whim.

Ruin (••)

With nothing more than a harsh bark, the werewolf destroys a man-made object. The object actively twists itself apart, metal bars crumple, and plastic plates shatter into pieces. The werewolf can't affect an object larger than about one square yard — he can destroy a car radiator or a ceiling beam, but not the whole car or ceiling.

Dice Pool: Wits + Crafts + Primal Urge

Action: Instant

Roll Results

Dramatic Failure: The werewolf's body writhes and warps. He takes two points of bashing damage.

Failure: The Dominion doesn't work.

Success: The item warps and crumples, taking one point of Structure damage per success. This damage ignores the item's Durability.

Exceptional Success: The item falls apart. Even if it's not destroyed, any attempt to repair the item fails automatically.

Shallow Heart (••)

Picking up on a victim's fears, the werewolf forces his dominance over the darkest parts of his prey's psyche. For a short time, his victim gives in to another set of base desires quite apart from her norm, yet must sit through the whole spectacle not knowing why she acts; becomes, only that she does. Some use this Dominion as a non-lethal punishment for those who betray them, others like seeing their prey fighting her own nature.

Dice Pool: Composure + Larceny + Primal Urge versus Resolve + Composure

Action: Contested; resistance is reflexive

Roll Results

Dramatic Failure: The werewolf twists her own inner nature. Assign the werewolf a new Vice.

Failure: Nothing happens.

Success: The werewolf twists the core of weakness inside his prey, molding it into a different shape. The Storyteller should assign the target a new Vice for the subject, which lasts until the end of the day and should be role-played appropriately. The new Vice entirely replaces the old one, though if the subject has already indulged himself during this scene he can do so again. The new Vice comes from within the character, and the werewolf has no control over his target's new flaw.

Exceptional Success: The victim begins to question who she is. This strange understanding is equivalent to committing a sin with a Morality Threshold of 6.

Slip Away (••)

Werewolves may find themselves in tricky situations, but sometimes they're in real trouble: hands bound or even hogtied while in human form, without a way to shapeshift. Tapping the core of rage within, the werewolf exerts his dominance over his bonds; they have no right to hold him, and let him free to have his revenge.

Dice Pool: Presence + Larceny + Primal Urge

Action: Instant

Roll Results

Dramatic Failure: The chains rebel, locking down even tighter. Any rolls to release the werewolf without an appropriate key suffers a -2 modifier.

Failure: The werewolf remains bound.

Success: The shackles fall from the werewolf's limbs, leaving him free. Rope, handcuffs, chain, duct tape, and even industrial adhesive are no match for this Dominion. The bonds remain locked and unbroken. If the werewolf is locked in a grapple by another person, he automatically breaks free.

Exceptional Success: The werewolf breaks out with such grace that his captors are caught unaware. If he uses this Dominion as the prelude to an attack, add 5 to his Initiative.

Warrior Ideal (••)

The werewolf focuses on one person among his prey, noting every twitch and involuntary movement, every strange scent and subtle sound. He moves with his opponent, already aware of anything she's about to do. Though she can try to defend, it's useless — the werewolf is just too strong. The werewolf must activate this Dominion at the beginning of his action.

Dice Pool: Wits + Brawl + Primal Urge – opponent's Resolve

Action: Reflexive

Roll Results

Dramatic Failure: The character misreads his opponent and gives away a weakness. His Defense doesn't apply against that opponent's next attack.

Failure: The werewolf finds no weakness to exploit.

Success: The werewolf finds a weakness and exploits it. Reduce the specific opponent's Defense by the werewolf's Primal Urge (to a minimum of Defense 1) until the end of the scene. If the opponent dodges, or has Merits that affect Defense, subtract Primal Urge from the total Defense. The werewolf's attacks can involve any kind of attack, as long as he's within close-combat distance.

Exceptional Success: Add one to the werewolf's Primal Urge for the purpose of this Dominion.

Three-Dot Dominions

Three-dot Dominions demonstrate the werewolf's command of the world. While the abilities granted at two dots are immediate and reasonably simple, this level of power allows him to demonstrate more finesse in his control of the world.

All three-dot Dominions cost a point of Essence.

Command Fire (•••)

With a glare and a snarl, the werewolf bends flame to his will. Though he cannot summon it from nothing, he can direct and twist existing fires in ways that defy nature. The flames from a bonfire arc through the air to scorch his foes, or a burning apartment cools for long enough that he can rescue his packmates.

Dice Pool: Strength + Survival + Primal Urge

Action: Instant

Roll Results

Dramatic Failure: Nearby flames lash out at the werewolf, dealing one point of damage.

Failure: The fire resists the werewolf's commands.

Success: The werewolf can control one source of fire within line of sight. He can use the fire to lash out at a target, dealing one point of damage to someone within 20 yards of the flames. Alternatively, he can encourage the fire to spread (doubling its rate of growth) or diminish (reducing the heat of the fire by one step for one minute). See p. 180 of the **World of Darkness Rulebook**.

Exceptional Success: The werewolf can bolster or diminish the flames. Increase or decrease the size of the fire by one step. If this power diminishes a fire that's the size of a torch, the fire goes out.

Death Grip (•••)

The powerful jaws of a werewolf in one of his animal forms can deal incredible damage. This Dominion makes her bite attacks even more potent, easily able to tear a foe's body in two. The werewolf must use this power in Bestial Hybrid, Near-wolf, or Wolf form, and must have successfully grappled his opponent when activating this Dominion.

Dice Pool: Strength + Brawl + Primal Urge

Action: Reflexive

Roll Results

Dramatic Failure: The werewolf wrenches his jaws, taking a point of bashing damage.

Failure: The werewolf doesn't inflict particularly grievous wounds.

Success: The werewolf's jaws lock in with incredible power. If the werewolf attempts to bite the target of her grapple, she doubles her dice pool. She also gains six extra dice for rolls to overpower her opponent. This Dominion lasts for as long as the werewolf grapples his foe.

Exceptional Success: The shock of the werewolf's savage fury immobilizes the victim (**World of Darkness Rulebook**, p. 157). The werewolf doesn't have to actively maintain this immobilization, and can bite or perform other actions.

Gridlock (•••)

The city is hunting ground for many werewolves. Some possess Dominions that allow them to bend it

to their whim, trapping their prey in a mass of coincidences — sudden mobs slow the prey's movement, or a subway station locks down and no trains arrive before the werewolves strike.

Dice Pool: Resolve + Streetwise + Primal Urge versus Resolve + Composure

Action: Contested; resistance is reflexive

Roll Results

Dramatic Failure: The city hinders the werewolf, rather than his prey. All rolls to follow the prey suffer a -1 penalty for the rest of the scene.

Failure: The city doesn't respond to the werewolf.

Success: The target can't leave his immediate surroundings in any vehicle, and his Speed on foot is reduced by the werewolf's Primal Urge score for one minute per success.

Exceptional Success: The target's Speed is reduced by an additional -1 when on foot.

Primal Fear (•••)

With a mighty howl, the werewolf brings back instincts buried in ancestral memory. The howl speaks of monsters prowling the night, and all who hear it fear that this time, the werewolf comes for them. This Dominion affects everyone within 20 yards per dot of Primal Urge who roll resistance separately. Note that this Dominion can be used in any form.

Dice Pool: Presence + Expression + Primal Urge versus Composure

Action: Contested; resistance is reflexive

Roll Results

Dramatic Failure: For the rest of the scene, treat all witnesses to the werewolf as though their Willpower were two higher for the purposes of Lunacy.

Failure: The target feels a momentary fear, but nothing more.

Success: The target is affected by the werewolf's Lunacy as if the werewolf were in his Bestial Hybrid form for the rest of the scene.

Exceptional Success: The target is affected as for a success, but counts his Willpower as two points less.

Talons of Guilt (•••)

Some werewolves stand in judgment over humanity. Faced with a creature that can end their lives so swiftly, a human relives every bad thing she's ever done — be it petty theft or grand larceny, harsh words, or murder. Those memories wrack the victim's body as surely as feelings of guilt overcome her mind.

Dice Pool: Presence + Investigation + Primal Urge – target's Morality

Action: Instant

Roll Results

Dramatic Failure: The werewolf's own sins come back to haunt her. She can take no action on her next turn, but still applies her Defense to incoming attacks.

Failure: Nothing happens.

Success: The target's sins inflict one point of lethal damage per success. He also suffers a -1 penalty during his next turn as he reorients himself. The werewolf doesn't learn anything about the target's sins, only how much they hurt.

Exceptional Success: The disorientation and associated penalty last for the rest of the scene.

Four-Dot Dominions

Four-dot Dominions are the stuff of most hunters' nightmares. The werewolf is an apex predator, and the spirits of the world acknowledge that. If he prefers subtle manipulations, he can change the world in dramatic ways. If the werewolf is more direct, he can amplify his own power to an incredible degree.

All four-dot Dominions cost two points of Essence.

Beast Control (••••)

The werewolf's Dominion extends to other beasts. Rather than facing the rage of a werewolf, they give up their very bodies that a werewolf can continue his hunt. The werewolf's body falls comatose, but his mind remains abroad in the world. This Dominion only works on carnivorous animals and birds, including carrion-eaters.

Dice Pool: Wits + Animal Ken + Primal Urge

Action: Instant

Roll Results

Dramatic Failure: The werewolf takes on some of the animal's mannerisms. All Social rolls suffer a -2 modifier for 24 hours.

Failure: The animal resists the werewolf's possession.

Success: The werewolf rides the animal's mind. He can act as a passenger, leaving the animal in control and sharing its senses, or can take full control of the host body. Any injuries to the animal also appear on the werewolf's body — if the animal takes three points of lethal damage, the werewolf's body takes the same amount of damage. If the werewolf's body is injured, he's aware of the wound and can choose to return at any time. If the werewolf's body dies while his mind is away, he is subsumed into the animal's consciousness, and if the animal dies, the werewolf dies as well. The werewolf can control an animal for one hour per success.

Exceptional Success: The werewolf can control the animal for one day per success rolled.

Fracture (••••)

Often, a werewolf must remain cautious when killing his prey. While his Bestial Hybrid form can devastate a human, it might not be the best option in the middle of a packed shopping mall. Instead, he exerts his own Dominion over his prey's bones, causing them to crack and twist with every blow. The werewolf must strike her target for at least one point of damage, and cannot use a weapon.

Dice Pool: Strength + Medicine + Primal Urge

Action: Reflexive

Roll Results

Dramatic Failure: The werewolf wrenches his own bones as he strikes, taking one point of lethal damage

Failure: The werewolf hits no harder than normal.

Success: The werewolf deals one extra point of lethal damage per success rolled. This damage isn't affected by Dominions that affect the damage a werewolf deals (such as Savage Rending, below). If the werewolf aimed for an arm, the target drops what he was holding, if he hit a leg the target halves his Speed for the rest of the scene, and a torso or head strike inflicts an additional -1 modifier on all Physical actions for one turn per success.

Exceptional Success: The bone shatters into splinters. Without immediate medical attention, the bone will not set right and the limb may require amputation.

Graveyard Chill (••••)

The werewolf inhales, sucking the heat from the area. When he has finished, only the chill of a hundred winters remains. Frost covers the ground and water turns to ice. In a rainstorm, the sudden freezing rain wreaks destruction on tree branches and power lines both, and people subjected to the open air soon feel the incredible cold in their bones.

Dice Pool: Manipulation + Survival + Primal Urge

Action: Instant

Roll Results

Dramatic Failure: The cold strikes at the werewolf's heart. He takes two points of lethal damage.

Failure: The temperature drops, but only by a couple of degrees.

Success: The temperature plummets below freezing within 10 yards of the werewolf per dot of Primal Urge. The sudden onset of cold deals two points of bashing damage to living creatures in the affected area. Strength and Dexterity rolls suffer a -2 penalty until the cold lifts. Inanimate objects take one point of Structure damage. The freeze lasts for one turn per success.

Exceptional Success: The temperature shift is particularly harsh, dealing three points of bashing damage rather than two.

Savage Rending (••••)

The werewolf becomes an incarnate force, the original beast that destroys men and animals without thought or effort. His claws and teeth grow longer and sharper, easily able to cleave through flesh and bone to deal devastating wounds.

Dice Pool: Strength + Brawl + Primal Urge
Action: Instant

Roll Results

Dramatic Failure: The werewolf's claws and teeth grow out of control, dealing one point of aggravated damage to himself.

Failure: The werewolf's claws and teeth remain as sharp as ever, but do no more damage.

Success: The werewolf's claws and teeth deal aggravated damage. Only the kind of damage changes, not the amount of damage being dealt. The enhanced weapons last for a scene.

Exceptional Success: The werewolf's natural weapons more easily frighten his opponents. He gains a +2 bonus to all Intimidation rolls

Shadow Hunter (••••)

Nothing can keep the werewolf from his chosen target. With a low growl, she transforms her body into a shadow, able to travel through the smallest cracks to find her prey. Only a place without shadows — either powerful lights or complete darkness — can force the werewolf to resume her physical form.

Dice Pool: Wits + Stealth + Primal Urge
Action: Instant

Roll Results

Dramatic Failure: The werewolf's shadow rebels. For the rest of the scene, she casts a shadow of a different form — as a Man she might cast the shadow of Bestial Hybrid, while her Wolf form casts a Nearman's shadow.

Failure: Nothing happens.

Success: The werewolf transforms into a two-dimensional shadow, projected against a surface. She gains a +3 bonus to Stealth rolls and to Defense. She can only manipulate objects — turning a doorknob, typing on a keyboard, or pulling the trigger of a gun — when they're under her shadow, and then at a -2 penalty. She can pass through any gap, as long as there's enough light (or darkness) for her to remain a shadow on the other side. The shadow form lasts for one minute per success.

Exceptional Success: The werewolf can remain in her shadow form for the duration of the scene.

Five-Dot Dominions

Not many werewolves possess five-dot Dominions, and that's a fact for which most hunters are thankful. These powers are the hallmark of a being that commands total respect from one aspect of the spirit world — and through that, the physical world. The sheer scale of these Dominions puts them on their own level, with incredible destructive power.

All five-dot Dominions cost two points of Essence.

Discordant Howl (•••••)

All battlefields are chaotic places. Some werewolves hold Dominion over spirits of chaos and disorder, and turn that insanity to their advantage with a howl — SWAT teams fire on each other, prey find themselves running in circles, and phone calls are hopelessly garbled. The werewolf must howl or drum in any form to use this Dominion.

Dice Pool: Manipulation + Expression + Primal Urge versus Resolve
Action: Contested; resistance is reflexive

Roll Results

Dramatic Failure: Chaos spreads through the spirit world. The werewolf cannot use any Dominions for the remainder of the scene.

Failure: The listener isn't affected by the werewolf's power.

Success: The listener succumbs to the werewolf's song. For as long as the werewolf concentrates on his howl, all of the target's actions are reduced to a chance die. The werewolf can't take any non-reflexive actions while howling, and inflicting a wound on the werewolf ends the howl instantly.

Exceptional Success: The listener's first action when hearing the werewolf's howl is automatically a dramatic failure.

Devastation (•••••)

The city exists apart from the humans who dwell in it. Normally, the city and the population live in harmony, but a werewolf with Dominion over cities can invert that relationship for one block. Fire hydrants explode like cannon shells, streetlights over-charge and ground out through hapless humans, and windows rain razor-shards of glass on the people below.

Dice Pool: Intelligence + Streetwise + Primal Urge
Action: Extended (35 successes needed; each roll represents five minutes' concentration).

Roll Results

Dramatic Failure: The werewolf suffers a -1 modifier while he remains in the same city block.

Failure: The city doesn't react.

Success: The city block lashes out at the humans within. The block makes two attacks per turn on the werewolf's Initiative until the end of the scene, with a pool equal to the werewolf's Primal Urge score. Treat the attacks as thrown weapons for the purposes of Defense. An exploding fire hydrant is a 3(L) weapon, falling glass is 2(L), and a collapsing billboard is 2(B). Everyone in the block subtracts two from their Speed, and suffers a -1 penalty to other actions due to smoke and falling debris.

Exceptional Success: A building within the block collapses; anyone underneath or inside takes 10 points of lethal damage. Armor reduces that damage, but Defense doesn't apply.

Savage Fury (•••••)

Most werewolves are lethal combatants. Some rise beyond that, applying their Dominion to the chase and the slaughter. When such a werewolf indulges her Rage, nothing can stand in her path. Any weapons her prey brings to bear refuse to strike with their full force, and the werewolf tears through her foes like a bloody whirlwind.

Dice Pool: Dexterity + Empathy + Primal Urge

Action: Instant

Roll Results

Dramatic Failure: The werewolf loses her Defense for the remainder of combat.

Failure: The werewolf is no more formidable an opponent than she was before.

Success: The werewolf becomes a blur of fangs and talons, dealing death wherever she treads. For one turn per success, she receives the benefit of a dodge against all incoming attacks *and* can make attacks with the benefit of an all-out attack (**World of Darkness Rulebook**, pp. 156 and 157 respectively). This Dominion lasts for one turn per success.

Exceptional Success: The werewolf applies his enhanced Defense against firearms attacks as well as close combat attacks.

Terrible Might (•••••)

There come times when even a werewolf's strength isn't enough. Calling on his Dominion over the world, he pours his own Essence into bone, muscle, and sinew. For one single extraordinary display of strength, the werewolf is stronger than anything else on Earth.

Cost: 1 Willpower
Dice Pool: Strength + Athletics + Primal Urge
Action: Reflexive

Roll Results

Dramatic Failure: The werewolf's Dominion turns against him. Reduce his Strength by one for the duration of the scene.

Failure: The werewolf is no stronger than he was before.

Success: The werewolf gains one point of Strength per success rolled. There's no upper limit to the Strength granted by this Dominion — a werewolf who rolls four successes adds four to his Strength in any form. This enhanced Strength lasts for a single turn, and can be used for both attacks and non-attack actions.

Exceptional Success: A remnant of his enhanced Strength lingers. Increase the werewolf's Strength by one for the remainder of the scene.

Spirits

The world of flesh is not the only one to hold creatures that prey on humans. Hidden just beyond normal perception, spirits lurk in the darkness. Not the helpful forces that most occultists believed, the spirits that dwell in the World of Darkness know only their own nature, and damn anything that gets in their way. To a spirit, humanity is of no more consequence than rocks and trees — some would say less, for though rocks and trees have spirits, humans have no reflection of their own.

Animism is a fact of the World of Darkness. Everything has a spirit, from the lowliest flame of a candle to the sun and moon themselves. Man-made creations aren't exempt from that law — spirits of guns foster gang-wars while the spirits of every city on Earth shape their abode. Spirits aren't limited to just physical things — Hate, Pain, Lust, and even Friendship have spirits of their own. Mostly, they reside on a plane that no conspiracy can access, but some spirits feel confined, and decide to take an active role in this world.

Spirits live for the specific facet of the world that grants them power. They don't think like humans and don't act like humans — everything they do, they do to further their aspect. A spirit of medicine might inhabit a hospital and speed people to good health, hoping to increase the hospital's reputation. Not many spirits have the patience for such a deal — they'd rather slow the healing of everyone in the hospital, and sway the minds of doctors to recommend experimental treatments and unnecessary surgeries. If that doesn't work, the spirit has to go further afield, creating an outbreak of a headline-grabbing disease like H5N1 or MRSA, or even causing a freeway pile-up that injures hundreds of people. Individual people *do not matter*. All that matters is that "medicine" becomes more important to the local area.

The spirit world itself is a strange place, a world of symbolism reflecting the physical world close to it. How an area feels matters more than what it looks like; human emotions and expectations shape the spirit world even though humans have no spirits themselves. Most hunters never see the spirit world (sometimes called the Shadow), dealing only with spirits who materialize in the physical world or possess people or objects. Others can perceive immaterial spirits, and in special places where the barrier between the physical and spiritual are weak, the hunter can see the spiritual reflection of that place.

Most spirits aren't active. They passively accept whatever happens in the world without making their presence known. A few awaken from their slumber-like state, taking an active interest in the world around them — both physical and spiritual. Once awake, they remain so, desperate to increase their power. A few active spirits cross over into the physical world. It's risky for them to make that crossing, because they become prey: for werewolves looking for a shot of Essence; for other spirits trying to carve out a place for themselves; and even for unscrupulous human occultists who seek to bind them. Every spirit has a reason to cross into the physical world. Weak spirits seek refuge in the physical world, hiding from powerful foes that would destroy them. Powerful spirits cross over to set up an unassailable power base close to their aspect. Particularly twisted spirits might want to steal a human body and taste the pleasures of the flesh for themselves.

Glossary

The alien nature of the spirit world and its dependence on things that humans consider abstract concepts can make it difficult to define spirits. The

BEYOND A HUNTER'S EYES

This chapter portrays spirits as they're encountered by hunters — spirits who cross into the physical world and make life hell for normal people. Their focus is thus as an alien threat, something beyond normal reckoning that's an intrinsic, natural part of the world. Some groups may want to go beyond that remit, taking the fight back beyond the physical world. Book of Spirits, while not essential to one's understanding of spirits, provides additional information on the spirit world for hunters who travel there.

These places, called Loci, each have a magnitude and a resonance. Magnitude reflects the area that the Locus covers around the landmark that defines the Locus. A Locus of magnitude 1 may only affect an area a few yards across, while one of magnitude 3 may be a forest clearing or a floor of a building, and a Locus of mag-

terms below, used throughout this section, pin down the core elements.

Aspect: The defining trait of a spirit, a noun describing what the spirit is. A spirit of pain has the aspect of "Pain," a spirit of lust has the aspect of "Lust," and a spirit of guns has the aspect of "Guns." Note that the spirit of Guns is different to the spirit of .45s, and that's a different spirit again to the spirit within a specific .45. Each has a different aspect to reflect that. When a powerful spirit consumes a weaker one, it takes the weaker spirit's aspect as part of its own and changes accordingly.

Essence: The substance of the spirit world. All Essence has a Resonance that affects its flavor. Spirits must consume Essence to live, and werewolves use it to power their physical abilities. Essence doesn't have a manifestation in the physical world.

Influence: The specific aspects of reality over which a spirit has some sway. Usually, a spirit's Influences all reflect its aspect. One spirit of Justice might have an Influence over Honesty, another might have Vengeance. While a spirit's aspect is what it is, its Influences are what it can affect.

Resonance: A "flavor," as it applies to a part of the world, usually a descriptive term. Resonance applies to Essence and Loci in the same way that an aspect applies to a spirit. A pain-spirit would rather devour Essence with an "anguished" resonance if it had a choice, while a spirit of a sports-car would only consume that Essence if nothing else were available. Resonance usually reflects the character and "feel" of the area that generates it.

Loci

In some places, the walls between the physical and spiritual worlds have thinned. Perhaps generations of people believed it a sacred site where they made dark offerings to blasphemous gods. Maybe a particularly bloody murder left its stain on an alleyway, and nobody can walk through it without noticing the otherworldly sense left behind. In these places, spirits can slip into the physical world.

Jim Di Bartolo

nitude 5 would be the size of a whole lake or city block. A Locus generates Essence each day equal to three times its magnitude, which is available to whoever takes it — whether that's hungry werewolves or desperate spirits.

A Locus's resonance is a one- or two-word description of the spiritual "feeling" generated by the focal point and felt throughout the Locus. A torture-site's resonance may be "Fear" or "Pain;" a statue in a graveyard has a resonance of "Grief" or "Loss;" and an asylum cell resonates with "Madness." A spirit can use any Locus that resonates with its aspect to slip into the physical world. In addition, when within the area of a suitable Locus, a spirit heals twice as fast as it would otherwise.

Spirits who slip into the physical world remain immaterial, in a non-corporeal state of Twilight (similar to ghosts). They can't be detected by beings that can't perceive Twilight, though werewolves can sense them with a Wits + Occult roll. Anyone who can perceive spirits in Twilight doesn't see the normal world at a Locus — she instead can see straight through to the spirit realm.

To cross into the physical world, the spirit spends three Essence and must roll Power + Finesse. The

spirit remains in the physical world for one hour per success, after which the spirit loses one Essence per Rank every hour. A spirit can go further, manifesting physically, but only if it's already in Twilight and at a Locus of appropriate resonance. Physical manifestation requires three more points of Essence and another roll of Power + Finesse. The spirit remains active in the physical world for one hour per two successes, and must spend a point of Essence per Rank for every *15 minutes* after that.

Every source of Essence has a resonance as well. While werewolves overpower the resonance of any Essence they consume with their own unmistakable spiritual signature, spirits can and do take advantage of different Essence sources. A spirit who has consumed Essence of an appropriate resonance within the past day can use a Locus of that resonance as if it was aligned to the spirit's aspect. Consuming Essence with a resonance opposed to their aspect drives many spirits mad as they attempt to reconcile the conflicting aspects of meaning within themselves.

Rank

The alien laws of the spirit realm revolve around resonance and Essence. Some spirits work these laws to their advantage, gaining in power and influence. Others try their best, but never rise beyond the lowest ranks. The tie to resonance makes the spirit world a reflection of the physical — as concepts grow in power in the physical world, so do their related spirits. Conversely, as spirits gain and lose power through the strange politics of the spirit realm, their related concepts in the physical world gain and lose importance. The relationship is truly symbiotic.

A spirit's relative importance is measured by its Rank.

Weak spirits (Rank 1) are the lowest of the low, glimmers representing an e-mail message or a candle-flame. They've no inherent importance and little understanding of the world, but make excellent pawns for powerful spirits and have a single-minded devotion to their aspect.

Minor spirits (Rank 2) have gained a measure of awareness and subtlety. They're cunning and clever enough to play the game, but they don't have the leverage to get any further, the drones of the spirit world. Many have plans afoot that would grow their power, at the expense of other spirits — plans that bring them to the physical world.

Major Spirits (Rank 3) grow more complex. Though the majority of spirits still embody specific concepts, some no longer having a particular physical representation — a spirit of Fire, rather than a fire-spirit birthed from the Great Fire of London. Others grew in power by consuming lesser spirits, and thus have absorbed the aspect of their prey, giving them a dangerously divided nature.

Greater spirits (Rank 4) are the most powerful spirits that most hunters will encounter. Lords over their aspect, these spirits have a wealth of power at their disposal and considerable influence over spirits of lesser Rank. These spirits usually keep close to a prominent example of their aspect, either in the spirit world or the physical, and can call upon support from spirits of lesser Rank. If a spirit of this Rank manifests physically, it's impossible to miss.

Superior spirits (Rank 5) are minor gods of their aspect. Only two things matter to them: maintaining their rank, and ensuring their aspect remains at the forefront of the world. Fortunately, such powerful spirits have strong ties to the spirit world, and risk traveling to the world of flesh only rarely. When they do — and worse, when they condense themselves into physical form — it's nothing short of a localized apocalypse.

Bans

Every spirit has a ban — a specific weakness that affects its behavior or robs it of a part of its power. There's no getting around it, every spirit suffers from one specific weakness. It's just the way things are. The spirit of the Great Fire of London may weaken in the presence of water drawn fresh from the River Thames, while a spirit of disease must flee from the presence of antiseptic, and the spirit of Justice cannot tell an outright lie.

A spirit's ban is directly tied to its Rank. A minor spirit will have a ban that's relatively easy to trigger: the spirit of a candle flame weakens in the presence of bright light; a wolf-spirit can't attack a wolf or were-wolf who outranks it; a superior spirit's ban is likely strange and obscure. On the other hand, there's only so far a less-powerful spirit can fall when a hunter triggers its ban; finding the exact conditions necessary to weaken a superior spirit is the only way that hunters stand a chance against it.

Hunters can make use of spirit bans in a range of ways. A spirit who can't set foot on asphalt won't be able to enter the world at a Locus when the hunters bribe a planning committee to pave the area. Likewise, if a cult's warped master can't stand the presence of lavender then a hunter cell can stop the spirit and drive it out of a human that it's possessing.

Discovering a spirit's ban requires patient research, whether it involves asking other spirits or digging through an occultist's library. Any attempt to uncover a spirit's ban is an extended Intelligence +

Occult roll, requiring 20 successes, with each roll taking one hour. The hunters must have some reasonable resource that might hold the ban — an occult library, a captive spirit, or access to secretive underground websites — and each roll suffers a penalty equal to the spirit's Rank.

Sample Bans

A weak cat-spirit cannot turn away from a puzzle or riddle without first solving it. The minor spirit of a traffic light can only travel on asphalted roads.

A minor wolf-spirit can't attack a wolf or werewolf that outranks it, while the spirit of a sports car weakens when forced to remain still.

Several major spirits of disease can't stand the presence of one medicinal plant — a different plant for each spirit. They flee from the smoke if it's burned and can't cross a line drawn with a paste made from the plant. A major death-spirit is struck powerless by the light of a candle made from human-fat.

Some greater spirits of war cannot refuse a drink of blood that is dedicated to them, and must consume the whole offering. A spirit of the desert sun cannot accept or grant mercy, and the sight of someone treating a hated enemy with kindness is enough to drive them away.

Superior spirits have truly unique bans. The spirit of the New York subway is powerless to act against anyone who touches the third rail and lives.

Spirit Traits

Spirits don't have the same traits as humans. Being abstract creatures, they use suitably abstracted Attributes, and don't have Skills at all. For material creatures, dice pools are built from an Attribute and a Skill, spirits instead combine Power, Finesse, or Resistance with either each other or an appropriate Influence. If a spirit doesn't have an Influence that applies to the task, they suffer a -3 penalty to the roll.

Power: A spirit's Power represents the raw impact in the spirit world, either through its form or through sheer force of will. There's no distinction between mental, physical, or social power to spirits — raw ability is all that matters. Use the spirit's Power for all rolls that would normally involve Intelligence, Strength, or Presence.

Finesse: A spirit's Finesse measures how well it can manipulate spirits, people, and the very world around it. While a spirit may have a great deal of Power, it takes Finesse to use that power appropriately to impose its own concepts on others. Use the spirit's Finesse for all rolls that would normally involve Wits, Dexterity, or Manipulation.

Resistance: A spirit's Resistance represents the strength of the idea behind the spirit and how easily it is damaged or changed by outside factors — rather than changing as a result of the spirit's own actions. Use the spirit's Resistance for all rolls that would normally involve Resolve, Stamina, or Composure.

Corpus: Much as Health represents the endurance of living creatures, Corpus measures the resiliency of the spirit's ephemeral form. Corpus dots equal the spirit's Resistance + Size. Spirits heal Corpus at the same rate that humans heal damage (**World of Darkness Rulebook**, p. 175). If a spirit loses all its Corpus to aggravated damage, it discorporates back to the spirit world and cannot return to the physical world for at least a lunar month. If a spirit loses all of its Corpus and Essence both, it is destroyed.

Essence: A spirit's maximum Essence is determined from its Rank. A spirit can hold at most five points of Essence plus five more per Rank — a Rank 3 spirit could thus hold 20 points of Essence, while a rank 5 spirit could hold at most 30 points of Essence. A spirit must spend one point of Essence per day to remain active. Over and above that, most spiritual abilities cost Essence, and those who don't have a regular supply become desperate for their fix of spiritual energy. Spirits can also use Essence to boost Power, Finesse, or Resistance, on a one-for-one basis. The boosted trait remains until the end of the scene.

Essence also allows a spirit to remain in the physical world after slipping through at a Locus. The only way to avoid paying the cost is through Possess (see p. 179). A spirit who loses all its Essence in this way slips back into the spirit world until it can gather enough resources to cross into the world once more.

Spirits can regain Essence in a number of ways. The simplest way is to remain in the vicinity of the spirit's aspect, though the spirit only gains one point of Essence per day. Spirits can also consume the essence generated at Loci, barter for Essence with other spirits, or attempt to absorb lesser spirits (contested Power versus Resistance roll, the attacker gains one Essence with resonance of the victim's aspect per net success).

Willpower: Spirits have Willpower dots equal to Power + Resistance. A spirit's very essence requires a strong will to survive and grow in power. Most spirits regain one point of spent Willpower each day. Additionally, a spirit regains one point of spent Willpower when the spirit consumes a point of Essence with appropriate resonance.

Speed: A spirit's Speed is equal to Power + Finesse + a factor determined by the spirit's form. Spirits of inanimate objects add 0, animals add between 4 and 7, and spirits noted for their speed — a wildfire, or a car notorious for killing people at freeway speeds — add 9 or 10.

Size: Generally, spirits of abstract concepts are Size 2, and spirits tied to physical objects have the same Size as that object. To create spirits whose size relate to their Rank, add the spirit's Rank to a factor depending on form — 2 or 3 for a human or wolf-sized spirit, 5 or 6 for particularly large spirits. Using this system, abstract spirits use their Rank as their Size.

Skills and Merits: A spirit doesn't possess either of these categories of traits, though Influences can take the place of Skills.

Combat: Spirits have the same secondary traits (Initiative and Defense) as human combatants. A spirit attacks with a dice pool of Power + Influence. Most spirits deal lethal damage, though some spirits of Rank 1 may only deal bashing damage if they're particularly inconsequential. Corpus takes the place of Health for spirits.

Influences

Spirits aren't just the passive creations of the things that gave them existence; they can exert influence over the material world in much the same way as the material world affects them. These Influences are more than a simple way for the spirit to affect the world; they measure the spirit's connection with its aspect.

Every spirit has one or more Influences, rated from 0 to 5 like Skills. Each one is freely defined, and relates in some way to a spirit's aspect. A dog-spirit would likely have Dogs as one of its Influences, while a snake-spirit might have Snakes or Poison as an Influence, depending on how the spirit relates to the concept of "snake." A few spirits take on the Influences of weaker spirits that they have consumed, becoming terrible amalgams of otherwise wholly separate concepts. A horse-spirit consumes a spirit of flame. No longer just one or the other, it becomes a massive horse without skin or hair, with a burning mane and hooves of molten iron — and Influence over Horses and Fire both.

Using Influences

Primarily, a spirit uses its influences in the same way that other creatures use Skills. If any task would fall under the purview of one of a spirit's Influences, then that Influence counts as the spirit's Skill for the roll in question. Influences are broad things, and many spirits only have one or two, so each influence should be read in a reasonably broad fashion; a spirit of any predatory animal can use their Influence over that animal as a combat Skill, for example, and a spirit of war can use its Influence as a Skill whenever it's in a formal conflict, even if that conflict is actually a debate.

In the physical world, spirits can change the world directly by using their Influences. The dice pool to do so is defined by what the spirit wants to do:

Strengthen: The spirit enhances its sphere of Influence, make an emotion stronger, a plant healthier, or an object more robust. If used on a living thing, each success heals one point of bashing damage, or two successes can heal lethal damage. Conversely, strengthening agony would increase wound penalties by one per success. Roll Resistance + Influence. Strengthen costs one point of Essence.

Control: The spirit can exert overt control over anything that comes under its Influence, twisting emotions, making an animal do as the spirit commands, or changing an object's functioning. If the spirit changes something's state, either the beginning or end state must fall under the Influence in question — a spirit of Lust could make angry men into angry lovers or turn a carnal relationship into a messy break-up, but couldn't turn hatred or sloth into friendship. Roll Finesse + Influence. Control costs two points of Essence.

Create: The spirit can use itself as a channel, refining Essence into a new example of its sphere of Influence. It can create a powerful emotion in people who felt nothing, create a new sapling, or manifest an object *ex nihilo*. Powerful spirits (Rank 4 or above) can create whole copses of trees, packs of animals, or even factories for producing the object of the spirit's Influence. Roll Power + Influence. Create costs three points of Essence.

Using an Influence to affect the world directly is an instant action. The changes made last for 10 minutes per success, though the spirit can increase that to one hour per success for one extra point of Essence, or one day per success for two points of Essence.

Numina

Some spirits have abilities distinct from their Influences. Whilst many of these abilities are of little use once they've crossed over at a Locus, some benefit the spirit in any plane of existence.

All spirits that enter the real world possess either the Claim or Fetter Numina, or both. They may have a range of other Numina, including those detailed for ghosts (see p. 210 of the **World of Darkness Rulebook**). Spirits can possess any Dread Power as a Numen, including the Dominions detailed above. If the power normally requires a Willpower expenditure, the spirit must spend Essence instead. Dread Powers requiring rolls substitute the appropriate spirit trait — if a physical creature would roll Presence + Empathy, the spirit instead rolls Power + any relevant Influence.

Blast: The spirit can strike opponents at a distance. A pain-spirit may conjure knives, while a glass-spirit hurls razor-sharp shards, and a gun-spirit can fire spectral bullets. The attack has a range of 10 yards per dot of Power and suffers no range penalties. The spirit attacks with Power + Influence as normal, and may add two dice per point of Essence it spends. The attack deals lethal damage.

Claim: The spirit can attach itself to a person, anchoring itself to them after entering the material realm. With a living anchor, the spirit avoids the pull of the spirit world, and can hide from spiritual pursuers — and can subtly steer its host to achieve the spirit's ends. The spirit spends a point of Essence to Claim a living creature within five yards. The spirit must beat the target at a contested roll of Power + Finesse against Resolve + Composure before taking root. The spirit remains attached to the person until he dies or the spirit is exorcised. The spirit does not have to expend Essence to remain in the physical world. A spirit must remain in contact with a Claimed individual at all times.

Discorporate: The spirit can discorporate willingly. The spirit voluntarily surrenders its Corpus and dissolves into the spirit world, rather than fighting a losing battle that could see it destroyed. Voluntarily discorporating is an instant action costing no Essence. The spirit must succeed on a Power + Resistance roll to return to the spirit world. A spirit that discorporates via this Numen doesn't have to wait a lunar month before returning to the physical world

Fetter: The spirit can attach itself to an object, anchoring to it after entering the material realm. Doing so shields the spirit from burning through Essence then fading back to the spirit world. Additionally, the spirit can hide within the Fetter, to the point that anyone who can perceive spirits must roll Wits + Occult to notice it. The spirit must spend a point of Essence to Fetter a person or object within five yards of its current location. Once it's fettered, the spirit remains attached until the object is destroyed and does not have to expend Essence. A spirit fettered to an object must remain within five yards of it at all times.

Merge: The spirit infuses its host with its Essence, creating a hybrid creature that's no longer either fully human or fully spirit. The spirit must first have Claimed the human with whom it wishes to merge via the Claim Numen. The spirit spends three points of Essence and rolls Power + Finesse in an extended, contested action against the victim's Resolve + Composure. Each roll represents one hour, and the spirit must gain 50 successes by the next dusk or dawn — whichever comes soonest. Use the victim's available traits except Willpower points, which are equal to the spirit's current Willpower points. If the victim wins or ties the roll, the spirit loses its Claim on the victim and cannot attempt to Merge with the same host for a lunar month. If the host is killed or knocked unconscious, the spirit is forcibly ejected to the spirit world as if it had lost all of its Corpus.

Possess: The spirit can temporarily control a human that it has Claimed (via the Numen of the same name), subverting his will to serve the spirit's ends. Spend one Essence and roll Power + Finesse against the host's Resolve + Composure. If the spirit wins, it gains complete control over the host for a single scene. Use all of the victim's available traits except Willpower points, which are equal to the spirit's current Willpower points. If the victim wins or ties the roll, the spirit cannot attempt the possession again before the next sunset. The spirit can spend a point of Essence and make another contested roll at the end of each scene to remain in command of its human host. If the host is killed or knocked unconscious, the spirit is forcibly ejected. Not only does the possession end, the spirit must attempt to Claim the victim (or another person) or lose Essence for remaining in the physical world.

Creating Spirits

1. Choose an aspect and a Rank for your spirit.

A spirit's aspect is the facet of reality for which the spirit takes responsibility — a spirit of air has an aspect of "Air," and remains distinct from a spirit of the North Wind, which has the aspect of "North Wind." A spirit's aspect will likely influence its traits and should play a major part in determining the spirit's Influences. Note that an abstract spirit not tied to a specific physical form (such as spirits of Pain, Lust, or Guns) must be at least Rank 3.

2. Select Attributes.

Divide a number of dots according to a spirit's Rank into the spirit's Attributes: Power, Finesse, and Resistance. Note that the amount of Attribute dots is variable, giving a rough measure of the power available at each rank. Going slightly over or slightly un-

der to meet a concept is fine, but double-check that the spirit really should be the Rank that it is.

3. Choose Influences.

A spirit has a number of Influence dots and a maximum number of Influences based on its Rank. At least one Influence must hold close to the spirit's aspect. This is the spirit's core Influence, and gives the spirit the 9-again quality when using it. No other Influences can have more dots than the spirit's core Influence.

4. Choose Numina.

A spirit gains a number of Numina determined by Rank. In addition to those detailed above, most werewolf Dominions work as Numina without much modification.

5. Determine Advantages.

Willpower (Power + Resistance); Initiative (Finesses + Resistance); Size (Equal to size of object or 2 for abstract spirits, optionally based on Rank); Speed (Power + Finesse + species factor); Defense (the *higher* of Power or Finesse); Corpus (Resistance + Size).

6. Determine starting Essence.

A spirit can have any amount of Essence stored up to the maximum for its Rank. Spirits can never hold more Essence than that, though several maintain hidden stockpiles for their own consumption.

7. Determine Ban.

Looking over the spirit's aspect, Influences, and Rank, work out either a limitation on the spirit's behavior or a condition that significantly weakens the spirit. The difficulty of uncovering the ban and the requirements for exploiting it should factor into the effect that it has on a spirit — a ban that's almost unknown or that requires the flowers of a nearly-extinct plant should cripple the spirit.

The Claimed

It's a strange feeling when a spirit latches onto your soul. Some people, mostly people who are already a little bit dead inside, just plain don't notice. Others do. Even if the spirit's one of the few that doesn't ever try to influence its host, the host feels its effects. Over time, the host begins to associate with the spirit's aspect. If the host remains claimed by the same spirit for a week, he has a harder time channeling his Virtue. Not only does he have to play to his own sense of moral rightness, but to regain Willpower the situation must be such that the spirit could use

SPIRIT TRAITS

Rank	Descriptor	Trait Limits	Attribute Dots	Influence Dots	Max. Influences	Max. Essence	Max Numina
1	Weak	5	5-8	1	1	10	1-3
2	Minor	7	9-14	3	2	15	3-5
3	Major	9	15-25	6	4	20	5-7
4	Greater	12	26-35	10	8	25	7-9
5	Superior	15	36-45	15	12	50	9-11

one of its Influences. After a lunar month, the host must work with the spirit's Influences to channel his Vice as well. When the host channels his Virtue or Vice in this way, he's infused with the energy of the spirit world. He becomes immune to Lunacy for the remainder of the scene.

A spirit who has used the Claim Numen on a person can "nudge" the host to take an action. If it's the sort of thing that the host wouldn't normally do, the spirit must succeed at a contested roll of Power + Finesse against the host's Resolve + Composure. Once a spirit has Claimed a host, it can only use the Merge or Possess Numina. It can't access any other Numina, though it can use its Influences to affect the world normally.

A spirit using the Merge Numen mixes its Essence with the host's flesh and blood. The host slowly transforms into a hybrid creature of flesh and spirit. Each of the spirit's dots in Power, Finesse, and Resistance are distributed among the host's appropriate Attributes, at a rate of one dot per week after the Merge. The host's derived traits, including Health, Speed, and Defense alter appropriately. These increases can raise the host's Attributes above their usual maximums, though when that happens, the host's body warps in some obviously inhuman way to accommodate the change. The spirit can also use its own Essence to heal the host, spending one point to heal a point of lethal damage or two points of bashing damage at the end of a turn. Some merged spirits can take their stolen body of flesh through into the spirit world, though by that point the host's mind is little more than a faint echo protesting against the spirit's will.

BIRTHRIGHT

BY MATT MCFARLAND

THE GREAT AMERICAN ROADTRIP....FUN AND ECONOMICAL

Rain sluices down over the windshield. I can barely see out of it anyway, what with the cracks. I've got to admit, this car impresses me. It's a Checker cab, so it's already a beast, and they've done some impressive mods on it. Thinking about it just pisses me off, though. Makes me remember why my ribs hurt so much.

She sits next to me and she doesn't say a word, and I thank her for that. It's been a bad night.

The corpses in the back are starting to stink. Linda doesn't notice it yet, but she doesn't have my sense of smell. We'll need to dump these. I'm thinking the Schuykill River will do. I've got an idea on how we might make this work. We might be able to get out. Her people are dead. Mine… maybe I can make it so they think I'm dead.

Fat chance, says the voice in my head.

Fuck off, I respond.

Look, says the spirit. I haven't told them yet because you all agreed that you'd keep some secrets from each other. But this…

I shake my head and nearly lose my grip on the wheel. Linda gasps, but she stays quiet. Good girl. I'm still too pissed to talk, and I'd hate to take it out on her.

I want out. There's got to be a way.

There's a way, Joey. Turn left.

I squint out of the window and try to see where the next left is. When I do, I feel my heart sink. Left will take me to North Philly, and just like that, I know what our pet spirit is doing. He wants me to go find the Old Wolf.

Linda takes a breath, but catches herself. I look over at her and see fear in her eyes. It hurts me to see that, and hurt makes me angry, and now we're right back where we started. She can't talk because the sound would trigger it, that god-awful feeling that turns everything red. I can't talk because I'd have to hear my own voice, that horrible strain that comes up when I'm angry. I breathe deeply, roll down the window, trying to air out the car. Finally it starts to subside, and I look at her again. She smiles a little, testing, making sure, and I nod. We've worked out these signals over our time together. I guess it's only been a few weeks.

"I'm sorry," I say, and she shakes her head and puts a hand on my leg. The touch feels good, and I let go of the wheel with my right hand. I take her hand and kiss it, and she strokes my face. Her hand is cold, my face is flushed, and I feel the rest of the rage leaving me. I can think again. I can look at her without hate or anger. And all I can do is try to hold it, try to keep that feeling without letting the knowledge that the rage is there drag me back down.

· · ·

Joey's face is hot. The blood on his hands has dried, but it's still smeared over his chin. I can't point it out. I did that once, and immediately I saw shame and guilt, and I know what that leads to. I can't say anything to make him mad.

It's a relief, in a way. I ran for so long, I got involved with so many assholes who thought they had problems with anger. Joey has a problem with anger. But he comes by his problems honestly, just like I do.

I glance in the back of the car, and I feel a surge of anger myself. I should feel guilty for getting them killed. I should feel scared that the others — or, Heaven help me, She — will find out what I've done and hunt us down. I'm a traitor now. But I love him. And I hate the family. I didn't choose this. I didn't choose to be one of the Seventh Generation. I sure as Hell didn't choose to have His voice in my head.

"No one chooses family," my mentor used to say before my first hunt. "You can't choose. All you can do is accept. This is what we are."

I don't accept. I choose Joey.

We turn left and head north. "Where are we going?" I know he's been talking to that bird-thing that watches over him and his people. I understand familiars, but he refers to the bird differently. The familiar-bond, from what Darren tells me — or used to tell me, since he's not likely to be saying much now — is one you constantly have to watch. The bird seems to represent Joey and his people somehow. I don't understand it, but I know it's important to Joey. It's something he chose.

"North Philly," he says, and he looks worried. "You've heard the stories, right?"

"Stories?" My former friends had left a great deal out of their initial "briefing" when I was brought in.

"About the Old Wolf." I shake my head. "I know she's got a reputation among human... well, among folks like you. If you see a wolf in North Philly, just run? That kind thing?"

"Right." I have heard those stories, but not from my "siblings." Just after I got here, I spent the night with a guy named Hickman. The Lucifuge wanted him as a contact, and so they asked me to get cozy with him. He told me about the "grey wolf of North Philly," but I don't think I mentioned it to the others. "Is she one of your people?"

"Sort of." He shifts in his seat and tries to wipe off the windshield. That'll just make it worse, but I don't say anything. "She's one of us, at least. But she's been around a lot longer than my pack." He drops his eyes for a second. He's feeling guilty, and I wish I could take that away. I know what guilt's like.

I just squeeze his hand, and he shoots me a tight smile. I wonder for a second if we can really do this. Can we really make a life for ourselves if I have to run from my family, and he has to constantly keep himself in check? What if we want kids someday? How's his animal side going to square with that?

But it's not fair that we shouldn't be together because of how we were born, and I'll be damned if I'm letting what we can't help stand in our way.

I'll be damned. That's kind of funny. I'd tell Joey, but I'm not sure he'd get it.

· · ·

She's up ahead.

Thanks. I look on the sidewalk, and sure enough, there she is. She's sitting at a bus stop, but I know better than to think she's waiting for a bus. She looks at our car, and suddenly I feel like I'm under a microscope.

I stop the car and turn on the blinkers. "Keep your window up," I tell Linda. I don't look at her. I need to be focused, because I have no idea what the Old Wolf is going to do. I get out of the car and walk around to her. "Evening."

She points to the car. "Busy night."

"Bad night."

"Yeah." She stands and walks over toward me. She looks like she should move slowly, like an old woman, but she moves just as fluidly as I do. "You kill them?"

"Sort of."

She looks at me dead in the face. "Not much in the mood for games, boy." Her eye lights up. "I know you. You run with that pack down by the river. Hirfathra Hissu, right?"

Our language. The language of spirits. I wonder, fleetingly, if Linda could learn it. "Right. River's Secret Pack." I hope to Hell she doesn't ask me where the others are, but I guess it's going to have to come out anyway.

"So who's in the car, then?"

"My… girlfriend." I hate the way it sounds. It's more than that. She's my mate. She's my love. But I can't say those things out loud, and I don't know the word in our language.

"I mean the dead ones." She sniffs. Figures she can smell death. Then again, I'm sure she can smell blood on me, so maybe that's what she means. "Just killed 'em, I guess."

"Yeah."

"No ghosts?"

"Nope." Linda told me that they never linger as ghosts.

She pulls a candy bar out of her pocket. "Want some?"

"No, thank you. Chocolate—"

"Right." She takes a big bite. "Weird that never happens to me. Anyway," she continues between chomps, "I guess you came looking for me. What's up?"

I take a breath. This is it. "I want out."

She swallows a mouthful. "Out of what?"

"Philly. My tribe." I shut my eyes tight. "My pack." I'm expecting her to hit me. She might be an old woman, but from what I've heard, she could probably kill me. She lost three packmates in Fairmont back in the 70s, and I cannot believe I'm asking her this.

She doesn't hit me, though. "This about the girl?"

I try to answer, but I can't. I don't like her being called "the girl." I nod.

"I can teach you how to do it, sure." She pitches the wrapper into the gutter, under our front tire. "But

why should I? That's just going to piss your pack off, and I've got enemies already."

She's got me there, I think at the bird. Any more bright ideas?

Show her the medal.

"Hold on," I say. I walk to the car and knock on the window. Linda puts it down, and I whisper to her for a second. She hands it over. I look at it again

— it's nothing special. A little pewter thing with an etching of St. Francis on it. I walk back and hold it out for the Old Wolf. "This mean anything to you?"

Her eye gets wide, and I see rage. I step back, preparing to fight, and I hear Linda start that chanting she does. But the Old Wolf calms down a bit, and growls through her teeth, "Where the fuck did you find this?"

"It was on one of their bodies." The guy that hit me with the fucking car, in fact, had it in his pocket. Only reason I found it was because I tore his pants pulling his body out of the car before we stole it.

She takes it from me, and holds it, lovingly. She smells it, and I see a tear roll down her face. "This belonged to a friend of mine," she says. "He died in the Slaughter." She spits on the ground.

We stand staring at each other for a long moment. It's possible that this guy just found the medal. It's possible, but it's not likely. The bird led me here and told me what to do, and what the bird specializes in is secrets; stuff that no one in the world could possibly know.

"Will you teach me, then?"

She nods, and we walk off together.

. . .

I watch them tromp off into the rain. I slide over the driver's seat and turn off the blinkers, and pull out into the street.

When we fell in love, we both knew there would have to be secrets. "You'll never be part of my world, not really," I told him. "And I can't be part of yours. This is what we were born with."

"But I don't want my world," he said, "or yours. I want ours." And at that moment, I knew we had to get out. Otherwise it would be a long betrayal, a march toward suicide. And how many would die in the process? Would he have to sell out his people, or I mine, one at a time? Was it any better to do it all at once?

But that decision was taken from us when Darren got the tip. I still don't know who it was that called him. I just knew that Darren came in all excited, tossed down a handful of photos. "This guy," he said. "This guy is someone we need to look into." And there was Joey, plain as day.

Oh, I tried to throw them off track, of course, but they didn't buy it. The photos were pretty damning by themselves, and a few days of William tailing him sealed it. They knew what he was. They didn't

bother to check for demons, to make sure he was in league with Satan. Everyone knows that the werewolves in Philly are corrupt. Everyone knows because they've read the archives from the 70s, and back to the Depression. They decided Joey had to die, so I did the only thing I could. I went along with it.

We tracked him down in Strader's old Checker cab. This thing would go through a brick wall, I swear, and there's room enough in the back for all of us. We piled out up ahead of him, and got ready for the charge. They distract, using charms and silver. I distract, using the fires of Hell. And then Strader hits him with the car, we load the body into the trunk, and get back to the garage.

But he saw me, or smelled me, and he knew something was up. He stopped short, and I willed him to run away. Change and run, I repeated in my head, change and run, change and run, they can't catch you if you're a wolf. But he kept walking. And then Darren and Skye were behind him, and Gabe and I were in front of him, and they pulled out the silver.

It has to be timed perfectly. Strader has to commit to the ram, because that car doesn't brake well. I got behind Gabe, and I reached down below the streets, below the subways and the earth and the water and worms, and I pulled up Satan's fire.

And I turned, and threw it at Strader.

He spun the wheel and the car fishtailed. The back end slammed into Gabe and threw him against the wall. I heard his skull fracture, and he dropped to the ground, leaving a shiny trail on the bricks. Darren went flying over the hood of the car, and cracked the windshield with his shoulder. The bulk of the car caught Joey and Skye, but Joey was rolling with it. He changed, and I covered my eyes.

When I opened them again, I saw Darren running away. I reached for my pistol, and then I saw Joey.

Joey, sweet-faced Joey, running on all fours, covered in fur and blood dripping from his fangs. Joey, my lover, jumping and landing on Darren's back. Joey, the man I'd sworn to give up everything for, pulling Darren's spine out through his back.

We stacked the bodies in the car, and headed out to find a place to stash them. I don't know how Strader died; his heart might have finally given out.

"Don't say anything for a while," Joey said as we drove away. I know better than to test that.

• • •

I finish, and I feel like crying. It's all gone. My connection to the pack, to my tribe, it's gone. All that remains is my tie to Mother Luna, and she's not speaking to me right now. The Old Wolf assures me that'll pass, but right now, I just want to crawl underground and never look up again.

I walk back to the road, and I see her coming. She stops the car, and moves over to the passenger's seat. We start driving south, toward the river, to get rid of the bodies. We don't speak. She thinks I'm angry, and I am, but it's not the same kind of anger as before. I was mad before because I had to let go, to let that awful, ugly rage drag me down into the mud, and if I'd looked at her during that, I'd have killed her like the rest. I'm mad now because I think I might actually miss some of this. It feels good having a pack. It feels good knowing that one of the most powerful spirits in the world has my back. And it feels good knowing that the secrets of the world's shadows are my birthright.

But fuck all that. I never wanted this birthright. I wanted to grow up in South Philly and get a job like my brothers and be normal. I wanted to go to Eagles games and drink beer. Instead I got nights running down alleys on all fours and trying to talk myself out of eating homeless people. The only good thing about this was — is — her.

We get to the river, and she helps me throw the bodies in. I know the spirit of the Schuykill, and it's a sucker for a sacrifice. It promises to keep this a secret for as long as it can. I know that won't be long, that my pack will sniff this out and find out what's happened, but the spirit should buy us a day or two.

Enough time to start heading west; enough to try and outrun our birthrights.

I look over at her, falling asleep against the window. I love her, and I tell myself that shouldn't make me angry.

The first part of this chapter discusses werewolves, hunters, and the themes that bind them. How can you tell a traditional werewolf story, complete with consuming human flesh, the full moon shining down, and bloodied fingers chambering the last silver bullet in a **Hunter** context? Likewise, we examine how the themes and milieu of **Werewolf: The Forsaken** gel with **Hunter**, including how you might run a game including both hunter and werewolf characters. And, of course, we look at different takes on the lycanthrope myth; **Forsaken** uses a particular kind of werewolf, but other options exist.

The second half of this chapter takes us back to the City of Brotherly Love. This time, we examine the city through the yellow, hungry eye of the werewolf, and that of the hunter who has unquestionably become the prey.

Hunters, Killers and Gluttons — Werewolf Themes

The werewolf represents many different ideas and concepts in different mythologies and cultures, and given that role-playings often incorporate material from several different cultural backdrops, the werewolves in your **Hunter** game can use any or all of them. The characters of **Werewolf: The Forsaken**, of course, have a specific set of symbolic and thematic nuances that resonate with them, and we'll discuss these in more depth presently. For now, however, consider the *werewolf*.

The Monster

The werewolf is a monster, and that remains fairly consistent throughout different paradigms (though there are exceptions). Medieval bestiaries reported that the wolf could not turn its head backwards, and that if it stepped on a stick while stalking prey it would punish itself by biting its own paw. This kind of harsh, uncompromising behavior is typical of popular portrayal of wolves — they attack relentlessly and ruthlessly, seeking to fell their prey and gorge. *Gluttony* is a common theme for the wolf, and the werewolf reflects some of that in his insatiable hunger for flesh (typically human).

Going a little deeper, werewolves are the monsters from the woods. They stalk sheep in their pens, and attack the helpless and the infirm. This behavior makes perfect sense to a predator, of course — if one has to kill to survive, one picks the easiest kills. But human beings love to anthropomorphize, and so an animal that would rather feed on an innocent lamb than a healthy sheep develops a reputation for cruelty, cowardice, and inhuman viciousness. The wolf emerges from the dark and snatches away that which is most precious. From an allegorical standpoint, it's easy to see how

Outside, its tracks begin to fill up with snow, and the shriek of the wind seems savage with pleasure. There is nothing of God or Light in that heartless sound — it is all black winter and dark ice.

— Stephen King, The Cycle of the Werewolf

THE KENNEL

Deep in the urban jungle of Detroit, Null Mysteriis operates the Lycanthrope Reclamation project, informally known as "the Kennel." The block surrounding the project is abandoned, the buildings boarded up and condemned (though a careful observation would note that the condemnation notices tacked to the buildings are fakes). The project itself is underground, accessible only by special elevators, which are monitored by live staff 24 hours a day, although a clever and determined foe might manage to get in through the sewer system.

The Kennel is dedicated to curing lycanthropy. At present, the staff has captured three werewolves. It keeps them in specially designed cells, and the captives are constantly under watch. One flies into a berserk rage whenever he is awake, and so is kept sedated. The other two are more cognizant — one even knows that she is being held against her will and repeatedly asks for a lawyer. The werewolves receive treatment that are intended to cure them of their shapeshifting curse, but the treatment is slow going, in part because the staff doesn't have a good idea of what they are dealing with, and in part because of the ongoing problem with Lunacy.

Storytellers Note: Any of the Hunter compacts or conspiracies could run the Kennel, of course. Null Mysteriis takes a scientific approach, but a Kennel run by the Malleus Maleficarum might look like a monastery more than a science lab. The Lucifuge's Kennel might be more naturalistic, allowing the werewolves to indulge their primal instincts, but keep them contained through magical means. A Kennel run by Task Force: VALKYRIE, of course, probably resembles Guantanamo Bay. The Cheiron Group's version is likely a combination of testing laboratory and concentration camp, as werewolves are lobotomized, forcibly bred, and harvested for blood, organs and hormones.

out actually seeing or feeling the deed done.

Regardless of the reaction to it, this staple of the werewolf story is one that can throw a serious moral quandary into a **Hunter** story. If a man is changed into a werewolf against his will (which isn't in keeping with how **Forsaken** werewolves work, usually, but that's not important) and commits murder, is he really a murderer? Even if he doesn't have control, is a hunter cell justified in putting him down anyway, because he's a threat to everyone around him?

The Hunter

One of the most visceral themes of the werewolf (and a central theme of **Werewolf: The Forsaken**, incidentally) is the hunt. The lone werewolf stalks prey that he can kill alone, drags it back into the darkness of his den, and feasts. He represents many of the same terrifying motifs as the serial killer: he strikes without warning, he is implacable and bloodthirsty, and his hunger is craven and depraved (because he eats his kills). The werewolf *pack*, however, is a different kind of horror altogether. Werewolves, like natural dogs and wolves, don't have any sense of six against one being an unfair fight, where a hunt is concerned. That's just how they operate, and it's one of their biggest advantages. They hit a foe from all sides, tearing him apart before he knows what's happening. He doesn't have time draw his weapons, to call for aid, or even to scream.

But doesn't that sound a lot like the Tactics a hunter cell employs? A werewolf pack can be inspiring for a cell (if they have the means to watch the pack operate from a safe vantage point). What lessons could the cell learn from these predators? Do they start to question their own brutal methods, or do they look on the pack hunting of the lycanthropes as a good model for their next escapade?

a creature that kills a lamb (considering the symbolic relevance of the lamb in Christian mythology) is identified with the Adversary. And indeed, the werewolf is frequently painted as a man who sold his soul to the Devil for the power of shapeshifting. It bears noting, however, that even when a werewolf is a man who traded his soul for power, the "power" in question is very different than, say, a Faustian bargain in which the foolish mortal receives wealth, knowledge, and magical power. The werewolf in these stories is very much a rampaging beast, and the "gift" he receives is uncompromising, brutal strength — strength he can barely control.

Blind Rage

This aspect of the werewolf remains fairly consistent regardless of the portrayal. Classic werewolf stories, from literature to poetry to films, show us the man waking up after a long night of hunting and feasting with no knowledge of what he did. Sometimes that terrifies the man, sometimes he ignores it or displaces it, and sometimes he simply revels in a kind of pseudo-voyeuristic thrill. *While I sleep, the wolf hunts*, he thinks. That means he discovers who died last night, and knows *he* was responsible, with-

The hunter/hunted relationship is one that a Storyteller should definitely exploit when telling a **Hunter/Werewolf** story. Werewolves, especially as presented in **Werewolf: The Forsaken**, take an extremely dim view of becoming the prey, while the characters of **Hunter: The Vigil** are probably used to it. At what point does the relationship change? When and how does one side acknowledge that they are now the quarry? Can the hunters exploit the werewolves' tracking skill and lead them into an ambush?

Consider, too, the appeal of a story that highlights the bloody-mindedness of the shapeshifters. Human characters have to sleep, but how can they, knowing that the werewolves are after them? They can get into cars and flee, but how far can they really go? And where can they go that the world's greatest trackers cannot find them? Yes, Tactics such as Confuse the Scent can help with a temporary escape, but a dedicated pack will figure out the ruse and get back on the trail eventually. And every hour that the cell runs while the pack pursues is another hour that either side can complicate the final battle, which in turn complicates the hunter/quarry relationship even further.

The Intruder

A certain amount of xenophobia also comes into play when talking about werewolves. If the wolf is the creature from the woods, come to eat its fill, and the stranger is the man from *somewhere else*, come to rob us and take our women (or whatever unsavory be-

havior you'd prefer), then the meeting of the two is the werewolf. The fact that the werewolf is a beast that looks human is just a way to express this — if the characters have no way to detect the supernatural (probably the case for first-tier cells) or to detect werewolves in particular (potentially any cell), then that charming stranger might just be a monster. That's true for any supernatural being that looks human, of course, but consider the dramatic potential of that charming stranger turning into a *wolf* versus just growing fangs. Everything about the stranger that was human or appealing vanishes in an instant, and all that is left is menace.

This kind of story can also be tweaked to fit a "whodunit." If a group of people gets together in a secluded place, and one of them is suspected of being a werewolf, the entire bunch of them can drive each other insane trying to identify the monster. The characters might comprise the entirety of this unfortunate group, or they might just be thrown into the mix.

The Wrath of Nature

As mentioned previously, people like to apply human mores to animals and natural events. In our world, they don't apply, and so we're surprised when animals kill their young or do other "horrible" things to survive. In the World of Darkness, however, the spirit world works just as much on symbolism as on reality. A wolf-spirit might be ever hungry. A dog-spirit is fanatically loyal. And Nature has will, desire and agenda — but none of those things makes Nature interested in mankind, necessarily.

The lycanthropes of **Werewolf: The Forsaken** are capable of interacting with this spiritual world much more easily than most other characters (though that doesn't mean they've mastered it or that they are comfortable with it by any means — the spirits are, in fact, often antagonistic towards werewolves, as will be discussed anon). They are also better

---

STORY HOOK: THE PARTY'S OUT OF HAND

An Ashwood Abbey function, held in a mansion out on the moors (if you want to be traditional) or in a big house in the suburbs (if you want to play up a "protect the unknowing neighbors/maintain a good reputation" angle), suffers tragedy when a werewolf attacks the party. Maybe the werewolf was caged for later fun and broke free, maybe it was hunting down a particular member of the Abbey, and maybe the farmer down the way (or the next-door neighbor) has a bloody secret. Either way, the lights go out, screams and crashes ensue, and when someone finally gets the power back on, the place is trashed and a lot of people are wounded. At least one was probably bitten. Who? And does that mean that the victim will become a monster himself?

As with the Kennel story seed above, consider how this changes if you alter the hunter organization. What would a gathering of the Loyalists of Thule do in response to this kind of event? Would the Ascending Ones race to find an ointment that might cure the infection… if applied in time? Would the Aegis Kai Doru kill a bitten member outright? (Note that **Forsaken** werewolves aren't infectious, but this possibility is discussed later in the chapter.)

acquainted with the world beyond human influence, the wilderness, by dint of being part animal. Nature is red in tooth and claw, and werewolves embody that concept in a quite literal fashion.

Animal Magnetism

While the werewolf isn't usually as seductive as his cousin the vampire, a certain air of raw, animal carnality does permeate many werewolf stories. If you're telling a werewolf story that highlights the danger and mystique of the natural world, this kind of sexual overtone can be appropriate. Werewolves aren't sexy because they're beautiful and delicate; they're sexy in the way that an athlete, a warrior, or a soldier is sexy. They are confident and dangerous, and this kind of attitude can be extremely appealing. Likewise, the werewolf carries with him the appeal of animal carnality — sexual energy uncontrolled, clothes being ripped aside, passion more violent than loving. A hunter, used to taking his life into his hands, might find an infatuation with a werewolf in the right circumstances.

A better way to use this theme, though, might be to involve a hunter with the relative of a werewolf. As presented in **Werewolf: The Forsaken**, people who carry the werewolf "gene" but are not themselves shapeshifters have a measure of the spiritual awareness that their cousins do, as well as a bit of predatory

menace. A person like this might even *be* a hunter, especially if relations with the bestial side of the family have gone sour (and since werewolves sometimes treat their "wolf-blooded" relatives like second-class citizens or, worse, breeding stock, this happens). What happens when a hunter develops a romantic (or just sexual) relationship with the cousin, sister or spouse of a werewolf? And what about the fact that a wolf-blood can suddenly undergo the Change, becoming a werewolf herself, without warning?

The Many Faces of Lycanthropy

The World of Darkness has a particular vision of what being a "werewolf" means, but just because there's a game line dedicated to that vision is no reason to ignore the multiple other possibilities for shapeshifters. As a Storyteller, when you use werewolves in a **Hunter** chronicle, you need to consider what that means for the story. The thematic approaches you can use are discussed above. In this section, we're going to discuss the nuts and bolts — the "rules," if you will,

for being a werewolf and how you can mix and match them. Some game mechanics are included along the way, but any of the werewolf "types" described here can be given the powers listed in the previous chapter of **Spirit Slayer** or from the "Dread Powers" found within **Hunter: The Vigil** (p. 276).

Where Does the Power Come From?

A werewolf is, at the most basic level, a creature with the power to change into a wolf and a human being. The Storyteller needs to decide *why* that happens: How does a person become a werewolf? Below are three broad answers to that question.

Infection

Task Force: VALKYRIE lists werewolves as "high risk for infiltration" entities, because intelligence suggests (but does not conclusively prove) that a victim bitten by a lycanthrope may become one. Network 0 has film (available for free download, of course) that shows a werewolf chasing down a hapless person, biting her, and then running off into the night… as its victims begins to shudder and grow fur. And the legends are unmistakably clear on this point: the curse of the werewolf can be passed along by a bite.

Actually, as far as **Werewolf: The Forsaken** is concerned, lycanthropy *can't* be passed along this way, but again, that's not important. If it's more interesting for your chronicle to make werewolves infectious, feel free. Consider, however, that a bite isn't the only possible vector:

- **Sex:** Lycanthropy as a sexually transmitted disease isn't quite in theme for werewolves (it works better for vampires, whose condition actually involves *dying*), but if you consider the condition to be a possession of sorts, it makes more sense. The "spirit of the wolf" enters the person's body and soul, and if the human cannot reject it, it consumes them (this principle can be found at work in the 1994 film *Wolf*, in fact). This spirit, whatever it truly is, needs an extremely intimate way to enter a person, and sex is a perfect vector, as is a bite.

- **Curse:** The werewolf is the result of a curse from a powerful mystical source. This curse might be deliberately inflicted. What if a member of Les Mystéres offends the wrong spirit, and it decides to claim him fully, making him a werewolf? Or, what if the Loyalists of Thule discover an immortal being locked away in a forgotten Third Reich bunker, and he punishes them for their predecessor's crimes by cursing them with lycanthropy?

Then again, the curse could be accidental. A magical item recovered from a dead wizard's collection, a passage of a book read during a full moon, a batch of Wolfsbane Tea (see "Wolfsbane" sidebar, p. 143) made with the *wrong* kind of Wolfsbane… any of these might turn someone into a werewolf.

- **Science:** In an attempt to make a better, stronger, faster human, it's not hard to imagine scientists in the World of Darkness turning to so questionable sources. A strain of spiritually awakened virus, or a serum drawn from the endocrine glands of a werewolf, might enable shapeshifting, though possibly on a temporary basis. What might a person thus changed have to do to maintain the condition, presuming he wants to? Maybe consuming the cerebrospinal fluid of other people is the only way to keep the chemical "mix" intact. And what happens when it goes awry? Does the condition wear off… or become uncontrollable?

Genetics

This is the assumption that **Werewolf: The Forsaken** makes about its characters: They are werewolves because of family heritage. The child of a werewolf is not automatically a werewolf, but the Change isn't something that can be foisted upon a character from the outside.

A story which includes this kind of lycanthrope might focus on developing an identification test or a "vaccine" to determine or prevent a person's chances of undergoing the Change. It might also see a cell digging deep into a given person's past, trying to link a known werewolf to the subject's family. Consider, for instance, what happens if a member of the Union has a cousin who Changes. Everyone's going to start looking askance at the person's family (the hunter character included). And suppose that character is Irish Catholic, and has a huge family with multiple cousins, second cousins, cousins twice removed, etc? Obviously, the compact can't (and shouldn't) kill them all, so some other strategy is needed.

Faustian Bargain

Another classic method of becoming a werewolf, the would-be lycanthrope makes a deal with otherworldly powers (Satan, spirits, and beings from the Outer Dark) and receives the dubious gift of shapeshifting. The question here is *why* this person made the deal. Maybe he's sick and won't live to see another birthday without the mystical strength lycanthropy provides. Maybe he has an ill-defined lust for "power." Maybe he just wants to run with the wolves

— perhaps he thinks he identifies with a wolf, believing it to be his "totem" or "daemon" or some such lofty concept. Whatever the case, lycanthropy is a commodity that another being can grant. And, in the World of Darkness, this is indeed an option.

A mage, for instance, might grant the power of shapeshifting on demand, but with a catch: the spell only lasts a month, at maximum, after which the "contract" needs to be renegotiated. A powerful spirit might enable shapeshifting, but it takes up residence in the lycanthrope's body and sometimes assumes control. A demon (whatever that term means in your chronicle) might change a man into a wolf, but make him perform hideous acts of slaughter before it will change him *back*.

The Faustian bargain is always, *always* rigged. Someone using it to become a werewolf probably winds up killing someone he didn't mean or want to, or becoming the trained hound of a greater evil. Someone who takes on the Vigil might make this kind of bargain if she feels that becoming a werewolf will facilitate her punishment of the supernatural, but this sort of motivation very often ends with the werewolf being put down by her former cohorts. Unable to explain what happened, she dies as a beast, human-like howls issuing forth from her throat. Her fellow hunters probably even kill her thinking that the beast was responsible for the death of their former comrade, and thus get to watch in horror as the body of the monster *becomes* that comrade (another classic "scene" in werewolf stories).

The Beast Becomes the Man

One possibility we haven't considered is that of the werewolf being a wolf that changes into a person, rather than the other way around. This can happen through any of the methods discussed above, though of course the Faustian bargain isn't a likely course of action for a wolf to take. Instead, a wolf might become possessed by the ghost of a human (probably a mage, or at least someone with some occult knowledge). It might be caught in a ritual gone wrong and merge with one of the attendees. Or, perhaps the wolf develops a taste for human flesh, and just eats enough to absorb some analog of the man.

Many of the same questions are appropriate for a lupine-born werewolf as for a human-born one, but you might also consider whether the werewolf only has human cognitive abilities when in human form. If the wolf is a dumb beast when walking on four legs, but gains the capacity for reason, language and even compassion when walking as a man, what does it *do* while it is human? Does it try to make the change

THE SKIN-CHANGER

What of the werewolf who changes forms by donning a wolf-skin? This method of shapechanging is actually possible under several of these "origins." Consider: an Aegis Kai Doru character finds a wolf-skin belt used to bind the pages of an old witch's tome. Without thinking, she tries it on and… too late, sees the full moon shining down on her as she starts to change. A scientist of Null Mysteriis trades away a book of the names of known monsters for a wolf pelt that will, in the words of the mysterious stranger who proffers it, "grant you a wealth of knowledge about werewolves." A scion of Ashwood Abbey inherits a necklace made of wolf teeth, and is told that *someone* in the Abbey has to spend a night as a beast every year… and guess who drew the short straw?

A werewolf that changes form by means of skin needs the same consideration as any other lycanthrope in terms of powers, motives, and vulnerabilities. You just need to consider whether the *skin* can be destroyed, whether it's got a mind of its own (probably from having a spirit bound into it), and what the victim/user needs to do to activate it. Will simply putting it on suffice, or must it be donned at a particular time? Maybe the wearer has to taste blood while touching the skin, or succumb to a primal emotion like fear, rage or lust. In any case, items like this typically have history, and the characters should be able to research the item, even if the current wearer is no one of note.

permanent, or does it long to go back to its original state? Does it use a human's capacity for reason to trap its prey? How easily does it learn to speak, if at all? Does it develop any capacity for social graces, or does it grunt and growl and behave like an animal (and probably wind up incarcerated for its trouble)?

And if other werewolves exist, what is their opinion of such creatures? Do they know that they exist, and if so, do they hunt their even more bestial cousins down? They might find and teach them, or try to reverse their conditions, or they might simply tear them apart as threats to the secrecy of their race. Of course, if that's the case, the human-born werewolves are likely to hunt down whatever changed the wolf into a werewolf in the first place.

The Werewolf's Mind

What happens to the man when the beast's skin appears? Some werewolves have complete control over their shapeshifting, some can only change at certain times, and some change without warning and lose their rational minds while wearing the animal's skin. As Storyteller, you'll need to decide the particulars for the lycanthropes in your chronicle.

Werewolf: The Forsaken takes a hybrid approach — the werewolves can change forms at will, but run the risk of succumbing to rage at any time. When that happens, they attack anything that moves, no matter what or who it is. Not even packmates are spared. Note, though, that when these werewolves fly into this frenzy (called Death Rage in the context of the game), they don't normally eat their kills. It happens, but it's not a given or even especially common. This is at odds with many of the classic werewolf stories, which paint the lycanthrope as forever hungry for human flesh. Your werewolves, then, might kill with the express intention of eating their prey… again, no matter *who* that prey is.

Does the werewolf remember his time as a monster? It stands to reason that if a werewolf retains the use of his human mind, he'll recall what he does during his hunts. But if reason sleeps while the beast hunts, does the human simply wake up with no recollection of what happened? Many classic werewolf stories and films (including the ones mentioned previously in this chapter, as well as John Landis' *An American Werewolf in London*), simply have the cursed individual wake up in the morning with a full belly, often naked and in an unfamiliar locale, ignorant of the night's predations… until he hears about them from another source or discovers the kills he has stashed away for later.

Another option, though, is that the human *does* remember his time as a beast, but is unable to control himself. This option works well for a werewolf created through the merger of a spirit and a human, or through a curse from a malevolent power. The victim is trapped inside a beast's body, fully or partially cognizant of what he is doing but unable to stop himself, and probably wracked with remorse all the more vividly because being a werewolf feels *good*. The victim might secretly revel in the primal energy of chasing down prey and feeling bone snap between his jaws, but when the sun rises and he must account for what he has done, the memory of the hunt seems horrific and nightmarish.

STORY HOOK: THE MADNESS OF ELLIOT FRIEND

A contact of the characters, Elliot Friend, becomes a werewolf. Elliot has a job that makes him extremely useful to the characters, but not one that requires them to meet him often. Perhaps he is a researcher that finds ancient secrets and dogma for a cell of Long Night hunters, or a lab technician running tests for Network 0. In any case, Elliot becomes erratic and insane as the curse takes hold… but he makes excuses with the best of them. The news is full of reports of murders that the characters identify as werewolf-related, but nothing (immediately) leads to Elliot. He might even supply them with good leads that take them into other dangers — not necessarily deliberately, of course, but Elliot's in denial as to why he can't remember what he did last night or why he drools when he sees someone with a bloody nose.

The characters notice changes in his habits: rare steak instead of medium-well; pulling the lettuce off a beef sandwich… and then not bothering with the bread, either; pacing when nervous or bored, when he used to sit still; and shunning coffee, because it's started making him sick. How well are the characters paying attention? Will they notice something's wrong before Elliot just snaps, Changes forms, and attacks out of nowhere?

The werewolf might degenerate. The Storytelling system has a mechanic for this in the Morality trait. A werewolf that can control itself and still chooses to hunt and kill others probably loses Morality fairly quickly. A werewolf that *cannot* control itself and has no memory of its actions, though, might not. This is a decision the Storyteller needs to make: if the character has no knowledge of what he is doing, is he still accountable for his actions? One option is that the character only risks degeneration if and when he finds out what he has done. Another is that the character slips into denial and maintains his Morality (and functionality). But unless the werewolf in question is a player-controlled character (and you aren't using the **Werewolf: The Forsaken** rules, which present a werewolf-specific take on Morality), it's probably best to just decide on Morality and derangements that fit the character.

The Forms

What, exactly, does the werewolf become when it Changes? Mythology, film and literature offer several possibilities, and **Werewolf: The Forsaken** uses most of them. Below are suggestions for what a man might become when the wolfsbane blooms. These terms correspond to the forms described in Chapter Three, p. 161.

The Near-Man

The near-man is humanoid and can pass for a person in bad light. It is generally taller and more muscular than the average person, and much hairier — eyebrows knit together, beard grows coarse and dark and covers most of the face (or even the entire head), and the hands and arms sprout thick fur, too dense to be confused for human hair. This form might or might not have claws capable of inflicting any real damage, but the canines also increase in size (such a monster usually inflicts lethal damage with a bite, though the character still needs to grapple before doing so).

This brute hearkens back to the werewolf-as-intruder described earlier in this chapter. The werewolf here is human-looking enough to get close to its prey, but once it does, its bestial nature becomes apparent. The horror in the brute is the merger of man and wolf, and the fact that the creature's origins are obvious. The near-man *was* human, but all that remains of humanity is form. Additionally, if he is discovered eating, it calls to mind acts of cannibalism, rather than being eaten by an animal. The horror here is therefore still very much rooted in the human sphere, rather than the wilderness.

The Wolf

On the other side of the coin, we have the werewolf that becomes a natural wolf. The wolf is not immediately supernatural, and sheltered or foolish people might mistake the creature for a dog initially. But when the wolf gets closer, that mistake becomes impossible — the wolf has in its eyes and bearing a wildness that terrifies people. In the werewolf's song is loneliness and fear, and in the werewolf's growl is the nightmare beast that cannot be outrun.

A werewolf that can *only* change into a wolf isn't as immediately threatening as one that can become a giant wolf, but don't overlook the potential for juxtaposition. The characters are walking down a city street, and the wolf exits and alley, blood on its muzzle, and runs off into traffic. Or, better yet, what if the characters hear a scratching noise at their door and assume it's the family dog… only to hear the growl as the dog enters the room behind them. What's at the door, then?

The Near-Wolf

A wolf might be able to chase a person down and take out his throat, but even a big wolf isn't much more massive than a good-sized dog. Some werewolves, however, are able to change into a wolf not seen on Earth in thousands of years, one that stands five or six feet high at the shoulder and can decapitate a man with a single bite. This giant wolf takes the horror of the normal wolf and makes it raw, visceral and immediate. The near-wolf can't be intimidated, wrestled or felled with a sharp blow to the head. The near-wolf is much more likely to disembowel its prey and start feasting before the light in the quarry's eyes goes dim.

The near-wolf is the horror of the natural world taken to an extreme. It is a monster, as is the wolf-man discussed in the next section, but it is a monster that is recognizable as an animal. The size of the wolf marks it as supernatural, but the form gives the human observer a frame of reference. It's a wolf, even if it's a freakishly huge one, and so some context exists for it and its hunger. Everyone has heard stories of wolves attacking humans, even if those stories began "Once upon a time, there was a little girl named Little Red Riding Hood." The giant wolf also underlines the threat of being eaten by a predator more vividly than the natural wolf does, because the giant wolf is capable of eating a whole person by itself, and that's apparent just from the size.

The Bestial Hybrid

The wolf-man is largely a product of modern cinema (*The Howling*, in particular), but has rapidly become an archetypal vision of the werewolf. It walks on two legs and has human-like hands, enabling it to grab and throw, or even open doors, but it retains the canine muzzle and head shape, marking it as unmistakably bestial. It sports vicious fangs and, usually, wicked claws, and thus is a creature obviously of the supernature rather than an animal gone wild. Even the near-wolf might be some freakish mutant, a horror, yes, but still a wolf. The wolf-man is a nightmare, clearly born of something beyond human experience, and therein lies its appeal in a **Hunter** story.

The hybrid is usually portrayed as unstoppable. It can power through most attacks against it (until someone gets smart enough to use silver or exploit some other weakness, which is discussed in the next section), and is strong enough to kill multiple human opponents in seconds. As such, it makes for a good opponent against tough, well-prepared and trained hunters. Even if they know what they are in for, that doesn't make the savagery any easier to face.

The wolf-man combines all the worst aspects of animal and man. It might have some of the human's intelligence left (figuring alternate ways around routes, basic lateral thinking, etc.) combined with animal instinct, cunning and senses. It assuredly has a wolf's strength and speed, combined with a human's ability to fight creatively. Creatures like this don't run; they retreat strategically, often to find the rest of the pack.

Killing the Beast

The beast must die — but how to accomplish that? In some stories, the werewolf is no more resistant to physical damage than any living creature, and can be felled with a few well-placed bullets or knife thrusts. Most of the time, though, a werewolf is highly resistant to physical harm; some lycanthropes are immune to physical attacks and cannot be killed (this is more common with werewolves who cannot control their shapeshifting and for whom lycanthropy is a curse). Even after being blown to pieces, they reform, howling at the moon. More commonly, though, werewolves simply heal damage almost as fast as they suffer it. Wounds close in seconds, and the beast rises, hungry and enraged.

The shapeshifters of **Werewolf: The Forsaken** fall into this latter category; they regenerate one point of bashing damage per turn, and heal lethal damage the way normal humans heal bashing damage (one point every 15 minutes), *whether or not* they are resting. This means that a werewolf with Stamina 2 in human form can sustain injuries that would incapacitate a normal person (seven points of lethal damage), but be completely healed in less than two hours. Is it any wonder, then, that hunters often go to ridiculous lengths to make sure werewolves are dead before they turn their backs on the corpses?

Silver and Other Remedies

Even someone who knows nothing about the occult, when asked the best way to kill a werewolf, can probably come up with "a silver bullet?" The origins of the werewolf's allergy to silver are unclear, perhaps dating back to stories of the Beast of Gévaudan in 18th century France, but it remains the most commonly known weakness of shapeshifters. In the context of **Werewolf: The Forsaken**, it's quite accurate — silver weapons inflict aggravated damage to these werewolves, and they cannot regenerate the damage anywhere near as quickly as they can other forms of harm.

That said, there are other, more esoteric methods of combating werewolves, and you might decide the

lycanthropes in your chronicles can shrug off a silver bullet just as easily as a lead one. Below are a few methods of harming, killing or at least inconveniencing werewolves that are drawn from folklore.

- **Blood of the werewolf:** One legend says that drawing three drops of blood from a werewolf would cure it, but, of course, the blood had to be drawn when the werewolf was in its bestial form.

- **Wolfsbane:** This plant, in some legends, acts as a deadly poison to werewolves. In others, wolfsbane repels lycanthropes, and even the scent is enough to keep them away. Wolfsbane, in some modern works of werewolf cinema, suppresses the werewolf's hunger and ability to change. Rumors suggest that the Ascending Ones know how to prepare wolfsbane in just such a way so it can be used to force a werewolf into human form, where he is easier to kill (should you decide that this rumor is true, feel free to write it up as an Endowment using the R&D rules in **Hunter: The Vigil**).

- **Iron:** According to some 19th century legends, throwing a piece of pure iron over a werewolf's head or shoulder would reveal him for what he was. In the case of a skin-changer, the skin would fall off and the werewolf stood naked. In the case of other types of shapeshifter, the lycanthrope was forced to immediately change forms, which obviously carries some risk. The Aegis Kai Doru has access to objects with similar effects, some of which are indeed made from iron.

- **Moon cycles:** Werewolves have long been associated with the full moon, and in some sources, the werewolf is sluggish and weak on the new moon. Hunters might therefore choose the timing of their attacks based on lunar cycles. Note, though, that the lycanthropes of **Werewolf: The Forsaken** do not all draw strength from the full moon. Some, in fact, align themselves with the new moon and are even more deadly during this phase.

The Cell and the Pack

A pack of werewolves and a cell of hunters share more than a few similarities. Both groups are optimized for hunting, after all, even if they come by that specialization in different ways. The cell is composed of people who, for whatever reason, chose to embark upon the Vigil. The pack is composed of people who were *chosen* to be hunters. The werewolf's hunting prowess is inborn, the hunter's is learned. But even so, the two groups both track down their prey and, quite often, kill it.

That means, of course, that a story in which the werewolves are the antagonists is going to incorporate "the hunter's hunted" as a theme — which group, at any given point in the story, is on the defensive? Who is the hunter, and who is the target? How can one turn the tables on the other?

But consider, too, a story in which the cell and the pack are not working at cross-purposes, but are working together. Under what circumstances might this kind of story arise, and how can the Storyteller make the most of it? And, what happens when the players want to mix the games, taking on the roles of both hunters and werewolves in the same story? This section examines all of these concerns.

Coming Together

Why would a pack and a cell ever work together? It's more likely with some cells than others, obviously. It's easier to imagine a rough, practical group of Task Force: VALKYRIE operatives agreeing to band together with a pack, especially in the face of a greater threat (and especially if the pack in question embraces a warrior or soldier-like ethic). It's perhaps harder to picture the Aegis Kai Doru doing so, as they see werewolves as inherently monstrous on moral grounds. Likewise, the more rational compacts (Network 0 and Null Mysteriis) might welcome the chance to observe a pack, but wear out their welcome quickly. The Union might have some initial problems, since werewolves are monsters, after all, but once the cell and the pack establish a respectful basis for communication (namely, "we both have to *live* here"), they might form a lasting alliance.

Below are several reasons why a cell and a pack might wind up working together, and how it might come to pass, along with suggestions for the Storyteller in setting up this sort of event.

Common Foes

One possibility is that the cell and the pack are tracking the same target. This might be general (the pack is hunting down vampires in its territory, while the Union is trying to clear out the bloodsuckers from the city), or specific (both the pack and the cell have lost members to an elusive slasher). In either case, one group probably doesn't know about the other until they both investigate the same crime scene, try to interrogate the same witness, or blunder into one another's ambushes. As a **Hunter** Storyteller, you can set the cell up to find the werewolf pack by seeding hints:

- Witnesses are all suffering from a strange form of memory loss (which is, in truth, Lunacy). It responds to mitigating methods like drugs, hypnosis, and perhaps the Deprogramming Tactic, but all of the witnesses know that *something* roughed them up, and then asked them the same questions that the cell is trying to get answered.

- An odd substance found at all of the scenes related to whatever the cell is tracking turns out to be urine, as though something is marking its territory. Oddly, sometimes it's canine, sometimes human.

- Wolf prints leading into an area, human prints coming out.

- Three vertical scratches on the back of a character's car (the werewolf pack marking the car as something to watch in future).

Connections

Werewolves, at least as **Forsaken** imagines them, were born human, and usually don't realize their supernatural heritage until they reach adulthood (or at least puberty). As such, they have plenty of time to make the same connections that other people do before they are sucked into the bestial side of the World of Darkness. A hunter character's childhood friend might be a werewolf. A werewolf's online friend might belong to Network 0. And, of course, it's not impossible for a hunter to be related by blood or marriage to a werewolf. Any of these connections might make cooperation between cell and pack a little more palatable.

A story that plays upon this kind of connection, of course, raises questions about loyalty and commitment. Exactly how dedicated to the Vigil is the hunter, if she's willing to consort with werewolves? Is the werewolf risking the ultimate sin among his kind — betrayal of the pack — by sharing information with a cell? Loyalty is an appropriate theme for both games. In **Werewolf**, loyalty is instinctive, and only the worst criminals and vilest traitors take action against their own packs. In **Hunter**, loyalty is a matter of survival, because the creatures that hunters fight exploit any possible lapse in vigilance that they can. But what about loyalty to friends, family, or lovers? How does a werewolf approach the notion of fidelity, and how does a hunter do so? These kinds of conflicts can make for strong bonds between hunters and shapeshifters, or set the stage for bloody, epic tragedy.

Good Neighbors

Another possibility is that the pack and the cell are working parallel to each other, but are not working at cross-purposes. They might wind up choosing the same targets at some point, but for the most part, they have their own investigations and activities, and don't harm each other through them. The World of Darkness has no shortage of supernatural activity, after all, and a cell of hunters might have to prioritize which otherworldly being it wants to pursue. By whatever criteria the cell makes that choice, a local pack might not be much of an issue, especially if the pack just wants to improve its territory.

Hunters and werewolves aren't necessarily looking for the same kinds of things, after all. A werewolf might be looking for spiritual intrusion, and thus miss vampire activity entirely, since vampires don't seem to have much in the way of spiritual knowledge. A cell might place special emphasis on a slasher, but to a werewolf pack, it's just another serial killer. But if the two groups become aware of the others' activities in a way that doesn't make one view the other as a threat, the two sides might eventually come to accept the other as part of the supernatural landscape. That doesn't mean their relationship can't evolve (or devolve), but it does mean a certain level of tolerance can happen.

Shoulder to Shoulder

What if players want to mix the two games, with some taking on the roles of hunters and some taking on the roles of werewolves? This is by no means impossible, but it does require a few considerations, both in terms of game mechanics and the chronicle itself.

For the record, however: a hunter *can* become a werewolf. It's not something that the players can engineer, of course (unless you've decided to make lycanthropy communicable, but we'll keep things in a **Forsaken** context here), but it's not impossible. A hunter that undergoes the First Change, though, probably doesn't get the best of both worlds: read on.

Impact on the Chronicle

What does it mean to have werewolves and hunters rubbing shoulders? The first hurdle that must be overcome is that the hunters are mingling with monsters, and werewolves are assuredly monsters. Werewolves don't tend to remain near their human families, and that's because it doesn't take much for them to go from completely contented to bloodthirsty rage. It stands to reason, then, that even if a werewolf has the best of intentions, he knows that being in a stressful situation alongside human beings (and what else is the Vigil?) is asking for trouble. If the werewolf flies into a frenzy in the middle of a hunt with his pack, he

has other werewolves to help subdue him before anyone dies. If he does the same thing while surrounded by humans, they'll either have to put him down or flee before he tears them apart.

But going beyond the base issue of murderous rage, consider that werewolves are not human. Their Morality is quite different than a human's, in that it aims for balance between spirit and flesh. A werewolf risks losing Morality (called Harmony) for doing things that throw this balance off, such as betrayal of the pack, needless killing of humans (but not killing in and of itself) or murder of his own kind. A hunter, on the other hand, risks losing Morality for killing a human being under any circumstance, until his Morality drops low enough that it isn't an issue (which presents other problems) or until he adopts a Code (if the Storyteller is using this system). It's not an exaggeration to call werewolves inhuman. They can understand a human perspective, having been born and raised with it, but Harmony presents a worldview that might be, on some points, irreconcilable with it.

Having a werewolf working with the cell does require that the cell can come to terms with his inclusion. Leaving aside the broader question of why groups like Aegis Kai Doru would *ever* accept a werewolf (this question is discussed in more detail below), the players need to decide individually if their characters would consent to it. Note that if the Storyteller is including a supporting character who happens to be a werewolf, the same kind of care might not be required — if the characters suddenly decide that having a lycanthrope around is unacceptable and some silver bullets are the perfect solution, so be it. But if the werewolf is a player-controlled character, it's fair for the player in question to demand some advance notice if cooperation is going to turn to murder. After all, the point of the exercise is to have fun, and that requires communication from all parties.

The proportions of the group are another important factor. If the troupe's characters include three hunters and three werewolves, that makes for a very different kind of story than five werewolves to one hunter, or five hunters to one werewolf. A story with the characters is roughly equal numbers probably focuses more on the two groups coming together and dealing with a common threat or learning to coexist. A story in which the numbers are profoundly uneven is probably more tense, and might deal with the "odd man out" learning to cope with this new group of people. Why isn't he with his own kind, after all? One option is that some supernatural threat killed all of the other hunters (or werewolves!) in the area, and the lone character is the last survivor, turning to un-

WEREWOLVES AREN'T THE NEIGHBORHOOD WATCH

References are made in this section to werewolves policing their territory and trying to improve things. Those aren't invalid statements, but don't be fooled: werewolves aren't human, either. They have a set of values and priorities that *intersect* with human-seeming concerns on several points, most notably that they want the area where they live to be pleasant and comfortable. But they also have concerns that don't make any sense to humans (and thus hunters), and that in some cases can be downright offensive or unacceptable.

Consider: a pack of werewolves that makes its home near a river has to drown a person in that river every year. The pack tries to make it a point to pick someone who deserves it, or at least who won't be missed, but if the deadline creeps up and no murderers or homeless people are to be found, they'll grab someone off the street. The reason is that if they *don't* fulfill their obligation, they run the risk of losing the spirit's favor, and that's important to their continued dominance in the area. Werewolves are part spirit, and spirits behave in ways that are sometimes maddeningly simplistic, sometimes dizzyingly arcane.

This section makes the assumption that whatever the werewolves are doing, it doesn't involve actions heinous enough to catch the hunters' attention, at least not immediately. But what if a cell makes contact with the above-mentioned Drowning Pack just *after* their latest fulfillment of that obligation? The pack and the cell have a whole year to get to know each other before the next murder.

Doru follows a moral imperative to *kill* werewolves, so what might they do to hunters who befriend them? Null Mysteriis might accuse any of their members who fraternize with lycanthropes of biasing their own experiments, and exposing themselves to possible contamination.

Mechanics

The Dread Powers listed in Chapter Three of this book do a perfectly serviceable job of representing werewolves in a **Hunter** context. If, however, you have access to **Werewolf: The Forsaken**, a few other considerations become appropriate:

- Hunters are *not* immune to Lunacy. There might be Endowments that enable resistance or even complete immunity, but without such resources, hunters suffer the same debilitating effects as any other person does. Lunacy and how it feels to hunters is described in more detail anon.

- Werewolves cannot use (most) Endowments for the same reasons that unaffiliated hunters can't. More specifically, a werewolf generally does not have an RFID chip (meaning most of Advanced Armory is useless) and doesn't possess the proper breeding as it were, to learn Castigation rituals. Benediction rituals are based on Catholic teaching, but also on human Morality, which werewolves don't have (simply put, their quasi-spirit nature prevents the Benediction from having any effect, even if properly performed). Elixirs produce only a slight tingle and a moment of dizziness before the werewolf's enhanced metabolism rejects them. Thaumatechnology, like Advanced Armory, requires body modifications. Relics, of course, work for werewolves just like they do for anyone else, but a werewolf carrying one of the treasures of the Aegis Kai Doru had better be prepared to defend himself from a steady stream of attackers.

- A werewolf can participate in Tactics, but the usual penalties associated with having an untrained member perform the Tactic apply (see p.

orthodox places for help.

Finally, consider that werewolves and, to a lesser extent, hunters have larger societies to consider. Werewolves belong to *tribes*, spiritual brotherhoods bonded by powerful totems. The pack is probably more important, just as one's immediate family is generally (though not universally) considered more important than one's nationality. But if the cell often runs with a werewolf of, for instance, the Bone Shadows tribe, what happens when another Bone Shadow pack moves into the area and starts making trouble? Can the werewolf character smooth things out before this causes a rift? And if he can't, which way do his loyalties go?

If the cell is composed of tier-one hunters, with no support from larger organizations, this probably won't be an issue on their end (though consider what might happen if one hunter is a cop). Second- and third-tier groups, though, might have to justify what they are doing. Task Force: VALKYRIE hunters work for the government, and as such, don't have as much autonomy as other groups. The Aegis Kai

216 of **Hunter: The Vigil**). A werewolf can learn Tactics along with hunters, of course, but must be mindful of flying into Death Rage during a fight.

• Werewolves cannot risk Willpower, nor do they gain Practical Experience. If a cell wishes a werewolf to learn a Tactic, the hunters must pay the Tactic's cost — the werewolf can't shoulder any of that burden.

The Forsaken and their Hunts

Werewolf: The Forsaken presents a rich, immersive look at the lives and culture of its shapeshifting protagonists. While **Spirit Slayer** deals with lycanthropy as a whole, and not just the *Uratha* of **Werewolf**, the remainder of this chapter focuses on some of the elements unique to the Forsaken and how they might play into a **Hunter** chronicle.

The Forsaken at a Glance

The Forsaken claim spiritual ancestry from a god-like being called Father Wolf; supposedly, he sired nine powerful spirits called the Firstborn with Mother Luna. These wolves later went on to become the totems of the various tribes of werewolves. His other children, also with Luna, were the first werewolves. Perceiving that Father Wolf was growing weak and his abilities as a hunter were slipping, they rose up and killed him. For that crime, other spirits rejected them and they were cast out of the paradise of Pangaea, hence their moniker "the Forsaken." Mother Luna, however, forgave them, and thus modern werewolves enjoy her patronage.

Of course, the above is about as much a part of a given werewolf's modern life as the fable of Adam and Eve is to a modern human's. It's a story, an explanation for why things are the way they are. On a day-to-day level, a werewolf is probably more concerned about what threats from the spirit world might menace her pack, how she can live among humanity while keeping her rage in check, and how she can balance her loyalties to her pack, her tribe, and herself.

Lunacy

Werewolves engender a strange kind of instinctive response in humans when they take on their bestial forms (not including that of a "normal" wolf). This response is referred to as "Lunacy," and it drives humans into a panic. Some people flee, some hide, some even fall catatonic. A very few stand and fight, or attempt to protect their fellow humans. In any case, most people forget their encounter with the werewolf, inserting whatever explanation allows them to keep functioning. Lunacy, despite its apparent utility for werewolves as a cloak for their activity, is actually a defense mechanism for humanity more than anything else. It allows a human witness to lycanthropy to go back to his life without panicking every time he sees a dog or hears a police siren (which might be confused for a howl). Some people, of course, aren't lucky enough for that to work — including hunters. Generally, the response to the Lunacy, both in terms of immediate reaction and memory, is defined by mental fortitude and the ability to stay calm in the face of danger: Willpower, the sum of Resolve and Composure, in game terms.

Most people (those with a Willpower rating between 3 and 5) will run from a werewolf, only stopping to fight if they have no other choice or an incredibly strong impetus to do so, such as a parent protecting her child. Those with higher Willpower ratings might be able to take some rational actions; locking doors behind them, getting in a car and driving away, and so on. Those with truly superlative Willpower ratings (9 or 10) might muster the strength to fight the beast — their fear turns to rage.

Hunters do experience Lunacy, but anyone who takes up the Vigil has already dedicated herself to the pursuit of the supernatural, for whatever reason. As such, hunters don't forget as easily as most people. Even if a given hunter's traits aren't particularly high, the obsessive nature of the Vigil provokes a different response than for most people. A hunter who sees a werewolf in one of its nightmarish forms feels terrified, to be sure. But most hunters feel, in that moment of terror, a sense of dedication and purpose. Here, in front of the hunter, is the greatest reason for the Vigil, a true monster. As such, when a hunter sees a werewolf, the player should roll Resolve + Composure. Success on this roll means that the hunter responds to the werewolf as though his Willpower was *three points higher* than it actually is (if you have access to **Werewolf: The Forsaken**) or that the hunter can function normally (if you are working from the **Hunter** core book and this book). When the time comes to try to remember what happened during the scene, the hunter's player also adds three dice to any relevant rolls.

Note that the Deprogramming Tactic and the Moral Support Tactic work normally on the effects of Lunacy. ("Lunacy" is described in greater detail in the prior chapter, on p. 163).

Biology of a Werewolf

Werewolves heal rapidly, regenerating one point of bashing damage *per turn*, and one point of lethal damage every 15 minutes. They heal aggravated damage at the same rate humans do, however.

Beyond the mechanical facets of regeneration, though, consider that a werewolf has a hyperactive metabolism. Drugs and poisons work on werewolves, but their regeneration affects this damage, meaning that the toxins get absorbed and passed through the system much faster than in humans. Werewolves do not get sick, and they age slowly.

Werewolves cannot breed with each other. Rather, they can, but the result is a powerful and malign spirit called a Ghost Child. These creatures hunt the spirit worlds, hoping to find and kill their parents. As such, a werewolf that mates with another of his kind can expect punitive measures, possibly even exile. This is something that a *very* clever and well-informed cell might capitalize on.

A werewolf can mate with a human being and produce a werewolf child, but the result is more likely to be a wolf-blood. Wolf-blooded humans are slightly more resistant to Lunacy than other humans, but they attract spiritual activity. See the Kin Merit on p. 139

for more information. In Forsaken society, wolf-bloods are sometimes treated as breeding stock and little else, kept captive by their lycanthrope mates. Anyone they turn to for help is put at risk, and so many wolf-bloods in this situation simply give up. A few, however, wind up becoming hunters. The child of a wolf-blood, whether with a werewolf or a normal human, has a strong chance of becoming a werewolf, though, and so werewolves don't let wolf-bloods escape easily.

Werewolf Culture

The society of the Forsaken is composed of several tribes, each of which claim one of the Firstborn children of Father Wolf as a spiritual patron. The tribes teach different outlooks towards spiritual and temporal matters, and are somewhat analogous to third-tier hunter organizations. They provide werewolves with spirit magic, and a werewolf can usually count on a tribemate for some degree of hospitality and support, though a werewolf's first loyalty is generally to his pack.

A given pack's status can be measured by how much territory it can claim. A pack claims territory by being able to defend it from other beings that wish to partake of the same resources. For instance, a prime territory might include one or more *Loci* (see below), a spirit population that is easily manageable, and any other qualities that a specific pack might favor. For instance, a pack that prizes the ability to move around a city quickly might claim the subways as its territory. One that prefers to spend time hunting in wolf form might claim a large swath of wilderness.

Werewolves don't, obviously, make any overt claims to ownership or dominance of any area as far as humans go. They might police an area for certain kinds of human activity. A pack that wishes to keep spirits of addiction, misery, and greed away from its turf might go after drug dealers and users, and depending on their methods, this might attract hunters.

War

A werewolf's primary enemy is arguably another werewolf. Their society has deep rifts that stretch back to Pangaea. Specifically, not all of the Firstborn accepted Mother Luna's offer of forgiveness. Three of them denounced the werewolves that killed Father Wolf, and took other werewolves as their spiritual children. These tribes, referring to themselves as the Pure, are the bitter enemies of the Forsaken, and are perhaps more likely to be on the receiving end of violent hunter activity. The Pure behave more like the werewolves of legend, for the most part — they kill and even eat humans, they consort with powerful and dangerous spirits, and they renounce any claim to their pre-Change lives. The Forsaken and the Pure don't necessarily attack each other on sight, but they do battle over turf, wolf-blooded mates (see above) and on ideological grounds.

Some werewolves give themselves over entirely to worship of unclean spirits. These spirits might embody violence, spite, hatred or gluttony, and they originate from places in the spirit world that no sane being should tread. These werewolves, called Bale Hounds, care nothing for humanity and nothing for the principles of Harmony. As such, if a pack and a cell were to join forces, a Bale Hound (or a pack of them) would make for a good common foe.

Of course, if a pack goes to war, it doesn't have to be over anything more than turf rights. Two packs belonging to the same tribe might even be involved in a protracted battle for territory, although such battles are far less likely to involve fatalities (deliberate ones, at least) than battles with the Pure or the Bale Hounds. A hunter cell caught between two battling packs, though, might find that playing one pack against the other is difficult. The werewolves will probably circle their wagons against an outside threat, leaving the cell facing two (or more) packs instead of just one.

Fetishes

Any werewolf with the proper training can craft a fetish. A fetish is an object with a spirit bound into it, and such objects are prized among the Forsaken. Fetishes range in their effects from inflicting extra damage (weapon fetishes, known as *klaives* among werewolves) to forcing spirits to materialize to disguising a lycanthrope's wolf form as a dog. If a fetish is broken, the spirit inside is freed, and it might well be hostile to its erstwhile captors. On the other hand, a spirit that enjoyed having a home (and such spirits do exist) might well attack its liberators instead.

Fetishes, unlike Relics, cannot be activated by non-werewolves. They require special entreaties or the expenditure of spiritual energy, neither of which is possible for humans. This doesn't mean, of course, that hunters, especially of the Aegis Kai Doru, don't zealously pursue fetishes. It's impossible to tell the difference between a useful relic and a fetish at a distance, and some hunters figure that any magical item can be activated with the right ritual or trigger, anyway.

Fetishes are often passed on to packmates or family, and as such they can have a great deal of sentimental value to a werewolf. A hunter who loots the body (or the home) of a werewolf might find himself in possession of a trinket that seems useless, but that makes him a target for the werewolf's pack.

Spirits

Werewolves are not masters of spirits, nor are they necessarily their friends. In fact, spirits generally dislike werewolves. This dislike is sometimes thought to stem from the werewolves' ancestral crime, but in fact, spirits kill each other frequently. The enmity has more to do with the fact that werewolves are part spirit, part flesh, and spirits dislike this inconsistency.

Spirits are powerful, but limited in what they can accomplish in the physical world. As such, if a hunter cell encounters a spirit, it is generally either acting under direction, or powerful enough to force its way out of its own realm somewhat. Either demands caution.

Spirit Mindset

The important thing for the Storyteller to remember when portraying spirits is that they don't have free will. A spirit *cannot* act out of its nature. A car-spirit can only be a car-spirit, and depending on the specifics, might be impatient and impulsive (a spirit of road rage), imposing and haughty (an SUV-spirit) or imperious and unbending (a police-car spirit). A spirit of violence *cannot* show mercy, no matter how deserving someone might be. In that way, spirits are refreshingly honest and simple, but as the example of the car-spirit should show, a myriad of possible spirits exists for any given concept.

Note, too, that every spirit has its own name and personality. As a spirit grows in power, the personality becomes more individualized and less like a "typical" member of its species. The spirit of a police car might, over time, become Car Number 234, and relish the idea of chasing down fleeing felons. Anyone put in the back of this car feels the handcuffs grow tight around his wrists and the doors and windows close in on him. The car enjoys torturing those it is transporting to jail, and it firmly believes that the police who ride in it (no matter who they are or whether they're honest cops) never arrest the innocent, and are always acting within the law. Pity the hunter who gets arrested by those cops, especially if he resists.

Spirits seem to want to cross into the physical world, though many lack the ability to do so. Some werewolves make it a point to stop this kind of intrusion, but many only care insofar as it affects their territory. Once a spirit crosses over, it needs a way to anchor itself. Some spirits do this by possessing a living being or an object, and powerful spirits can make such a change permanent. The Exorcism Tactic can get rid of a spirit controlling a person, but if the spirit has claimed the human entirely, warping his flesh to suit the spirit, then the only "cure" is death.

More information on spirits in a **Hunter** context can be found in Chapter Three.

Totems ("Familiar Spirit")

Most werewolf packs have a totem spirit. This spirit represents the pack and grants it power (usually in the form of a reserve of Willpower, a few dots of Skills, or even a Dread Power that they can all call upon). In return, the werewolves agree to observe a ban of some kind. Some spirits demand a special ritual in their honor, others proscribe a certain kind of behavior. A pack following a totem strongly related to stealth or secrecy, for instance, might be forbidden from referring to their totem by name, even while alone. A more bloodthirsty totem might demand a special hunt culminating in feasting on the flesh of the target. Totems can take the forms of animals, but some are more abstract (spirits of emotions or concepts). A pack's name and agenda are almost always related to the totem in some way.

As Storyteller, a pack's totem can be a way to define the pack a bit more and provide you with some

insight into how they will approach a problem (like a cell of hunters, for instance). A pack that follows Mother Bear might be inclined to leave the hunters alone, provided they stay away from the pack's family. If the cell steps over that line, though, the pack attacks with all the ferocity it can muster — Mother Bear demands no less. A pack that follows Starving Rat knows every nook and cranny in the city, and might be bound by their totem to take a bite out of their prey. If the werewolves follow their Morality, they'll spit the flesh out, but that might be just as horrifying as watching the werewolves gulp down the gobbet.

Loci

As has been mentioned before, a locus is a place where the barrier between the physical world and the spirit world grow thin. Spirits gather at loci like watering holes, drawing energy from them. Werewolves use loci to step into the spirit world, and can even pull unwilling targets across the barrier at these places, leaving troublesome hunters stranded in a decidedly hostile environment.

Strange things happen at loci. The surroundings alter themselves, both in mood and in form, to fit the resonance of the locus. As such, loci are often identified as "haunted" sites, which might attract hunter cells expecting to find ghosts and instead encountering spirits and werewolves.

Below are three possible loci for use in your **Hunter** chronicles:

• **The Mirror in the Hall:** A rich man's mansion contains a gigantic mirror large enough to drive a car through. The mirror's frame is inscribed with astrological and date-keeping symbols, originally put there by a deranged offshoot of the Ashwood Abbey. The mirror, over time, became a locus with an "inviting" resonance. Looking into the mirror often portrays the viewer as more attractive than he actually is, and those who primp in the mirror for at least five minutes gain a +1 to any

Social roll made in the next scene that benefits from physical appearance (similar to the Striking Looks Merit). Over the 40 years it has resided in the mansion, the mirror has disgorged a host of small, mischievous spirits. They have plenty of room to hide (the old man and his staff are the only inhabitants), but they are bored. When the mirror next opens, they intend to coax a more powerful spirit through, one that can give them direction and purpose.

• **Mr. Barry's Basement:** Earl Barry was executed recently for six counts of rape and murder. The police removed his victims' remains from his basement, but they couldn't wash away the spiritual taint. The basement stairs are now a large locus. The resonance is horrifying, a mixture of the pain of his victims and the exuberant glee he felt in violating and dismembering them. The worst part is; the stairs might be used to bring Earl Barry back from the dead. A powerful murder-spirit is looking to coax or possess a vulnerable human into exhuming Barry's body and bringing it to the basement, whereupon the spirit will possess it and turn it into a kind of undead slasher.

• **Lover's Lane:** The stretch of road overlooking Almes Quarry is notorious among nervous parents as a lover's lane. Many of the locals were actually conceived while their parents parked on that stretch of road, and some randy teens joke about being second or third generation "Quarry Kids." Every few years, when spring comes early to the area and a creeping fog covers the lane, though, a couple will emerge from their car after a romp and find themselves in the Spirit Wilds. As long as they don't leave the fog, they'll be fine; the "crossing" disappears with the fog and leaves them back on Earth. A pack of bloodthirsty werewolves hunts the area, however, and considers anyone on "their" side of the Gauntlet to be fair game for the hunt.

HUNTING GROUND: PHILADELPHIA

Welcome to Philadelphia, the City of Neighborhoods. Where even the most civil city-dweller can turn aggressive if the block he comes from is challenged. The average Philadelphian is a creature full of pride and territorial spirit. Imagine then those citizens who have the blood of beasts pumping through their veins.

The years have not been kind to the City of Brotherly Love, a city mired in tragedy, political scandal and a meteoritic rise in its murder rate. Life in so-called

"Killadelphia" is only getting worse. The youth of the city are increasingly driven by an almost unnatural hostility, drawing lines literally down the middle of streets. This sort of posturing and territoriality isn't altogether strange amongst youth, but the violence in Philadelphia is severe even by gangland standards.

All of this unchecked violence in Philadelphia makes it the perfect setting for a game of high stakes violence and territory. Street by street, the struggle spreads through the City of Brotherly Love leaving no corner untouched. The crack of gunfire mixes with the cracking of bones; and the howling of sirens mixes with the howling of wolves through the night. Parents lose their children on all sides of the conflict between wolves and human. No one is innocent, and no one gets by unscathed.

Welcome to Philadelphia, the City of *Territory*.

Theme: Degradation

Philadelphia, once a place of great hope, idealism and revolutionary spirit has slowly eroded with cynicism, isolation, and corruption. Under William Penn, Philadelphia and the surrounding boroughs were remarkably free of the tension with natives or religious hysteria that plagued early colonial culture. Peace with the natives, peace between religions, and even peace with the changing men once ruled Philadelphia. While falling short of a utopia, it's small wonder Philadelphia drew the attention of the Founding Fathers to become the nation's first capital. However, it seems all good things must come to an end.

The vision of the City's founder and patron slowly withered, natives were persecuted and pushed off the land they had kept since their ancestors. Ancient compacts with the local spirits fell apart as there was no one left to keep their bans and traditions. Philadelphia has been seemingly cursed ever since to be mired in greed, intolerance, and violence.

Mood: Escalation

One night it's an argument, and then it's a fight. One side brings friends, so the other brings a knife, and the first pulls a gun. At a glance, this is the worsening condition of Philadelphia. It is not a new condition; Philadelphia's relationship with violent crime dates back to the Revolutionary War. Since then, race riots, religious riots, and other violent expressions of xenophobia ruled the 1800s, and the 20th century was overrun with mafia and gang violence under the nose of one corrupt establishment after another.

A brief lull of peace through the 1990s into the early 2000s saw a renewal in civic pride and a push toward gentrification largely welcomed throughout the city. This élan proved short-lived as those residents pushed out of their homes couldn't go far were forced to move into already overcrowded neighborhoods. The kettle is coming back to a boil and that brief peace seems like a distant memory as the murder rate spikes in Philadelphia and neighboring cities.

A Paradise Lost (History)

The land that became Philadelphia was occupied by the tribes of the Leni-Lenapé, who dominated much of the coastline on all sides of the Delaware River. Common to many aboriginal people, their term for themselves (Lenapé) simply meant "People." The qualifier, "Leni," held a special and terrible meaning to immigrant European werewolves; it means *Pure*. These Pure People worshipped spirits to maintain peace and balance locally. Most notably, Misinkhâlikàn or "Misink" their patron, a spirit of the forests who offered his protection so long as the Lenapé honored him and kept his bans. Misink was described as a beast man, a large powerful creature who walked on two legs with a face half-red, half-black. Modern interpretations liken the creature to Bigfoot or Sasquatch, or what the Algonquin people further north called Wìdjigò (Wendigo). The European werewolves recognized the Native *lenateme* (wolf people) packs and their relationship with spirits as their ancient enemies.

Penn and Tamanend

William Penn perhaps said it best: "A *good end cannot sanctify evil means; nor must we ever do evil, that good may come of it.*"

Philadelphia came to be with none of the bloodshed or calamity that many other colonies came to accept as part of the rugged New World. This almost unique peace came down to two men, William Penn, Quaker and Tamanend, Sakimâ (chief) of the Unami.

Penn had been persecuted as a Quaker in England and came to the New World with a vision of a place of utmost tolerance. As a pacifist he saw a place where all disputes could be resolved through reason and all differences overcome in peace. True to his ideals, he approached the Natives differently than many Europeans and his message of tolerance resonated between the natives and the settlers. Penn insisted on being fair in any and all negotiations with the aboriginal people and insisted his people did the same. Despite possessing a Royal Writ to the land surrounding the river, Penn bartered, paid for, and shared the land among his Quakers, the established Dutch and Swedes, and the native cultures. He paid fairly for land and established a charter that stated any Indian wronged by a European would be seen to by a court of equal parts Lenapé and Englishman.

COMPACT WITH THE MASKED ONE

Long ago, there were three young Lenapé who were treated rather poorly and in fact, their parents did not seem to care whether they lived or died. They were Unami (turtle) eldest and wisest of the boys, Unalachigo (turkey) the middle boy, and Minsi (wolf) youngest and of fierce temper. One day, the boys were in the forest hunting and talking about their troubles when they saw a strange-looking hairy person with a large face painted half black and half red. This creature said, "I am Misinkhâlikàn, I have taken pity on you and I will give you strength so that nothing can ever hurt you again. Come with me and I shall show you my country."

He took the boys into the sky to the place where he came from. It was a great range of mountains up in the sky reaching from north to south. He promised that they would become stout and strong and should gain great power to get anything they wished. Then he brought the boys back down to Earth again. So it was the three boys experienced their first change of the *lenateme*, and the three Pure Tribes of Lenapé were born.

In later years, the boys had grown up and gained respect for their strength and influence with spirits and none dared their wrath. As they would hunt, they might see Misinkhâlikàn occasionally, riding on a buck, herding deer together, and giving his peculiar call, "Ah-ho-ho!"

Now, the Lenapé had always used a bark long house to worship in, where they would sing about dreams and visions. However, while the three *lenateme* men were away making families and hunting, the people gave up the ways of Misinkhâlikàn and for 10 years they had none. Then a great many earthquakes came lasting 12 moons and gave much trouble to the Lenapé. In one town, an old Sakimâ (chief) of the Unami people, remembered the forgotten ways and built a new house, to bring an end to their strife. When it was finished, they worshipped there, and sang and prayed all winter for relief, but the earthquakes continued, and ill will between the people grew out of such hard times.

Just after springtime came, the men returned to find the Lenapé broken, hungry, and fighting against one another. They held a meeting immediately to bring their people together again when they heard a noise in the forest to the east, "Ah-ho-ho!" The three men recognized the call of Misinkhâlikàn and went to find out what he wanted and why he had lifted his protection from the people.

So, they went outside and found Misinkhâlikàn in the woods, and asked him what he wanted. "Go back and tell the others to stop holding meetings and to attend to their crops," he answered. "Do not meet again until the fall, when I shall come and live with you. I will give your people help through a new ceremony, Xinkwikàn (Big House). You must carve a mask of wood to look like my face, painted half black and half red, as mine is, and I shall put my power into it, so it will do as you ask. When the man who takes my part puts the mask on, I shall be there with you, and in this way I shall live among you and bring you peace. The man must carry a *taxoxi kowàni'kàn* (turtle-shell rattle), a bag and a staff, just as I do now."

Misinkhâlikàn told them to carve 12 faces on the posts of the Big House and on drumsticks to be used in the ceremony. Then he said, "You must also give me hominy every year in the spring. I take care of the deer and other game animals. That is what I am for. Wherever you build a Big House, I shall keep the deer close by so you can get them."

"Never give up the Xinkwikàn, for if you do, there will be more earthquakes or other things just as bad." The people did as the *lenateme* said, the earthquakes stopped, and the Lenapé kept the Xinkwikàn and the mask thereafter.

The big question — the question to both the hunters and werewolves of this city is — what happens if this deal isn't kept? Certainly someone must be keeping it, since there haven't been earthquakes. But who?

Tamanend represented the Unami at the time and thus the other Lenapé tribes looked to him as the voice of reason and peace among them. He found Penn to be true of heart and his people to be respectful. The two men forged a treaty of friendship under a tall elm tree at Shackamaxon, in what is now the city's Kensington section. So profound was this notion of peaceful cooperation in Philadelphia that other seaboard cities such as New York and Boston dubbed the Indian leader Saint Tammany and Patron Saint of America and celebrated King Tammany Day on the first of May.

Both sides had their detractors, of course, not the least of which were the Pure *lenateme* and their European counterparts. Many wolfmen and their kin came to the Colonies for the same reason other men did: persecution by government and Church. Also their population increasingly clashed over territory between Pure and their own Forsaken tribes. To their horror they discovered the same conflicts awaited them in the New World in a land controlled almost exclusively by their enemies. Without centuries of open war however, their squabbles were almost tame in comparison to what they had left behind.

Walking Purchase

By 1737, William Penn and Tammany were long dead and the Penn's Woods colony fell under the governance of lesser men. Penn's children had less the virtue and fairness of their father, and inevitably the peace they held with the native population wore thin. Penn's legacy turned to greed, and Tamenend's people turned to resentment, a situation which culminated in the land swindle known as the Walking Purchase.

Penn's son (Thomas) and grandson (John) claimed to have found a deed giving his father the right to as much land as three men could walk in a day and a half. In truth, he had already sold most of the land throughout the Lehigh Valley (north of the city) and needed to clear that area of natives before it could be settled. The legacy of peace was still strong among the native population, and the name Penn carried a lot of weight. The document was almost certainly a fake, but due to most Lenapé being illiterate and largely unfamiliar with English law, they conceded to the letter of this found treaty. After all, how far could a man walk in that time? Not enough to be of any consequence, they presumed.

The trickery of the Penns wasn't done yet, and the governor hired the fastest runners they could. The men set out and stopped only briefly to rest through the night. The pace set by these "walkers" was so intense that by the end of the time limit they had acquired a piece of land roughly the size of Rhode Island. The Lenapé were outraged but believed themselves bound by their word and English law to honor the deal. Many of the Leni-Lenapé moved on by coercion or self-imposed exile from the lands of their ancestors. Werewolves fell on either side of the divide; some among the *lenateme* had come to side with the European tribes and vice versa.

The European werewolves did not have the same deals in place with the area spirits, the bans of Misink were not upkept and the situation was coming to a boil just below the surface in the spirit world. The wolves kept the situation a secret from even the local hunters they managed a loose cooperation with.

Peace eroded, corruption festered, and dread loomed larger and larger. Well before the historic signing of the Declaration of Independence, Philadelphia's golden age was past. The wolfmen were losing control over disturbed spirits and people were caught in the middle of their increasingly desperate mission. Area hunters found themselves butting heads more with the Lupines than they ever had before.

Violence and Discontent

Post-Revolutionary Philadelphia enjoyed a brief stint as the nation's capital but that distinction moved to Washington D.C. soon after and the city stewed in growing trends of crime, civil unrest, and corruption. Misink's curse had come true and the Forsaken tribes watched hopelessly as spirits of murder, hate, greed, lust and violence burbled through the boundary between the spirit world and the tangible world.

The insular and territorial Philadelphians engaged in a seemingly ceaseless string of riots. Worker riots, election riots, anti-Catholic riots, race riots; Philadelphians seemed ever-prepared to take to the streets and dish out their prejudice with torches, sabers, and rifles. Multiple meeting halls, community centers, and churches were lost every year throughout the mid-1800s to fire and fear. The situation became so bad that special militias were chartered to keep the peace, and a guideline of "one watchmen per thousand tax-paying citizens" was established.

These struggles didn't leave hunter or werewolf at peace anymore than any other citizen. In fact, they were at the heart of many local squabbles. The wolfmen knew the riots were often fueled by malignant spirits while making those spirits stronger. Spirits of despair, violence, and hate fed well and grew in power and there was little the combined packs could do to hold back the floodgates. Hunters often misunderstood the behavior of the wolves and inadvertently hampered efforts to get a handle on the situation. The wolves were losing their invisible war while churches burned and weavers rioted.

Frustrated with the seemingly bottomless well of malice and greed, the werewolves lashed out at the symptoms — i.e. humans — as often as the disease. Hunters were caught in the middle trying to protect humanity from what spirits they could affect, and a wolf problem that seemed equally out of control. The werewolves were confronted with the awful possibility that they were becoming infected with the very malignance they were trying to stem. Something had to give.

A meeting was held between the packs of Philadelphia in what is now Fairmount Park, to discuss the hunter problem, and the growing darkness in their hearts. In a rare instance of swallowed pride, the werewolves acknowledged they needed help.

Penn Treaty

The elm under which William Penn and Tamanend had signed their treaty blew down in a storm in the early 1800s. A marker was quickly put in its place but the area had long since been developed by the local logging industry. This was the place hunter and werewolves would come together, and discuss their terms. Whether this meeting would lead to drafting a treaty or declaration of war remained to be seen. One of the hunters procured a small wooden box, unexceptional in almost every way save its origin: it was crafted from the elm tree that had once stood in the very place they held their midnight senate.

Agreeing both factions desired peace was the easy part; neither side could afford the time or casualty to keep interfering with one another. All present swore a pact of non-aggression and established jurisdiction where their respective word was paramount. The treaty's conditions stated no hunter could knowingly kill a wolfman or their kin unless in direct defense of his own life. It further stated no werewolf would harm a human unless they posed a direct danger to the spiritual climate of the city and peaceful intervention had failed.

Local legend claims this meeting is when Center City was proclaimed neutral territory and both sides agreed to rescue the site on which they stood. To take it from being a forgotten corner of some rail yard to a park honoring the spirit of peace and friendship it was meant to represent, Penn Treaty Park was set aside as public land shortly thereafter and the park endures to this day. The same cannot be said for the treaty.

New Relic: Box of the Treaty Elm ••••

Records of the box's whereabouts have been lost over time. It is widely believed a representative of either the hunters or wolfmen present at the treaty were assigned as steward of the box as a token of good faith. Accounts vary as to even which faction was left in charge and what became of it thereafter. Individuals on either side blame the other for knowing the box's whereabouts or having lost it. Regardless, one thing most agree on: the box still exists somewhere within the city limits. Many desire to find and use it to return peace to the City of Brotherly Love; and still others who would want to destroy it.

Function: This Relic makes any oath spoken over it completely binding. All parties who wish to participate in the compact choose a representative. The chosen individuals contribute their Willpower for the activation cost and supply the necessary token representing their faction. The token should be an item of some sacrifice or importance to the respective side of the agreement and able to fit inside the box (approximately one foot by six inches and six inches deep). If an appropriate item can't be procured, one should be carved or crafted by the representative.

Each represented faction agrees on the letter of the pact and its conditions then each representative puts their selected token within the box, closes it and hands it to the next participant who follows suit. Once all the offerings are placed within, each side puts their hands on the box, and swears aloud to the oath. The Storyteller or relevant players make their rolls and add together the results of all the rolls to determine success below.

Cost: 2 Willpower from all participating parties, and one physical token

Action: Instant

Roll: Resolve + Empathy (combine participants' results)

Roll Results

Dramatic Failure: All participants and represented factions immediately lose all Willpower. Furthermore, the offering items disappear. The participants may attempt to swear to the same treaty by waiting one full turn of the moon (28 days) and repaying the full activation cost.

Failure: The Willpower is spent, but the items remain within the box and nothing happens.

Success: The offerings disappear without a trace and the oath is made binding to the participating representatives and the groups they speak for. Anyone claiming membership to one of the represented bodies are responsible for the oath's upkeep. If a faction betrays any part of the treaty everyone within their ranks immediately lose all Willpower and suffer a -2 penalty to all dice rolls against or defending against the opposing faction (provided that faction remained true to the letter of the oath). In addition, oathbreakers gain a severe derangement (Storyteller's choice).

Exceptional Success: As a success above and the oathbreakers immediately suffer two aggravated damage upon committing the offense.

Suggested Modifiers:

+2	Offering is of deep personal significance.
+1	Offering is emblematic of the organization (badge, seal, or heirloom).

Jim Di Barbur

+1	Offering was crafted by the participant.
-2	Offering is profane.
-3	Representative is in any way insincere.

Breaking the Oath

For more than a generation, a fragile peace subsisted. Despite this cooperative effort, the spiritual turmoil continued unabated. For every spirit sent back to its locus another two would pop up. Hunters did their best to help as inexpertly as they could manage, but were less equipped to handle the special breed of monsters pouring into the city. How do men fight greed and hate made manifest?

The wolves lost ground to despair; the young ones knew only constant warfare and the old ones knew in the dark of their hearts they were to blame. The Curse of Misink could not be stopped now. It had gone on too long, and none were left who could enact the ancient rite to stem the spiritual deluge. Packs abandoned the city for easier territory, spreading the available manpower even thinner.

Philadelphia through the 20th century became well known for its graft and was accurately described as "corrupt and content." Gangs and mafia warred for control over those parts of the city not in the grip of the Republican government. Often the two factions worked hand in hand, mutually looking the other way. By the time of the Great Depression, the city

had been through enough bank scandals they were old hat at destitution; losing pay, pension, and industry to outlying towns was an almost yearly event.

The city wasn't immune to the desperation of the time, and the corruption continued. The situation was made worse when the mayor denied rampant starvation and accused the unprecedented unemployment rate on laziness while cutting thousands of city jobs to keep Philadelphia in the black. The fat cats stayed fat while people starved in the streets. The werewolves were no different, and starving wolves make for troublesome enemies.

In the mid-1930s, hunters investigated a rash of grisly murders that led back to a pack of hungry and desperate werewolves who resorted to man-eating to fill their bellies. The pact of the Treaty Elm shattered; the last good will between wolf and man was spent. Accusations followed, the backdrop of depression, hunger, and desperation drove the conflict to open warfare and the wolves found themselves weakened by the breaking of the treaty. The actions of a desperate few had damned them all. The spirits of anger, hatred, and intolerance finally won, driving a lasting spike between the two perennially cooperative factions.

Fairmount Slaughter

Unfortunately for the wolves, the penalty for breaking the treaty carried over to every pack in Philadelphia, their families, and extended kin. The humans gained a supernatural edge over their foes. Peace was already a distant memory in Philadelphia, now it would seem an unachievable dream. Despite the odds being against them, the werewolves' sheer strength allowed them to hang on to what territory they had left for several decades thereafter, retreating to the few strongholds they had left — primarily Fairmount Park.

A coalition of cells made a concentrated push to pry loose what hold the creatures had left within the city. The hunters didn't consider the consequences of weakening the city's only guardians against the spiritual overflow. What few cool heads remained on either side suspected the terrible truth: they had all fallen prey to the same spirits they were meant to battle against.

After decades of fighting, it was in the mid-1970s that the wolves felt their control of Fairmount Park threatened. Their last great holding, home to werewolves for centuries (even before the European Forsaken had come) would be taken away from them, and not through the violence of war which they would have at least been prepared for. No, the attack came as a mix of public and legal pressure to "clean up" the area.

The battle for stewardship of the park dragged through the courts and streets over a few years until one chilly September night. As many cells as could make it converged on the park. They started at various points around the perimeter of the park, and moved inward. From the riverside, from the street side, and through the woods they came. They formed a human dragnet moving inward and killing everything that stood in their way.

Bloodlines were still hampered from breaking the treaty and proved far more ineffectual than they would have thought. Some packs openly fled with the hope of surviving to fight another day, others sent word to their kin to hide but stood to defend their home. The hunters call it the Reclamation; the wolves call it the Fairmount Slaughter.

Werewolves intended retribution to be swift, but with heavy losses and their weakened state they found themselves too evenly matched for the hunter population. Instead revenge has been a long, scrabbling, bloody affair. Consumed with their war between each other, the spirits grow unchecked, the Pure have made inroads back into the city and the long traditions of the Forsaken have been lost to madness.

(More information on Forsaken versus Pure can be found be found under "War" on p. 204 in this chapter.)

Modern Nights

The murder rate spikes as another generation of guideless and tribeless wolves come of age and misspend their youth violently. Too many young souls march willingly through the meat grinder and the old guard can't expect to stand idly by and expect the situation to heal itself. Will their intercession galvanize their youths to band together with or *against* them?

For the first time in a century, hunter cells and werewolf packs have to consider what good they might accomplish together or die trying. Something has to give, that much is certain.

Spirit of Philadelphia

The spirit world reflects history's scars: catastrophes that ripple through history and don't heal quite right. Generally speaking, this conjures images of tragedy over triumph. A look into the spirit world of Philadelphia reveals: desperation, desolation, corruption, greed, hate and a savage enough death toll to support a personified murder spirit. "Killadelphia" doesn't call to mind sun-shiny spirits ready to lend a helping hand.

It isn't all bad however—it couldn't be or no one would live here. Other spirits are at work in the city: community, family, pride, hard work, and strong ethics. Philadelphia is all of these things, and more; one doesn't need to travel to the spirit world to see the extremes between streets in Philadelphia. The same avenues where the first American zoo, university, public library, national flag and Capital building were constructed, which played host to every forefather of the United States is bound to have positive spirits as well.

When designing the spiritual landscape of Philadelphia (or any setting), not every textile fire or economic nadir is going to have an effect on the local spiritual reflection. Scars may be caused by any source, great or small: from the violent murder of a five-year-old child found beneath a bush in a carriage box at Fox Chase known only as the "Boy in the Box;" to the 1844 Southwark riots against Catholics resulting in multiple churches burned to the ground, cannons fired into crowds, and dozens of deaths requiring the intercession of the military and local militia.

The wide variety of spirits and loci peppering the cityscape stand as testimony to the city's long-lived character, below are a few examples to get Storytellers started.

Spirit Story Seeds:

• Revolutionary spirits left over from the War of Independence still hang around. Area residents find themselves compelled to take up the fight against tyranny… over 200 years too late. It begins as minor civil disobedience, but before long all of Center City stage demonstrations daily against the most mundane of ordinances. Can the players free the populace from these effects or will they be swept up in the furor?

• Yellow Fever or other spirits of sickness from the multiple epidemics throughout Philadelphia history still lurk in alleys and the backstreets of poorer districts. The players discover a mysterious spirit sickness resembling a disease long thought vaccinated. Perhaps connections in the Cheiron Group could synthesize a cure, or perhaps it will take more supernaturally potent methods.

• Centennial/bicentennial celebration spirits linger representing the spike in civic pride, national identity, and hopeful tourism of their respective eras. During a street fair, concert or other celebration, attendees find themselves suddenly connected to the past; literally walking in and out of other time periods. What's more, other time periods are walking into the modern day. Is there a way to barter with the Spirit of '76 and wrangle everyone back to their own time; and why now so far from those notable anniversaries? In addition, don't forget that civic pride can become a lot like nationalism… which can turn into violent, prejudicial behavior by anybody who doesn't salute the Liberty Bell or support the Eagles.

• The streets at 9th and Washington seem to catch spiritual fire late on winter nights. Reportedly from when coal and oil poured from a heating oil manufacturer into the snow-banked streets, becoming trapped and creating a "sea of fire" in the street. Hunters can see this strange aurora, but are unaffected by it. Werewolves however, are not so lucky. This makes it the perfect place for an ambush if the characters can successfully lure their foes to the area — but doing so breaks the neutrality of Center City.

• Spirits of twisted metal and the screams of injured and dying still echo in the night in the Philadelphia suburbs. These spirits still hang on from when two trains collided head on outside of Ambler killing 50. Until recently, this remained a terrifying but harmless neighborhood haunting, but recently the phenomenon has gotten louder and more insistent. Witnesses even claim the still extant railroad tracks have been violently shaking to accompany the cacophony. Does this portend another disaster and if so, are the spirits the cause or a warning?

The Vigil at a Glance

Wolf hunting in Philadelphia has taken many shapes through the years. Once content to remain ignorant of one another, the hunters and wolves forged a fragile peace through non-aggression; until desperate times drove otherwise reasonable creatures to the far edges of sanity and war broke out. The wages of war weigh differently on all who take up the Vigil but can be summarized as follows.

Ascending Ones: *Profiteering.* The Jagged Crescent observes the struggle from their street corners. Weakening the young wolves and their kin with the poisons they deal while turning a profit in return.

Ashwood Abbey: *Entrenched.* There's enough old money to support the Abbey in Northwest Philly. They proved instrumental in the Fairmount Slaughter but find they're quite unwilling to deal with the consequences these many years later.

Aegis Kai Doru: *Undermanned.* Philadelphia has a wolf problem the likes of which they've rarely seen. The few Guardians within the city have petitioned to get more manpower into the city to no avail.

Cheiron Group: *Overwhelmed.* TCG and its new director don't even like to think about what's happening outside of Center City. They've attempted to stay out of the conflict, but Corporate sees this as a waste of good wolf pelts and have begun to put pressure on the branch offices to get out in the streets and get involved.

The Long Night: *Clear and Present.* The Long Night's foot soldiers M5:5 under Isaiah Bellamy (**Hunter: The Vigil**, p. 352) make up the front lines of the struggle in Philadelphia's street war between werewolves and hunters. The short-term gain is looking more like long-term loss, but they're in too deep.

The Loyalists of Thule: *Disinterested.* For their part, the Loyalists seem largely unaffected by the war in the streets. What limited presence they have is more interested in keeping their information and land out of the hands of their other enemies. A mission best served with Loyalists finding a way to pit the beasts upon their foes and vice versa.

The Lucifuge: *Otherwise Entangled.* The Lucifuge have their own problems to deal with, which isn't to say they're not occasionally dragged into the struggle whether they like it or not. Only that they're quick to be doing anything else. Some of the members of the Seventh Generation are more sensitive to the spirit world, however, and it's becoming harder to ignore.

Malleus Maleficarum: *Irrelevant.* Lacking a strong enough presence to be truly effective, the hunters of the Malleus Maleficarum are forced to sit on their hands and watch their Protestant cousins do most of the work. This doesn't sit well, but they simply do not have the numbers or the tactics to change that situation. Yet.

Network 0: *Panicked.* There's a goddamn war going on in the streets, and too few among Network 0's ranks are fit for war journalism. However, a small snippet of film of a wolf cutting apart some gangbangers has made its way out on the Secret Frequency. That might finally get them and this situation the respect it deserves.

Null Mysteriis: *Smug.* Well, werewolves are a brilliant metaphor: gang warfare, aimless young turks traveling in packs wasting their lives on savagery to protect a postage stamp of meaningless real estate. The whole thing certainly is reminiscent of the unbending cruelty of nature beating in the breast of each of us. The nature of the trend isn't as alarming as the size of the phenomenon. With Howard Bloom's *The Lucifer Principle* firmly in hand, the Null Mysteriis on this topic are practically proselytizers.

Task Force: VALKYRIE: *Losing Control.* This city was supposed to be a milk run. That's why the staff and budget got cut during the 90s. Now all of a sudden the water is rising and everyone's drowning and the superiors are expecting the same results as before. With a quarter of the manpower? Yeah right.

The Union: *Ubiquitous.* Philadelphia is the Union, and the Union rules Philadelphia. The Long Night and other interlopers are only adding to the problem. Their problem. The Union was there when the pact was made, they were there

Jim Di Bartolo

when it was broken, and they'll be there in the end — come what may.

Not In My Backyard: Territories

Philadelphia is a City of Neighborhoods. Translation: every hunter and werewolf has a stake in his block of the city. It is an area of tremendous pride for all citizens, even as the city falls to disrepair around them. Every block has its own flavor even if the row homes look the same on this block as on the last. The denizens are as much a part of the street and the spirit of the area as the cracks in the wall and the signs on the street. Families might live on the same street for generations, spreading out as their children and grandchildren grow up. This is especially true for the city's hunters and werewolves with their tight-knit family/cell/pack structure.

Philadelphia makes the perfect setting for a game about territory. Obvious metaphors jump out, such as gangs as packs and city blocks as their pissing circles. The city is broken down to its component parts to grant a better understanding of the worlds existing between streets, highways, and rivers. Neighborhoods exist in every corner and crevice of the city, in the shadows of bridges and the bends of the rivers. Sometimes either side of the street within the same block claim different affiliations. Block, street, neighborhood, ward, district and city, Philadelphians have developed a complicated hierarchy of where they're from and what that means to them. Ask any collection of people where the bad part of Philly is and you will get as many answers as people you ask. Similarly no clear cut borders exist between districts; three Philadelphians might put the same street corner in three different neighborhoods.

Take a map of Philadelphia and get the players to mark their progress in thumbtacks as they march across the city, or play at a mission of peace in a war-torn city. Whatever the angle, family, pride, and territory are built into the fabric of Philadelphia.

Keep in mind that it's important to mix up the ideas of what werewolves are and can do. Yes, certainly some of them fall into the "Forsaken and Pure" model as discussed earlier in the book, but do endeavor to utilize weird infectious vectors and Satanic bargains to keep everybody on their toes. When the werewolf the hunters corner in an alley turns into a wolf with a human scalp in its mouth, or the creature returns to a fresh grave within a twisted copse of trees, enjoy watching the look on players' faces as they realize all the rules are out the window.

WOLVES AT THE BARGAINING TABLE?

One event that makes Philly so noteworthy is the formation of the Chestnut Street Compact, AKA the Candle Compact. Inspired by the Declaration of Independence, local hunters came together to forge an understanding, drafted by the largest cells of the time as a commitment of mutual cooperation and understanding within the Vigil.

A long-running rumor exists among the elder werewolf population that at least one pack was present at the signing of this historic document. This is largely attributed to confusion with the Penn Treaty, or simply a generational lie to detract from this historic event in the Vigil. However, a few isolated hunter historians believe the werewolves' claim… but they don't really speak loudly about it, lest they catch a bottle to the head.

Story Seeds:

• A pack of werewolves moves into the characters' neighborhood. Regardless of their predisposition toward the encroaching strangers, when a child is attacked by "wild dogs" within a week, the characters are going to have to get to the bottom of it, forcing a conflict. What if it isn't their new neighbors but a mutual enemy? What if the mutual enemy is the red herring?

• In chasing their prey the cell are made aware they're on someone's territory — whether they know already or the locals make it abundantly clear. Can they barter for safe passage long enough to pursue? Can they convince their unwilling hosts that their prey is a threat to them both?

• The struggle for territory has gone too far and each faction is quickly running aground. A truce has to be made, and fast. Whether using the Box of the Treaty Elm or simple God-given common sense, someone needs to put an end to the violence and strive for something better. Can they find enough sympathetic ears on both sides of the divide to heal the rift within the city?

• Maybe the wolf problem isn't in the city, so much as around it. The suburbs of Philadelphia run the gamut of traditional *cul de sac* laden 'burbs and large tracts of rural forest and farmland. Plenty of space exists to have packs of Pure and/or Forsaken lurking, making border strikes, and getting bolder every night like sharks circling the boat.

• Screw peaceful solutions. That's for housewives and little girls, this is war, and wars are for winning. The players and their cell are loading up their shotguns and silver and marching out to take the streets away from the animals that believe they have any business sitting at the people table eating their food. They won't stop until their neighborhood — and from there the whole city — is clear of those monsters.

Center City

Center City stands for the Downtown area where most high rises, professional districts, and historic areas stand. Little to no open hostility occurs within Center City, its heavy tourist traffic and police presence make such activity easy to zero in on and knuckle under. This allows the historic and social center of Philadelphia to remain neutral territory. Nothing beyond a longstanding gentleman's agreement holds this unspoken treaty; some of the younger elements have dared to break this code but were quickly quieted.

Center City is also where hunters will find the Graduate Hospital, where cheap medical attention with less questions asked are likely favor. Sure the doctors and nurses are students, but that makes them easier to keep quiet.

Greg Weiss, Loyalist Historian

Quote: *History is where we find most of mankind's greatest misperceptions. I have found — ahem — most energetically, that people favor their misperception greatly over the truth*

Background: Greg attributes his love of the past to growing up in an area of such historic importance. His family carries a long legacy of Loyalists dating back to the old country, and his predilection for knowledge made it clear Greg would take up the Vigil someday. Short of learning how to shoot a rifle fairly well, Greg doesn't consider himself a hunter. Not how most folks mean. His hunting is all done in history books and libraries. He grew up in the 70s and remembers the Fairmount Slaughter as his coming of age. He always found the event so sad and misguided and has since developed a fascination with lycanthropes.

Greg compiled a comprehensive history of the relationship between werewolves and humans in

Profession: Academic

Compact: Loyalist of Thule

Mental Attributes: Intelligence 4, Wits 2, Resolve 3

Physical Attributes: Strength 2, Dexterity 2, Stamina 2

Social Attributes: Presence 2, Manipulation 2, Composure 3

Mental Skills: Academics (History) 3, Computer 2, Investigation 3, Medicine 1, Occult 3, Science (Cryptozoology) 1

Physical Skills: Firearms 2, Larceny 1, Stealth 2, Survival 2

Social Skills: Animal Ken 2, Expression 1, Subterfuge 1

Merits: Contacts (University) 2, Language (Latin) 1, Status (Loyalists of Thule) 2

Willpower: 6

Morality: 7

Virtue: Compassion

Vice: Sloth

Initiative: 5

Defense: 2

Speed: 9

Health: 7

Philadelphia — and beyond where he can. He is one of the few hunters who believe werewolves were present at the Chestnut Street Compact (see sidebar), an opinion he has found is altogether unpopular. Few other things are as inviolate as the Compact in Philly and the idea is blasphemy to area hunters. Greg has learned to keep his papers and pet theories to himself, but practically begs for a willing ear. He doesn't know why people don't find it *more* remarkable that such a historic event was accomplished between hunters of both species, and how that obviously set the precedent for the later Penn Treaty.

Appearance: A slender man getting past his prime if only by a little. He squints when he talks not entirely accustomed to the glasses he's supposed to wear these days. He has a collection of fidgets and tics, but after spending any significant time with him these features

become less pronounced. Either Greg becomes more used to the viewer or the other way around.

Greg sucks noisily on hard candies most hours of the day. Yellowed fingers fidget with one another and all together Greg calls to mind a very nervous someone who only recently got over the habit of smoking.

Storytelling Hints: Though he was a little young for it, Greg is all too happy to tell any who will listen that he had no part in the Fairmount Slaughter — he refuses to call it the Reclamation as that land historically belonged to the wolves and was never the hunters to reclaim. Whether he's a werewolf sympathizer as many believe or not, he simply contends some acts are too gruesome even for the Vigil. If he has an audience and they belie any sympathy for their lycanthropic enemies, Greg is quick to acknowledge he has an affinity for the creatures.

TABITHA RASA
✦ LES MYSTÈRES MAMBO ✦

Profession: Religious Leader

Conspiracy: Les Mystères

Mental Attributes: Intelligence 3, Wits 4, Resolve 2

Physical Attributes: Strength 2, Dexterity 3, Stamina 3

Social Attributes: Presence 3, Manipulation 3, Composure 3

Mental Skills: Academics (Religion) 2, Crafts 2, Investigation 2, Medicine 2, Occult (Vodou) 3

Physical Skills: Athletics 1, Larceny 1, Stealth 1, Survival 1

Social Skills: Animal Ken (Spirits) 1, Empathy 2, Expression 2, Intimidation 1, Subterfuge 1

Merits: Contacts (Vodou) 1, Endowment: Rites du Cheval (Skin of the Loa 1, Elemental Rebuke 1, Light as a Feather 2, Hands of Raphael 3), Professional Training 3, Resources 2, Status (Les Mystères) 3

Willpower: 6

Morality: 6

Virtue: Faith

Vice: Pride

Initiative: 5

Defense: 3

Speed: 11

Health: 8

Tabitha Rasa, Les Mystères Mambo

Quote: *"If you already t'ink you know so much, why'd ya come in me store, then? Good, now shut up and pay attention. Ya might accidentally learn somethin'."*

Background: Tabitha runs a little occult shop off South Street, and has since the turn of the century. No one in the city remembers Tabitha before her appearance within the trendy shopping district. Not even Tabitha. She claims to be an amnesiac and her memory is only distinct this side of 2000, shortly before opening her shop. While she has nothing but hazy memories of who she was or where she came from, her base of knowledge remains intact and she is arguably one of the foremost religious and spiritual authorities in the city for those who know to ask. By all accounts from her parish, she makes quite the Mambo as well and has risen to some status within the Les Mystères sect. The young woman is abruptly sarcastic about her practice and often puts people off that Vodou is all a show to shoo away tourists and lookie loos. If pressed or she judges a request as genuine, she will provide her services for a fee (no refunds). The more

STORY SEEDS: TABITHA

What is the truth of dear Tabitha? Consider the following possibilities…

• Tabitha or someone speaking for her made a deal using the Box of the Treaty Elm. The pact was then broken, taking her memories with it. This makes her the last person to have used the Relic even if it's outside of her memories. If the players can only help her remember….

• Tabitha survived a great tragedy she doesn't wish to remember, such as surviving the MOVE bombing, escaping the clutches of Pure werewolves, or perhaps she's running from a Vodou cult. Perhaps what she's not remembering portends the cult or other organized movement is perched to move on the city.

• Tabitha is currently being spirit-ridden or worse, a zombi. It's not that she has no memory of her youth; it's that the spirit has no youth to remember. What's more, it's possible the spirit in possession of Tabitha's body doesn't remember any more than she claims to and will be as surprised as any to find out its true origins.

• True amnesia through emotional or physical trauma is exceedingly rare and bears little resemblance to anything seen in movies and television. Logic dictates Tabitha is lying. She is quite simply putting everyone on. She might remember any and all of the above, or simply uses it as a curiosity to draw in customers.

she likes the person, the lesser the fee; but none have walked out paying nothing. She is quick to point out she's not running a charity or library.

Appearance: Tabitha is a lithe young woman with an ageless quality about her. In certain light, characters could believe she was as young as 18, while in others she could be pushing 40. She has a sprout of thick unkempt dreadlocks atop her head. Her rich, brown skin is offset by piercing hazel-colored eyes. While performing for her customers she tends to be bright-eyed and intentionally mysterious, while regular customers are more fit to be greeted warmly and left to browse. While at rest or unaware she is being observed Tabitha is prone to long stretches of staring toward the light of day outside her shop window or simply gazing at her own reflection in the glass surface of her display case. At these times she looks haunted, and old.

Storytelling Hints: Tabitha is a quick wit and a friendly enough soul to customers she deems worthy of her attention. She's not above turning up her Caribbean accent and putting on a show to spook the few rubes who dawdle through her shop as if it's simply a curio shop. Her acerbic front is merely to weed out the gawkers and casual browsers, if a character stands up to her or persists; she's likelier to grunt out a begrudging respect which can grow to a genuine friendship given time. She maintains the Vigil in her own ways, but rarely goes out hunting as her duties as Mambo call her away.

She brooks very little irony about her name, despite her amnesia. Smartasses intent to press the issue are as likely to get a lecture on the eight Hindi *Rasas* as they are to get a rise from the diminutive terror. She will tolerate any religion under the sun

if hers is tolerated in turn. She has no patience for Long Night podium thumping or Malleus Maleficarum condescension. Unless looking for a demonstrative discourse on the origins of an individual religion or how Vodou was forced to adopt Abrahamic beliefs to survive, it's best to let sleeping dogs lie.

Antagonist: Dominic Chelemey, Pure Spiritualist

Quote: *"Come in. T-shirts are in the back, bowls in the glass case over there, and if you need any spiritual advice I'm your man, man."*

Background: Dominic first moved into the city shortly after the Fairmount Slaughter. He watched the situation from the suburbs, and seized the opportunity to slip past his lesser cousins to get a foothold within the city. Dominic set up shop in the trendy and open-minded areas of Center City, running a head shop with an occult flavor. Already encouraging two generations of university kids to embrace his spiritual, drop-out lifestyle. He's well aware of the newfound competition in that Rasa woman, but he's not particularly worried about her or her kin. In fact he finds them quite amusing, playing with spirits the way they do. The local spirits are out of control and while he doesn't know entirely why, that suits Dominic just fine. He fans the flames to keep hunters and other werewolves at each others' throats.

Several of Dominic's customers happen to be hunters who have no idea they are walking into the wolf's den. In fact, he has proven particularly helpful on the subject of how to fight werewolves. The kindly old man presents himself as a down to earth, non-confrontational hippie type. If it wasn't for his some-

DOMINIC CHELEMY
PURE SPIRITUALIST

Pack: South Street Pure

Mental Attributes: Intelligence 3, Wits 2, Resolve 2

Physical Attributes: Strength 3, Dexterity 2, Stamina 3

Social Attributes: Presence 3, Manipulation 3, Composure 3

Mental Skills: Academics 1, Crafts 1, Investigation 2, Medicine (Holistic), Occult 3

Physical Skills: Athletics 2, Brawl 1, Stealth 1, Survival 2, Weaponry 2

Social Skills: Animal Ken 1, Empathy (What You Want to Hear) 1, Expression 2, Intimidation 2, Persuasion 2, Socialize 1, Streetwise 1, Subterfuge 2

Merits: Contacts (Hunters) 1, Fleet of Foot 2, Meditative Mind 1, Primal Urge 4

Willpower: 5

Morality: 5

Virtue: Faith

Vice: Sloth

Initiative: 5

Defense: 2

Speed: 10

Health: 8

Dominions: Clarity, Unnatural Sense, Commandment, Slip Away, Ruin, Primal Fear, Talons of Guilt, Graveyard Chill

times accurate information most would blow him off as a harmless old kook. Still, even a broken clock is right twice a day, they think. Dominic is a literal wolf in sheep's clothing and hopes to keep the hunters and werewolves at war until both sides weaken enough to whistle up the rest of his tribesmen and packmates in the outlying counties.

Meanwhile, his pack chomps at the bit, not sure how either group could get much weaker, but Dominic is an old wolf and preaches patience. He knows the whole city stands on the precipice, but if they move too quickly, they have as much chance to put all of their enemies on the same side. At least that's

what he tells them; truth be told, he's too old for war, and hopes by sitting idle the situation will take care of itself.

Appearance: Dominic is getting on in years enough to be an old wolf, but he looks a young and fit 40 if he's a day. He's a scruffy old gray-haired hippie with sharp blue eyes and an overlarge grin. When he needs it, the predator is always there; like an optical illusion the wolf comes to the fore as readily as the grizzled old outdoorsman who smoked a little too much during his formative years.

Despite the sometimes sinister edge around him, he has found a way to pass off such weird behavior as be-

SOUTH STREET PURE

Dominic's pack are spread throughout the Center City and outlying areas but may be encountered individually or *en toto*.

Jacqueline, hard-nosed beta of the pack, is pushing for the old man to get off his haunches and get in the game. She shares none of his hippie trappings or characteristic patience and considers it well past time to strike out against their enemies. The werewolves are disorganized where they're not murdering one another and the hunters wouldn't know their ass from a hole in the ground if a fox came out of one. Her lingering respect for her alpha is the only thing that cools her claws, but packs from outside the city have contacted her and she can't hold out forever.

Meat-Hook is a gigantic mute who works down in the Italian Market in a butcher shop appropriately enough. Not the sharpest tool in the shed, but compassionless and a force to be reckoned with in any fight. Meat-Hook doesn't take sides in the pack and will do what he's told by whoever the alpha is. Right now that's Dominic and he behaves accordingly. If that situation changes he won't waste any time with remorse.

Skinny is the youngest member of the pack and the physical opposite of Meat-Hook: thin, little, black and female as opposed to the giant's pasty man-flesh. Skinny has a mean streak a mile wide. She stands ready to throw her chips in with Jacqueline when and if the time comes and plays number two to the beta. She is too eager perhaps and threatens to force the issue before even Jacqueline is ready.

Teddy is the weak link within the pack and the most sympathetic toward humans and Forsaken alike. The spiritual landscape in Philadelphia isn't fit for anyone, and he fears even the Pure won't be able to put the genie back in the bottle. Teddy supports a call to action, but his first plan of attack would be to try and stem the spiritual run-off in the city *before* they attempt to take control.

ing too burnt out and absent minded to catch himself staring and the like. And it works: his avuncular appearance coupled with a deep melodious voice put most of his customers at ease despite momentary lapses.

Storytelling Hints: Friendly, in an entirely creepy way if only how he watches customers too long, or holds a smile well past what's customarily polite. He is the stalking, talking big bad wolf — a predator in the skin of a man, but he knows how to play nice. Out of all of his pack and many of his kind, he's lived among the laymen most of his life and is particularly accomplished at concealing his nature. So he smiles too much like he's enjoying a private joke at the customer's expense? He's a harmless old man, right? He likes to boast that his mother never did teach him to not play with his food.

West Philadelphia

With sleepy areas such as Haddington to the blue-collar honesty of Mantua through the increasing gang presence of south Wynnefield, West Philadelphia is as diverse as any area of the city, maybe more so. Cobb Creek, also known as Southside based on its juxtaposition to Market Street, was popularized by gangs claiming the area since the 1960s.

After losing Fairmount Park many wolves spread between the crime ridden streets of North and West Philly, and this is the environment many young wolves are forced to undergo their already terrifying first Changes. The Lex Street Massacre is among the worst killing sprees in city history with seven dead and three wounded over a drug deal gone bad; a story largely spread among hunters as the effects of Lunacy covering a wolf's first change.

Location: 6221 Osage Avenue

This is the address of the infamous MOVE residence. MOVE formed a back-to-nature religion in the mid-1970s, in which members took the surname Africa (the source of all life). The group adapted their homes, tearing up surrounding blacktop and sidewalks to "let the earth breathe." Several confrontations with authorities eventually led to the death of two police officers and MOVE wisely disappeared for a few years, relocating to 6221 Osage Avenue in Cobb Creek.

They lived at this location for several years and residents were terrorized by their new neighbors. The members proselytized through an AV system all day, well into the early hours of the morning: decrying the laws and officials of the city, shouting profanity and zealous propaganda. They tore up the street around their home and dug into the earth under their floors, didn't wash and left all their waste within the confines of the home attracting rats and cockroaches.

The MOVE group entrenched themselves, removing the front steps and stationed guards on the roof with assault weapons. Residents felt like prisoners in their own home and begged the city to take care of the problem. MOVE was well fortified, and police weren't armed for the effort it would take to uproot the cult. A 10-year escalation between MOVE and police came to a head in May 1985.

With few solutions apparent, the mayor approved the use of a C4 charge dropped from a helicopter in tandem with an attack from the street to remove resistance. If police had been able to follow up decisively, perhaps the event would not live in such infamy; however, the decision was made to let the building burn to ensure minimal resistance. Eleven dead, 61 homes destroyed, and 250 people struck homeless later and city officials were left pointing fingers. The few survivors of the MOVE organization broke up or were imprisoned. After two decades and hundreds of lawsuits later the block is rebuilt, but spirits remain.

Story Seeds:

• The MOVE Project was Pure tribe wolfmen establishing a beachhead within the city. Their "back-to-nature" mentality was an extrapolation of their spirit-centric lifestyle. They slipped in the side door while the Philadelphia wolfmen were busy warring with local hunters. Dominic Chelemy and others spread throughout the city are spokes of this now-broken wheel.

• The MOVE Project was an otherwise civil group of naturalists who had the misfortune of straying too close to a locus and were overtaken by flesh-riding spirits, specifically *rat* and *cockroach* spirits. The locus is buried under a new foundation but still active. How long before new spirits come out seeking innocent vessels?

• The MOVE Project was tied to a faction of Les Mystères. Similar to the above seed only the invitation to spirits was entirely intentional. How might this connect to Tabitha Rasa and her lack of a past? Why is there 15 years between the bombing and Tabitha's appearance on South Street?

Konstantin Mittelos, Aegis Kai Doru Guardian

Quote: *"The Founding Fathers left me a trail of breadcrumbs I need to be following, but I can always spare some time to go wolf hunting, of course."*

Background: Konstantin has lived in Philadelphia since his family moved here when he was a boy. He instantly became fascinated at an early age with the rich history of the country, specifically the Masonic symbology seeded throughout the nation's fundament by the Founding Fathers. The deeper he dug, the more he became convinced it meant something and all roads pointed toward the first capital. Thus Konstantin was indoctrinated into the Aegis Kai Doru while maintaining his local roots. The rumor that fascinated him most was the Founding Fathers left a series of "Elemental Keys" behind — four Masonic artifacts said to lead to hidden treasure.

It is impossible to stay local and ignore the wolf problem, let alone Konstantin believes the monsters hold at least one of the keys. When Gunnarsen and the others sounded the call to march into Fairmount Park and root out the beasts, Konstantin was quick to jump on board and urged several other long-time residents to join the crusade. While instrumental in the Reclamation, killing two wolves personally and costing a third her eye, his efforts proved fruitless to his personal hunt.

He's become obsessed ever since, convinced that one-eyed bitch knows something about the keys and he plans to take the information from her by force. If she doesn't know, maybe young "Broken Arrow" will, or the next mongrel or the next. He will work his way through them one by one until he finds the evidence the perversions are hiding from him.

Aside from his lifelong quest — which even other members of the conspiracy consider a wild goose chase — he spends his time bumping heads with the Ashwood Abbey and sussing out other Relics tied to America's birthplace. He's freed many curiosities from the hands of witches and wolves, but still the Elemental Keys elude him.

Appearance: Konstantin has gotten old while he wasn't looking, and crested the proverbial hill years ago. He's a fit fifty-something, only having lost half a step to the younger set. Everyone within the Aegis fancy themselves cat-burglars; running around in black pajamas and night-vision goggles. In his day most of his time was spent in libraries wearing something sensible. He holds onto this attitude, prone to jeans and flannel and a good pair of sturdy boots.

Storytelling Hints: Some are of the opinion Konstantin has gone off the reservation, but hunters should find him completely reasonable to get along with. At least until he gets near the subjects of werewolves or his Great White Whale: the Elemental Keys. Then his heartbeat races, he yells without meaning to, and generally becomes belligerent cursing the whole race of them or sometimes specific wolves ("One eyed bitch," "scrawny little mongrel") regardless of whether anyone present brought them up. Konstantin has tied his two obsessions into one,

Profession: Occultist

Conspiracy: Aegis Kai Doru

Mental Attributes: Intelligence 2, Wits 3, Resolve 3

Physical Attributes: Strength 3, Dexterity 4, Stamina 3

Social Attributes: Presence 2, Manipulation 2, Composure 3

Mental Skills: Academics 2, Crafts 2, Investigation (Casing) 2, Occult (Artifacts) 2

Physical Skills: Athletics 3, Larceny (B&E) 2, Stealth 3, Survival 2, Weapon 2

Social Skills: Intimidation 2, Subterfuge 2

Merits: Contacts (Antique Dealers) 1, Professional Training 2, Relics (Skeleton Key 1, Blood of Pope Joan 2, Watchful Keris 3), Status (Aegis Kai Doru) 3

Willpower: 6

Morality: 7

Virtue: Justice

Vice: Greed

Initiative: 6

Defense: 3

Speed: 11

Health: 8

blaming the wolves for hiding the keys from him. He's quick to blame even the slightest bother on the interference of the city's werewolves.

South Philadelphia

A series of ethnic neighborhoods packed one on top of the next typifies South Philly. Restaurants, groceries and specialty stores announce the local majority between streets. Nicknames such as Little Italy, Little Saigon, Little Holland, Little Poland, etc. once populated the area; however, more and more the lines blur. Hunters and werewolves of all ethnicities are just as likely to come from these unofficial neighborhoods and add a whole new dynamic to the city as hitherto unknown conspiracies, compacts and wolfmen add to the melting pot of Philadelphia.

South Columbus Boulevard runs the length of the Delaware River through South Philadelphia where a lot of nightlife is attracted to the waterfront clubs and bars. Violence occasionally erupts at these hotspots as various factions bump into each other on their respective nights out on the town.

The far southern portion of the city opens up to allow for larger land use. The U.S. Quartermasters office, Naval Yard, airport and Fort Mifflin reside on all sides of Roosevelt Park, marking a large military quarter within the city limits.

HUNG DOI PHAM
NULL MYSTERIIS SKEPTIC

Profession: Technician

Compact: Null Mysteriis

Mental Attributes: Intelligence 3, Wits 3, Resolve 4

Physical Attributes: Strength 3, Dexterity 2, Stamina 2

Social Attributes: Presence 2, Manipulation 2, Composure 3

Mental Skills: Academics 1, Computer 2, Crafts (Civil Engineering) 3, Investigation (Problem Solving) 2, Occult (Parapsychology) 1, Science 2

Physical Skills: Drive 2, Firearms 1, Larceny 1, Stealth 1, Survival (Make Shift) 2

Social Skills: Persuasion 1, Socialize 2, Subterfuge 1

Merits: Kin 3, Professional Training 4, Resources 2, Status (Null Mysteriis) 1

Willpower: 7

Morality: 7

Virtue: Charity

Vice: Gluttony

Initiative: 5

Defense: 2

Speed: 10

Health: 7

Hung Doi Pham, Null Mysteriis Skeptic

Quote: *"Werewolves, huh? I've seen some werewolves. They were having a tea party with a Unicorn who crapped rainbow jimmies. Jackass."*

Background: Hung's family settled into the area two generations ago, long enough for Hung to be as American as apple pie if it wasn't for Grandfather. That old man refuses to let go of the old country — the old country which almost enslaved him and took all his earnings. There must be something nostalgic about oppression and constant warfare that Hung is missing. Among his other quaint trappings, the old coot would always go on and on about wolf-cousins in the family. Hung was always first in line to call bullshit on the old man and his Old World nonsense — in English because he knew that bothered him.

Despite harboring resentment toward his family, Hung stayed local and went to Drexel University where he pursued an engineering degree. He was a sharp kid and did well on debate squads and other intellectual pursuits, drawing the attention of Null Mysteriis, which hosts its national convention in Philadelphia every spring. Hung wasn't aware this kind of supernatural madness existed outside his family. Even within the organization he found his colleagues were a little too serious about the same things they disavowed.

Recently, he's heard a couple kids out of Chinatown talking about "wolf-cousins." The specific word-

WILSON STONE
T.F.V AGENT

Profession: Detective

Conspiracy: Task Force VALKYRIE

Mental Attributes: Intelligence 3, Wits 3, Resolve 3

Physical Attributes: Strength 3, Dexterity 3, Stamina 3

Social Attributes: Presence 2, Manipulation 2, Composure 3

Mental Skills: Computer 1, Crafts (Demolitions) 1, Investigation (CSI) 2

Physical Skills: Athletics 2, Brawl 2, Drive 1, Firearms 3, Stealth 2, Survival 1, Weapon (Knife) 1

Social Skills: Empathy 2, Intimidation 2, Persuasion 2, Streetwise 1, Subterfuge 2

Merits: Advanced Armory (Etheric Rounds 2, Frequency Pulse Emitter 2, Etheric Goggles 2), Contacts (FBI) 1, Professional Training 2, Status (TF:V) 2

Willpower: 7

Morality: 7

Virtue: Justice

Vice: Wrath

Initiative: 6

Defense: 3

Speed: 11

Health: 8

ing crawled under Hung's skin and stayed there. The kids claim these "cousins" only recently arrived under the name of Pham and that bugs him all the more. How would they know the name of monsters anyway, what are they, friends? Clinging to old-world superstitions isn't helping anybody, they're Americans now, dammit. For the first time, Hung feels the call of the hunt, even if it's just to couch this nonsense once and for all.

Appearance: Hung can be seen between South Philly and Chinatown. He's a stout man, with a crew cut and a flat, wide face that crinkles when he smiles. He smiles a lot, especially when he's being sarcastic, which is almost always (doubly so around other so-called hunters).

Hung cleans up nice enough, but will largely be seen in graphite-smeared, ink-stained Oxford shirts and cargo pants spilling with pencils, and measuring devices. He carries a briefcase with supplies and plans for various projects around the city.

Storytelling Hints: Mass hysteria is one way of looking at it, but it's more subtle than that. Someone tells someone else their gang-banging cousin is a member of the "werewolves" or "monsters" or something. Through the Law of Whisper Down the Lane eventually you have this localized insanity where people *believe* really-real werewolves live in the city. It's the worst sort of urban myth, at least stories of black-market kidneys and dog-sized rats sound remotely possible. It's all the worse to tolerate some otherwise

THE FENRIS PAYLOAD

The Fenris Payload is named for the giant wolf that will swallow the moon and signal the start of Ragnarok; a chillingly appropriate name for a sub-etheric exoplasmonuclear device. In laymen's terms, the device is a spirit bomb, designed to leave people and structures untouched, while eradicating the spirit of anything within the blast radius.

The boys in the backroom hope to have a working prototype up and running soon and Philadelphia's North and Northeastern neighborhoods are considered optimal conditions for a live field test. No system or cost is attributed to the Fenris Payload as its use is encouraged only from a story perspective. If a character gets her hands on the Fenris Payload and is tempted to use it or the characters otherwise fail in their attempt to prevent its use, the results should be no less than catastrophic.

If it works as intended every spirit — including at least half of a werewolf's soul — would be completely destroyed, torn from its respective hosts. The presumption is this would prove fatal to shapechangers but Storytellers may wish to reserve some darker fate for the creatures. If it doesn't work as intended the results may be even *more* catastrophic and may be no less than the results of a small nuclear device or dirty bomb.

Regardless of the immediate effects, who's to say what happens to an object once its spirit is destroyed in the animistic realities of the World of Darkness? Smart money's on "nothing good can come of this."

---

sober person trying to convince him they've seen a 12-foot monster no one remembers seeing but them. Hung tolerates none of this hoodoo.

Wilson Stone,
Task Force VALKYRIE Agent

Quote: *"Just the facts, please."*

Background: Agent Stone was brought into Philadelphia as part of a special FBI task force to quell the rash of violence in the city. Similar task forces have been successfully implemented in Chicago and Washington D.C. Stone is a double agent planted among the local FBI by TF:V to force a resolution to the werewolf problem. His superiors have passed down the impossible task to end all lycanthrope activity within the city boundaries. Whether that involves relocation or genocide depends entirely on the disposition of the wolves, he's told.

So far, Agent Stone is gathering the lay of the land, putting together a who's who and compiling lists of potential allies, liabilities and other contingencies. Between the Fairmount Conservatory and the situation in North Philadelphia, things are only getting worse. That's not to mention the etheric activity in the city is like nothing he's ever seen. It's literally flooded with malevolent etheric ENEs.

Wilson — Will to friends — doesn't like where this is going one bit. Regardless, the brass is looking to aggressively push forward with their agenda. Particularly R&D seems excited about something they're putting together right now and have contacted him about a potential test run within city limits. No, Wilson doesn't like this at all, he took this job to serve and protect not for… not for this.

Appearance: Agent Stone is emblematic of an old-school spook. He wears the stereotypical uniform: black pressed suit, black tie, white shirt, and mirror sunglasses. He's developed flecks of early gray at his temples and looks haggard when he's not standing at attention. The job is wearing on him and not in a way that he could ever anticipate. Every day proves harder to not wear it on his sleeve.

Storytelling Hints: Will is all business while on duty: taciturn and humorless. He cuts to the chase and isn't going to stand for a lot of running on at the mouth or getting away from point. If he asked a question, he wants an answer as concisely as possible. Conversely, Will has gotten old and tired and is that much more likely to show his general distaste for the job he's asked to do. If the time comes to follow orders or his conscience, even Agent Stone doesn't know what he'll do. It's worth mentioning, too, that he generally despises Moryken (**Hunter: The Vigil**, p. 348) with gross distaste.

North Philadelphia

The Reclamation robbed many coming-of-age wolfmen of any kind of positive cultural influence. Without anyone to guide them, they have no way to address the rage within them and it *will* find a way out one way or another. Compounded by the natural competition and lack of consequence of youth, most

Profession: Criminal

Compact: Long Night

Mental Attributes: Intelligence 2, Wits 2, Resolve 2

Physical Attributes: Strength 4, Dexterity 3, Stamina 3

Social Attributes: Presence 3, Manipulation 3, Composure 2

Mental Skills: Academics 1, Crafts (Repair) 1, Investigation 2

Physical Skills: Athletics 3, Brawl 2, Firearms 2, Stealth 1, Larceny 3

Social Skills: Intimidation 3, Streetwise (Local Area) 3, Subterfuge 1

Merits: Contacts (Street) 2, Mentor (Isaiah) 2, Professional Training 2, Retainers (M5:5) 2

Willpower: 5

Morality: 5

Virtue: Justice

Vice: Wrath

Initiative: 5

Defense: 2

Speed: 12

Health: 8

Armor: 1

Weapons/Attacks:

Type	Damage	Range	Capacity
Glock 17	2	20/40/80	17+1

of North Philadelphia has become a nightly warzone. Infested with drugs, gangs, guns, and crime; the situation continues to worsen for all involved be they hunter, werewolf, or simply human and trying to survive high school long enough to get out of here.

With the elder generation of wolf too caught up in their own battles, no one has taken the time to reach out to the young: wolves whose parents were killed in the Fairmount Slaughter and were secreted away by surviving kin so hunters wouldn't come for the babies in the night. Now any interest they do take is going to be an uphill struggle to instruct these young men and women on any place they serve in the grand order beyond their block. They're as likely to lash out at their own kind trying to help them, and that's if the Pure don't get to them first.

Tre, M5:5 Enforcer

Quote: *"Even though I walk through the valley of the shadow of death, I ain't scared, 'cause I brought backup."*

Background: Tre was approached by Isaiah Bradley outside school one day. Tre figured the old guy was bringing more of that feel-good "stop the madness" bullshit that most church folk were good for. Instead the guy impressed Tre: he acknowledged the need for violence if violence is the only language being spoken. Tre didn't sign on for God — though he does believe someone's paying attention. More than faith, the pastor gave Tre hope. Hope that there was a way to win this war. If Tre can just kill enough monsters it will all be over someday.

Tre was never stupid even if he didn't always have time for school. As he survived to the ripe old age of 26, he grows less sure of himself. The more he fights kids from his own neighborhood — last month the wolf he shot changed into a kid he'd known since the 3rd grade — he realized it's taking too much out of him. What's more, he's been reading that Bible Isaiah keeps stealing quotes from and he doesn't think this war is about winning anymore. Looking around the city it's hard to deny the Apocalypse is here — shit, Philadelphia is mentioned, *right there in Revelations*. But maybe things don't have to be this way.

He recently sent word to the opposition, specifically T-Bone; he wants to parlay. He hasn't told Isaiah, this was never about him anyway. This has got to get settled right here, right now; for better or worse.

Appearance: Tre is tattooed from head to toe with the names of dead friends, inspirations from the Bible, song lyrics, etc. Weather permitting, he's going to be showing off as much skin and ink as possible, wearing open button-down shirts or wife beaters and a bandana pulled low enough to cover the troubled look in his eyes.

Storytelling Hints: Tre's gone quiet lately, chewing on his bottom lip and frowning all the time. He's starting to forget his street manners, which is making other members of M5:5 nervous. If other gangs start to notice or sense weakness, this war is going to get a lot longer, they figure. He's not well spoken, but he's not ignorant either, although that sometimes gets lost in his brusque manner. Lately, he's been getting short even with his own crew, snapping at everyone and complaining that he can't think for all the noise around him.

Location: Penn Treaty Park

That the pact of peace between the Native American population and the intruding Europeans was established in what stands as one of the poorest and most violent neighborhoods in *America* is Philly irony at its finest. It is perhaps the simplest metaphor for the Philadelphia condition that exists.

When the famous elm tree fell during a storm in 1810 the city immediately erected a monument even as the area quickly developed. A small obelisk stood in a forgotten corner of an old lumberyard, before actions were taken to preserve the area and convert it back into parkland in 1893 (purportedly by a joint effort between werewolf and hunters). The park is located at Delaware Avenue (Columbus Boulevard) and Beach Street in Kensington with an uninterrupted view of the Ben Franklin Bridge. The obelisk marks where the elm tree stood and may have a lasting resonance with the Box of the Treaty Elm or at least might provide some clue to its whereabouts.

Locus: Tamanend's Obelisk

Magnitude: 1

Resonance: Peace

In the middle of the disused park is a tall white obelisk, marking the spot of the great elm tree under which the titular treaty was signed. Despite falling into obscurity, and only seeing revitalization in the past hundred years thanks to another treaty — just as short lived — this monument stands for an enduring peace that didn't endure long enough. Tamanend's Obelisk

is said to be where the spiritual turmoil first began to spread through the city, like a splinter in a lion's paw, however the area itself is remarkably tranquil.

Antagonist: T-Bone, Ghost-Wolf

Quote: *"Pack? This ain't even a gang, motherfucker."*

Background: T-Bone is the first among a generation of guideless young wolves in the city. T-Bone is an angry young man with a caged animal beating beneath his chest. His story isn't unique among the wolves of Philly, hell he's endemic of the so-called "wolf problem" in the city. The only thing he knows about his father is hunters killed him and having werewolf blood hasn't ever done him any good. So what the fuck's the point?

Whether he wants it or not, T-Bone serves as the *de facto* leader of the werewolves throughout the 'hoods of North Philly; his example of aimless lashing out has taken hold. Younger wolves look to him like he's got something to say. He doesn't. If they want some advice, it's simple: Trust yourself and no one else. He and the roughshod pack that formed around him have little to no information regarding their condition or the part they're meant to play as werewolves. It wouldn't occur to them to patrol the borders of the spirit world; they don't even know what that means. Many of them have been confronted by spirits (first change, etc.) but they have no words or basis of comparison for those experiences, so they mostly don't talk about them.

T-Bone recently learned he has a three-year-old son. It dawns on him he should be a better man if that son is going to grow up to be anything more than a scourge to the neighborhood like the packs have been. He's not without a tender side; he's well aware most of the boys and girls coming to him don't have daddies or mommies to tell them what's going on anymore than he did. While he doesn't see himself as any more fit to be that figure, he seems long out of choices and has seen what doing nothing and shitting where he eats has done. T-Bone is at a crossroads, but without anyone to guide him he honestly doesn't know which way he'll turn.

Appearance: T-Bone is a glowering young wolf who wears a perpetual expression like he smells something he doesn't like. He's tall, broad and powerful with a shaved head and dark black skin. It is small wonder the younger set looks up to him, even when he stands still he projects an image of strength like some form of God given flesh. He wears clothes loose to facilitate his Changes, often cut and ripped from same. As a wolf he is just as dark if not more-so, with fur that glints like tiny blades of polished ebon. He's

Pack: Ghostwolfz

Mental Attributes: Intelligence 2, Wits 2, Resolve 3

Physical Attributes: Strength 3, Dexterity 2, Stamina 3

Social Attributes: Presence 2, Manipulation 2, Composure 2

Mental Skills: Crafts 2, Investigation 2

Physical Skills: Athletics (Running) 2, Brawl 3, Drive 1, Firearms 1, Larceny 2, Stealth 2

Social Skills: Animal Ken 1, Intimidation 2, Persuasion 1, Socialize 1, Streetwise (Upper North) 2

Merits: Allies (Gangs) •••, Contacts (Underworld) •, Fresh Start ••, Primal Urge •, Resources •

Willpower: 5

Essence: 2

Morality: 6

Virtue: Justice

Vice: Pride

Initiative: 4

Defense: 2

Speed: 10

Health: 8

Dominions: Clarity, Terrible Strike, Malfunction

missing patches of fur from his side and belly from old gunshot wounds.

Storytelling Hints: T-Bone is an urban predator that walks like a man. He stews quietly, growls his words and snaps at anyone who didn't get the hint the first time. He is an irrational force of anger as often as not. He just wants to be left alone, and spends much of his time pushing even friends away. Despite this, he makes an excellent leader whether he wants to be or not — and he doesn't. No matter if he tells people not to listen to his advice, they do anyway; no matter if he tells people to leave him alone, they're still there when he turns around.

Recently he's begun to take a more active role in trying to advise those around him, but it's slow work and he's still prone to explosive fits of anger. But he's trying for the first time.

Northwest Philadelphia

Northwest Philly is a mixed bag of poor neighborhoods just trying to maintain, and a gentrified renaissance. Block to block is a different experience from leering faces out of alleyways to wide open streets bustling with people quick with a hello. The Northwest is perhaps the most disparate section of Philadelphia, which hosts many of the area's wealthiest residents, clubs and organizations side by side with some of the poorest.

WOODWARD MILLER
ASHWOOD ABBEY ENTHUSIAST

Profession: Professional

Compact: Ashwood Abbey

Mental Attributes: Intelligence 3, Wits 2, Resolve 3

Physical Attributes: Strength 2, Dexterity 2, Stamina 2

Social Attributes: Presence 3, Manipulation 3, Composure 3

Mental Skills: Academic (Economics) 3, Computer 3, Investigation 2, Politics 2, Science 2

Physical Skills: Athletics 2, Drive 1, Weapon 1

Social Skills: Intimidation (Social Standing) 1, Persuasion (Bribery) 2, Socialize 2, Subterfuge 2

Merits: Barfly 1, Contacts (Investors) 1, Professional Training 3, Resources 3, Status (Ashwood Abbey) 2

Willpower: 6

Morality: 6

Virtue: Hope

Vice: Lust

Initiative: 5

Defense: 2

Speed: 9

Health: 7

Chestnut Hill contains the Morris Arboretum, Wissahickon Valley and Pastorius Park, which are connected to the larger Fairmount Conservatory organization in an attempt to keep all the area parks free of the shapechangers. This effort has proven surprisingly effective.

Woodward Miller, Ashwood Abbey Enthusiast

Quote: *"If you're looking for smart investments in the next quarter, I'm the man you want to golf with, trust me. Oh, my colleagues just arrived — my card, call me, I always have time for the back nine here."*

Background: The Millers have put a lot of money into the neighborhood around Mount Airy, and Wood-

ward is proud to pick up where his father left off; as a philanthropist and member of the Ashwood Abbey. His father took part in the Reclamation, but all of that was before his time and the shaggies are practically tamed by now. Woodward wants to take down a werewolf — the only foe he hasn't beaten — if he's ever going to surpass his father's legacy within the compact.

He is a colleague of Elsa Gunnarsen if not quite her friend, due to her sometimes unfortunate views on the color of his skin. Their mutual interests are enough that he finds a way to transcend her ignorance, but it isn't always easy. If Woodward is being honest, there's not a lot of color in the Abbey, and he isn't one to rock the boat. Recently however, he's finding himself diverging from their — and Elsa's — focus.

The Broken-Arrow woman is having exactly the wrong effect on his morale. Woodward is increasingly torn between the compact and basic human dignity, which was never a problem before. He's trying to convince himself this isn't about the girl.

Appearance: Woodward is a mocha-skinned African-American with gentle eyes and a warming smile. He's always dressed as if he just came from work, even out on the golf course or sipping mimosas at the Country Club. He keeps his hair short, his face smooth and his nails trim. In all ways he comes off as square as they come, unless he's on the hunt. Even then he's more subdued than many within his compact, but the gleam in his eye and his devilish smile belies the rush he feels in the pursuit of his prey.

Storytelling Hints: Woodward speaks concisely and has a way of cutting to the heart of the issue. He's not without diplomacy, but at the same time, he knows when he's being bullshitted and/or having his time wasted. He carries this shrewdness over to any and all business dealings, Woodward didn't get to where he is today by being fast-talked by flash-in-the-pan ventures.

Socially, he's a friendly guy with a good sense of humor and a deep laugh. Nothing about his public presentation should give away the darker appetites he indulges with the Abbey. He only gets into those subjects with people he trusts or anyone he otherwise believes share those interests. It's possible to turn Woodward's head with a wink and a smile but he's not an easy man to take advantage of.

Antagonist: Diana Broken-Arrow

Quote: *"We — none of us — can afford this conflict any longer."*

Background: During her first Change, Diana received a vision of Fairmount Park burning. Seeing this as a sign, Therese "Old One Eye" Ross deputized the young woman to retrieve the park from the hands of Gunnarsen and her cronies. While Diana agrees in principle, the more she's dug into the city's history, the more she's coming across items her mentor didn't tell her. Therese says all the right things for someone dedicated to peace but Diana hears what she's not saying, sees a fire in the old woman's good eye. The younger woman worries that the fire from her vision is *them.*

Diana has come to believe the only way to guarantee an end to the generational struggle within the city is to find some common ground and forge a new treaty. It's time they made up for the past; and the first step — which Therese cannot abide — is admitting they were wrong.

The struggle between Diana, the hunters, and her mentor is driving her to drink these days. She is beginning to lose hope, patience, and faith. She fears time is running out, as the events of her dream seem to be encroaching. She can't explain how or why she feels that way, only that the city itself will barely survive unless an accord can be made to stop the coming fire. Nor can she can explain why her dreams feature a man in black with sad eyes.

Appearance: Diana dresses practically and as ready for a three-day hike in the wilderness as a walk to the store. She's broad-shouldered and stands straight as if at attention. However, recently her shoulders slump more and her eyes are red-rimmed.

Her appearance doesn't speak to any ethnicity in specific, and she's a self-described Euro-mutt. Her skin-tone bears a Mediterranean cast, framed with auburn hair, often pulled out of her face into a ponytail. As a wolf, Diana has a reddish-brown pelt with black streaks across her haunches.

Storytelling Hints: Serious and passionate about her words, Diana speaks with conviction and righteousness. Recently, she's become frantic as if she expects the world to end any minute — because she does. She's already passed through the other side of passion and become desperate for anyone to hear and help her. She still holds herself well but is increasingly distracted, getting lost in the middle of sentences only to recover a half a minute later. The astute nose can catch alcohol off her breath.

Location: Fairmount Park

Perhaps nowhere in Philadelphia is more prescient to the current climate between hunter and werewolf, than Fairmount Park. The area historically was controlled by wolfmen — both Forsaken and the Pure *lenateme* before them — through the 1970s. The area is considered sacred to them with no less than two loci within the park.

It went from seldom visited woodland to an ongoing news item throughout the mid-1970s. Local hunters and unwitting conservationists gained a controlling interest in the park, getting the city more involved. The park was finally taken by force during the hunter's Reclamation. The wolves call it the Fairmount Slaughter for the butchery that came that night.

The werewolves want it back but many of the younger generation — where so much of the wolves' strength comes from — are tied up in petty squabbles over city blocks. Someone will need to organize

DIANA BROKEN-ARROW

Pack: Fairmount Reclamation

Mental Attributes: Intelligence 3, Wits 2, Resolve 3

Physical Attributes: Strength 2, Dexterity 3, Stamina 3

Social Attributes: Presence 2, Manipulation 2, Composure 3

Mental Skills: Academics 1, Investigation 1, Occult 2

Physical Skills: Athletics 3, Brawl 2, Drive 1, Stealth 2, Survival 2, Weaponry 1

Social Skills: Animal Ken 1, Expression 1, Intimidation 1, Persuasion 1, Socialize 1, Streetwise 1, Subterfuge 1

Merits: Domination ••, Meditative Mind •, Mentor (Old One Eye) •••, Primal Urge ••

Willpower: 6

Essence: 4

Morality: 8

Virtue: Temperance

Vice: Gluttony

Initiative: 6

Defense: 2

Speed: 10

Health: 8

and return them to focus if they're going to deserve the park back, let alone do the job. The park land is one of the few areas within the city that remains largely untainted by the malevolent spirits growing unchecked throughout the rest of the city. Even with the staining of the Fairmount Slaughter, the park is one of few pure places left with enough spiritual energy to use as a base of operations. Maybe enough to push the spirit world back behind its boundaries.

The Fairmount Park Conservatory controls the park and beyond that, most of the other parklands within Philadelphia. While run by knowledgeable hunters, the Conservatory is a public entity and more influenced by money and legal pressure than tooth or claw. Recently, a legal has contributed a large sum of money to the Conservatory — too large for the hunters to turn away or raise questions from their laymen contributors.

The Fairmount Reclamation Pack is equally curious about the law firm as it's no party they know. Could it be the Pure invading the city through legal pressure and bribery? Or another, hitherto unseen player?

Loci:

Statue of Joan of Arc

Magnitude: 1

Resonance: Agony

Near the eastern entrance of the park, slightly off the path, a statue of Joan of Arc on horseback stands

Profession: Socialite

Compact: Union

Mental Attributes: Intelligence 3, Wits 3, Resolve 4

Physical Attributes: Strength 2, Dexterity 3, Stamina 2

Social Attributes: Presence 2, Manipulation 3, Composure 3

Mental Skills: Academic 2, Politics (Favor Currying) 3

Physical Skills: Athletics 2, Firearms 3, Survival 2, Weapon 1

Social Skills: Expression 2, Intimidation (Political) 1, Persuasion 2, Socialize (Conservatives) 2, Subterfuge 2

Merits: Professional Training 2, Resources 3, Status (Union) 1

Willpower: 7

Morality: 4

Virtue: Fortitude

Vice: Greed

Initiative: 6

Defense: 3

Speed: 10

Health: 7

Weapons/Attacks:

Type	Damage	Range	Capacity
Rifle	3	50/100/200	4

cast in bronze. The bronze-work has fallen into disrepair giving it a grotesque quality. Years of weathering give Joan the appearance of screaming in agony with discolored tears streaming down her face. The story behind the statue makes the countenance all the eerier: the model for the statue ironically burned to death later in life matching the fate of the woman she portrayed.

The Glen

Magnitude: 2

Resonance: Nature

Deep in the park, a copse of trees conceals a small waterfall-fed pool and cave. This area traditionally acted as a meeting place among wolfmen. Without

their ministrations, the area has fallen into perpetual autumn: leaves muck up the water and branches stand sparse year-round. At one time however, this area was conversely in a constant state of vernal bloom, and unmatched beauty. Despite this wilting signs of the city's corruption, the area still resonates with the spirit of untouched nature amid the urban landscape.

Elsa Gunnarsen, Union Ranger

Quote: *"Filthy creatures, all. Best bet is to wait until they're licking their balls and crack! Take them out with a rifle shot from a safe distance. I'd say to hang the mongrel on your wall and be happy — but it's too bad they look human after you nail them."*

Background: Elsa is the current steward of the Fairmount Park Conservatory. She was just a girl during the Reclamation and inherited her parent's love of the park and their prejudice toward its former inhabitants. Understandably, she has zero interest in returning the park to the umbrage of the wolves. She would sooner die than let those mongrels set foot back in her park. Contrarily, they have every interest in meeting that condition.

With new investors and that one-eyed bitch's bitch making moves in public, Elsa finds herself in a bind, one she can't shoot her way out of. While she's certainly more connected than the mangy critters, with enough numbers and pressure, they might actually make a case against her Conservatory. That is something she cannot abide.

Appearance: Elsa is a reedy and stuck-up middle-aged woman. Platinum blonde hair crowns her head which she wears in many styles — likely to change between appearances and trips to the salon. She always dresses well and typically in light colors and whites; however, she will dress darkly as appropriate. While content among the Country Club set, Elsa is an accomplished hunter in both senses of the word. Despite her prim manner, she would be just as comfortable dropped a mile into the woods with a pack of matches and a buck knife.

Storytelling Hints: Elsa is a remarkably charming woman with a dulcet tone to her voice, but she's as likely to drop a racial epithet or alarming profanity in the middle of a sentence like a turd in a public fountain. Her prejudice is rarely dormant for long, especially when on the subject of wolfmen. After all the mongrels took her parents from her and all they were doing was protecting their family. Beyond that, Elsa is more than a little racist even when it comes to her fellow man, if to a lesser extent. It's as if Elsa is two women, one a pampered bourgeoisie, and the other a spitting and cussing blue collar hunter. She knows how to play to her audience though falls short when it comes to people she deems beneath her consideration.

Northeast Philadelphia

Northeast Philadelphia is broken up between the Far Northeast toward the suburbs around Franklin Mills Mall and the Lower Northeast section closer to Center City and the city proper. The Lower Northeast includes much of the violence, burned-out factories, and abysmal property value that have come to typify Philadelphia.

Location: Corner of Four Faiths

At the intersection of Frankford and Cheltenham Avenues each corner is occupied by cemeteries — Mount Carmel cemetery and three lots comprising the North Cedar Hill cemetery. Each of these graveyards radiate outward in spokes from a sudden rise in the landscape and the intersection itself. Area residents know this area as a spooky short cut where pedestrians often hear moaning and wailing at midnight hours. Another interesting fact is the intersection is the only place in the world where four cemeteries representing four separate faiths meet. Truly a testament to William Penn's vision of religious tolerance that Jew, Catholic, Protestant and Quaker could share hallowed ground within the same district, let alone one street corner.

With banshee-like wails from the largest portion of the cemetery, and the religious distinction behind its origins, several stories present themselves.

Story Seeds:

• A mistress to a notable Philadelphian (perhaps a Founding Father or just one of many whose names grace the streets) became pregnant but was pushed out of her lover's life for fear of scandal. When the man passed away through Revolution, old age, or Yellow Fever, he took what meager support the woman had left. She went crazy with poverty and grief, haunting the man's grave every night before and after her death.

• The Founding Fathers, their hunter contemporaries, a pack of werewolves, and/or representatives of the attendant religions fought a greater spirit at this crossroads. Knowing it would return if not properly sealed, the foundations for the cemeteries were laid to bind the beast. The sharp rise in the landscape resulted from the creature awakening in mid-binding and its throes caused a swell in the ground before quieting.

• Before the site became so populated and well-traveled it was a locus to the Pure werewolves. It was this resonance that attracted the faithful to inter their dead here and made it such a popular corner for that purpose. The spirits gathered at this former locus are the voices who guide Javi "El Lupe" Chávarri.

Javi "El Lupe" Chávarri, Van Kirk Pure Alpha

Quote: *"Your problem, T-Bone? You have no rudder. You have no voice. I have something guiding me. Guess what it's telling me now."*

Tribe: Van Kirk Pure

Mental Attributes: Intelligence 2, Wits 2, Resolve 2

Physical Attributes: Strength 3, Dexterity 3, Stamina 3

Social Attributes: Presence 3, Manipulation 3, Composure 2

Mental Skills: Investigation 1, Medicine 1, Occult (Spirits) 2

Physical Skills: Athletics 3, Brawl 3, Drive 2, Firearms 2, Larceny 2, Stealth 1, Survival 2,

Social Skills: Animal Ken 1, Expression 1, Intimidation 3, Streetwise 3

Merits: Contacts 1, Fresh Start 2, Primal Urge 3, Resources 2

Willpower: 4

Morality: 5

Virtue: Faith

Vice: Wrath

Initiative: 5

Defense: 2

Speed: 11

Health: 8

Dominions: City Eyes, Commandment, Nightfall, Gridlock

Background: Javi grew up as a normal hood rat running the blocks between the Boulevard and Bustleton until his first Change came over him like a storm. Wracked by visions and his body betraying him, Javi came to wandering around North Cedar Hills Cemetery, shivering and nude with someone else's blood on his hands. Remarkably, he wasn't confused, rather he found a remarkable clarity among the frost wilted blades of grass and the stiff breeze drying the sweat and blood to his body. His confrontation with the spirits that night opened his eyes to a whole other world. Violence was nothing new to Javi, having to fight for respect growing up, but the spirits promised to elevate simple survival to an art form.

Javi, though younger than many of the other wolves in his area, quickly rose to dominance with terrifying simplicity of vision. Their blood isn't cursed as the more superstitious wolves thought; they're blessed, kings of men. Drawing from the immense fountain of spiritual energy coming off the Corner of the Four Faiths, Javi rose quickly to alpha of his gang and lord of his neighborhood. No one fucks with *El Lupe*.

Appearance: Javi grew up wiry, almost skinny, but ever since his Change he's grown out in all directions. Even in the dead of winter, Javi goes without a shirt, showing off a full back tattoo of a snarling white wolf. The Van Kirk Pure wear white or silver as their gang color, and their kin and human followers wear the same.

Storytelling Hints: Javi fancies himself Tony Montana from *Scarface*. With terrible strength, shapeshifting, and the ear of local spirits, he's so much more than a simple gangster but his mundane inspiration is all that keeps him from being a true thing of nightmares. Even with his limited scope, Javi is a remorseless killer and iron-handed ruler of his streets. If caught in his territory, one can expect to pay a terrible penance (starting with fingers) at best, a drawn out death at worst.

RILEY "2-WRONGS" WRIGHT
JAGGED CRESCENT PUSHER

Profession: Vagrant

Conspiracy: Ascending Ones

Mental Attributes: Intelligence 2, Wits 3, Resolve 3

Physical Attributes: Strength 3, Dexterity 3, Stamina 3

Social Attributes: Presence 2, Manipulation 2, Composure 2

Mental Skills: Computer 1, Investigation 2, Science 1

Physical Skills: Athletics 2, Brawl 2, Firearms 2, Larceny 2, Stealth 1, Weapon 2

Social Skills: Intimidation 2, Persuasion 1, Streetwise 3, Subterfuge 2

Merits: Elixirs 3, Professional Training 3, Mentor (Uncle Raj) 2, Status (Ascending Ones) 3

Willpower: 5

Morality: 6

Virtue: Prudence

Vice: Greed

Initiative: 5

Defense: 3

Speed: 11

Health: 8

Elixirs: Eye of Ra, Hunting Sight of the Asp, Elixir of Fiery Heart, Mind Talking Drug

Others began following him out of fear, but his vision became contagious and the more they travel through the cemeteries at night, the more empowered he's made his packmates and gang members. He is utterly dismissive of humans, though he tolerates them as necessary as foot-soldiers and breeders. When dealing with other wolfmen, he will first try to win them over to his nigh-religious fervor.

Riley "2-Wrongs" Wright, Jagged Crescent Pusher

Quote: *"What you need, huh? Bet I got it. Pills, weed, smack, what, man, what? Oh, I see, you're a refined taste. I got special stuff in the trunk, man. Follow me, 2-Wrongs gonna' make it right."*

Background: Riley comes from a big family, growing up on the hotly contested streets of Northeast Philly. His pedigree a motley of ethnicity, from Arab to Zimbabwe, Caribbean to Venezuelan, Riley claims it all. His religious upbringing was significantly more confused than his cultural heritage. *Tios* and *tias*, the city over filled his ear with everything from Catholic guilt to tithing household loa. Opened to a lot of ideas, Riley took what he could from each but settled on Islam after attending the fourth funeral of his sixth grade year. His Uncle Raj (Roger) read from the Koran about the strength to thrive under hardship

Mental Attributes: Intelligence 3, Wits 3, Resolve 3

Physical Attributes: Strength 2, Dexterity 3, Stamina 2

Social Attributes: Presence 3, Manipulation 3, Composure 2

Mental Skills: Academics 1, Crafts 2, Occult (Family) 1

Physical Skills: Athletics 2, Firearms 1, Larceny 2, Stealth (Hiding) 2, Streetwise 3, Weaponry 1

Social Skills: Empathy 1, Persuasion 1, Socialize 1, Streetwise 3, Subterfuge 1

Merits: Ambidextrous 3, Direction Sense 1, Kin 3, Status (Local Werewolves) 1

Willpower: 5

Morality: 7

Virtue: Hope

Vice: Sloth

Initiative: 5

Defense: 3

Speed: 10

Health: 7

and never giving up. Raj introduced Riley to the Ascending Ones, and for better or worse, the Jagged Crescent.

With his mish-mashed upbringing it would be difficult for anyone to proclaim "one true faith." While he's far from devout, Riley does consider himself faithful. More than Allah, he is loyal to the Ascending Ones and he's risen quickly within the ranks for a young man. His position on the street has allowed him to tip off hunters in the city when things are going to go down while remaining "undercover." With customers on both sides of the hunter/werewolf struggle, he's not sure how much longer he can maintain an air of neutrality. The wolves are onto the fact that someone is ratting them out. That no one suspects the dealer under the El at the end of the block can only last so long, especially with Riley being too small a fish to provide the amount of product he does.

Appearance: Riley is nebulously ethnic with a little bit of everybody swirled into his genes. He's a stocky guy, short and broad with a low center of gravity. His clothing is comprised of a perfect mixture of thug-wear meets religious affectation. He wears a gold chain with various religious symbols and figures, including a kitschy Virgin Mary charm, Star of David, pentacle and a chewed on Crescent Moon pendant. He wears a large, colorful tattoo of a phoenix on his right forearm.

Storytelling Hints: Riley likes to believe he's more than just some colors-wearing street thug. However the appearance of same is important to his mission. Upon first meeting, he's as likely as not to come across as dense and quick to fight. Once his trust is earned or he learns someone is a fellow hunter he'll arrange a private meeting somewhere other than his corner in Frankford. Riley isn't prone to sampling his own prod-

ANGRY JOHNNY THE DEVIL'S DOG

Mental Attributes: Intelligence 2, Wits 4, Resolve 3

Physical Attributes: Strength 2, Dexterity 4, Stamina 2

Social Attributes: Presence 1, Manipulation 3, Composure 2

Mental Skills: Academics 1, Crafts 1, Investigation 3, Occult 2

Physical Skills: Athletics (Foot Chase) 3, Brawl 3, Larceny 2, Stealth (Plain Sight) 3, Survival 2

Social Skills: Animal Ken (Stray dogs) 3, Empathy 1, Intimidation 2, Streetwise 1, Subterfuge 2

Merits: Direction Sense 1, Fleet of Foot 3, Iron Stomach 2, Primal Urge 2, Resources 1

Willpower: 5

Morality: 3

Virtue: Fortitude

Vice: Envy

Initiative: 6

Defense: 4

Speed: 14

Health: 7

Dread Powers: Dread Attack (Powerful Jaws) 3, Strange Form (German Shepherd) 3, Terrify 1

Strange (Dog) Form: +2 Strength, +1 Dexterity, +3 Stamina, Size of 4

ucts and is touchy about being accused of such, primarily because he feels guilty peddling the poison he does. He justifies it with the revenue and information it brings to the hunt, but it weighs on him.

Sophie "Short-Kut" Goodwyn, Neutral Kin

Quote: *"(sigh) Well, come on then, I'll take you through, but listen, if any of my brothers catch you, I ain't seen you. Fair's fair. I'll tell 'em the same, least as long as I can."*

Background: Sophie spent all 14 of her years in the shadow of this "war" between hunters and her cousins. Sometimes she wonders if she's the only one who sees how the fighting could just stop. Tomorrow they could all wake up and agree to not kill each other anymore. Short-Kut earned her name among the family when she happened across a skirmish between a gang of hunters and her brothers' pack; she showed the wolves a quick way to escape and saved all their necks.

What her cousins don't know is she did the same thing for some hunters the next week. She's been helping both sides ever since. Now whether she likes it or not she's stuck in the middle of the whole war. At least until she gets out of school and can get the hell out of this craziness. Unfortunately, the family has come to watch her more and more intently. They say her gift to know every back way and bolt hole in the neighborhood is a sign she's coming of age and might undergo her first Change soon.

Then they'll never let her go.

Appearance: Sophie is a skinny little 14-year-old girl with a gap-toothed smile and little afro-puffs tied up with ballies. She's almost criminally cute and flashes a smile that lets her get away with quite a lot. She dresses well, usually in the style of a school uniform despite attending an under-funded public school: sweater vests, drab colors, knee socks and a pleat skirt that falls below her knee. Dressed down, she's likelier to wear an oversized Eagles jersey and jeans with ballpoint doodles drawn on the knees.

Storytelling Hints: Sophie is an energetic and friendly young lady, but with a hint of sadness. She's never had a chance to just be a little girl, doubly so now that that the family watches her so closely. Still she tries her best to keep her spirits up, and brings to bear an alarmingly wit. Sophie is not to be underestimated and will call anyone out she catches patronizing her or treating her like a little kid. She's brighter than her older siblings and she knows it.

Antagonist: Angry Johnny, the Devil's Dog

Quote: *"Someday, you'll see. You'll see what Johnny can do."*

Background: Johnny's proof positive of the theory that abuse begets abuse. His dad beat his mother. His mother beat him. He beat his dog. The bullies at school punched his teeth in, so he punched in the teeth of those younger than him. It's the way Johnny has been and will be: afraid and in awe of anybody bigger than him, and meaner than hell to anybody weaker than him.

Sure, he used to kick the shit out of the family's many dogs, but he never tortured them, not really. Just gave 'em enough whackings so that they knew to tuck that stupid tail between their stupid legs and go sulk, you know? But then he started having these dreams. And hearing whispers. And they told him:

skin the dog. Take its pelt. Wear the pelt. Soak it in his own blood. See what happens.

Well, what happened was that Angry Johnny learned how to shapeshift into a goddamn dog. Not just any dog, but a stout, powerful German Shepherd, bigger than most and with overlarge teeth. He hunts with a pack of real stray dogs, going out and tearing up anybody who gives him shit during the day. Bartender overcharges him for a drink? Meter maid bitch gives him a ticket? Some frat fuck shoulders past him down on Market Street? Meet Angry Johnny and his big teeth.

Appearance: In human form, Angry Johnny looks a little like a meth addict. He's skinny, pasty, his face given over to cratered zit scars and weird sores. His eyes are perpetually bloodshot and his hair is always so slicked back it might as well be glued to his vulpine scalp. When he's a dog, he's a totally different animal (literally and metaphorically): broad shouldered, tall, stalwart, with mean dark eyes and monster-sized teeth.

Storytelling Hints: Here's the metaphorical part of his dog "side:" it gives Angry Johnny alarming amounts of confidence and fury. It allows him to carry what he perceives to be his strengths and bring them to bear against any who'd slight him. He's big, weak and sniveling in human-form, but when he's a dog, he's brash, loud, snarling, barking. Another interesting manifestation to this is the alpha-dog dynamic. Johnny's recently come to learn about the *real* werewolves of the city — the Forsaken and the Pure. And he's *fascinated* with them; basically, they're the alpha dogs, and he's the starfucker who spies on them and thinks of them the way a kid might think of Barry Bonds or Kobe Bryant. They don't know about him, yet, not really — but soon, they will, because Johnny's desperate to be a part of their lives.

ARMORY™
RELOADED

LOCK AND LOAD

Sometimes it's about tactics. Sometimes it's about personal skill. Sometimes it's about teamwork. And sometimes it's just about having a big enough gun to kill every last enemy in the room with a few squeezes of the trigger. There are a lot of options for mayhem. Why choose just one?

A CHARACTER BOOK FOR WORLD OF DARKNESS™

- An array of artifact weapons, both blessed and cursed, where each can be used as the focus of an entire story. These weapons are both blessed and cursed
- A new look at Fighting Styles in the World of Darkness: Old styles are reexamined, and several new styles are introduced, each with new rules, histories, and characters to go along with them.
- Rules for future weapons, the high-tech, bleeding-edge armament that characters might bring to bear against the horrors of the World of Darkness.
- A whole chapter devoted to hacking apart the combat mechanics of the Storytelling System and rebuilding them so they suit the needs of your game. Gritty combat? Blood-soaked cinematics? Monster-specific rules tweaks? All that, and more.

COMING NEXT
FOR THE WORLD OF DARKNESS

the World of Darkness